COMPUTER TECHNOLOGY FOR HEALTH PROFESSIONALS

A GUIDE TO EFFECTIVE USE AND BEST PRACTICES

SECOND EDITION

by Elio Spinello

California State University - Northridge

Bassim Hamadeh, CEO and Publisher
Kassie Graves, Director of Acquisitions and Sales
Jamie Giganti, Senior Managing Editor
Miguel Macias, Graphic Designer
Carrie Montoya, Manager, Revisions and Author Care
Kaela Martin, Project Editor
Natalie Lakosil, Licensing Manager
Alia Bales, Associate Production Editor

Printed in the United States of America

ISBN: 978-1-5165-1581-3 (pbk) / 978-1-5165-1582-0 (br)

CONTENTS

ACKNOWLEDGMENTS

This book would not have been possible without the support of my wife, Marie and our children Nicholas, Andrew, and Christina, who patiently provided support and encouragement throughout the process of me writing it. In particular, I also want to thank Marie for her eagle-eye proofreading abilities and my son, Nicholas for assisting with the photography.

A thank you also goes to Kurt Gunther of Mapgistics, Inc., who provided much input into the chapters on relational databases and Boolean logic. Thank you, Kurt, for helping to ensure that those explanations were conceptually sound. Also, thank you to my long-time friend, Ken Lee, for his expert advice and encouragement.

A special thank you goes to the many undergraduate students who have provided feedback over the years to much of the content and explanations that have been included in this book. That feedback has helped shape the approach used to explain and communicate the concepts.

Finally, a thank you is due to all of those at Cognella who helped this book come together, including Kaela Martin, Carrie Montoya, Rose Tawy, Rachel Singer, Miguel Macias, Sean Adams, and Dani Skeen.

Errata and updated images can be found on Active Learning.

INTRODUCTION

Blending the how-to aspects of technology instruction with the realities of professional practice is one of the challenges of technology education. At one end of the spectrum there are software tutorials that provide step-by-step guides to learning the how-to aspects of software use. At the other end of the spectrum lie the theoretical discussions in support of that practice. This text is designed to bridge both the "how" and "why" of computer technology usage, particularly as it pertains to the fields of healthcare and public health practice.

The issue can be thought of as a supply-and-demand equation in that the supply of instruction being delivered must align with the demand, which can be seen as the need for the technological tools in a professional setting. In today's environment there is no shortage of the variety of websites, tutorials, books, videos, instructor-led training, and other instructional resources available from which one can learn to use a variety of computer programs ranging from Microsoft Office to other specialized programs. Due to some of the unique aspects of the healthcare profession, although the use of computer technology poses a remarkable resource, the misuse of that technology poses significant risks in the form of security breaches, regulatory non-compliance, and poor organizational decision making. For that reason it is important to not only understand the how-to aspects of the various software applications, but also the best practices for their use.

This text addresses both of those issues by discussing the technology within the context of professional practice in the fields of clinical healthcare and public health. Each chapter focuses on a particular topic relevant to the use of personal computer technology in a healthcare environment, beginning with Chapter 1, which focuses on legal issues relevant to computer users in health-related fields. Chapter 2 focuses on the pertinent issues related to computer malware and approaches to minimizing risks from malware. Chapter 3 is dedicated to a discussion of computer hardware and is designed to provide an understanding of the key components of computers, while reducing the confusion surrounding the barrage of technical terminology. Chapter 4 provides a discussion of health research found on the Internet, with particular focus on how to discern whether the information that is found holds scientific validity. Additionally, the chapter includes some practical tips for how to develop an effective search strategy and for using common search engines more efficiently when conducting searches.

Chapter 5 provides a discussion of the use of Microsoft Excel. Although Excel has become a rather ubiquitous tool in most organizations, it can be often unintentionally misused, leading to errors. In addition to a step-by-step exercise designed to provide an introduction to the use of Excel, the chapter also contains a number of tips for best practices related to spreadsheet modeling. Chapter 6 continues with the use of Excel, but relates to the use of data visualization techniques, such as charts and graphs. Included is a step-by-step introductory exercise, together with a variety of best practices for the use of spreadsheet-based graphs. Chapter 7 is designed to provide an introduction to relational database theory, including an exercise using Microsoft Access, and Chapter 8 delves into the theory and application of Boolean Logic, as it applies to databases.

Chapter 9 focuses on the decision-making process of selecting and purchasing specialized computer software within an organization. Included are many practical tips for identifying, assessing, and comparing alternatives, as well as an approach for making a selection. Chapter 10 provides an overview of Geographic Information Systems, together with a list of resources that are freely accessible, in addition to an introductory exercise using on online mapping program and actual mortality data.

Included are commonsense approaches to using the hardware and software, as well a variety of hands-on exercises for the purpose of gaining basic familiarity with and skills in Microsoft Office programs such as Excel and Access.

HOW TO USE THIS BOOK

This book is organized into ten chapters, each focusing on a particular concept related to computer technology pertaining to the fields of healthcare and public health. It is designed to be useful as an undergraduate- or graduate-level textbook for courses focused on computer proficiency or as a guide for practitioners.

Each chapter includes a section titled "Apply Your Knowledge," containing practical hands-on exercises designed to allow the reader to apply the concepts presented in that chapter. Topics related to *Legal Issues*, *Malware*, *Online Research*, and *Software Selection* include discussion questions designed to guide the reader to apply key concepts in a realistic exercise and/or through the use of discussion questions. The exercises and questions are designed for use as assignments in a course, or as self-study resources.

Four chapters focus on particular types of software. Chapter 5 provides an introduction to the use of electronic spreadsheets using Microsoft Excel 2013, Chapter 6 provides an introduction to data visualization using Microsoft Excel 2013, Chapter 7 introduces the reader to relational database management systems using Microsoft Access 2013, and Chapter 10 provides an introduction to Geographic Information Systems using ArcGIS Online. In addition to discussion questions, the Apply Your Knowledge sections of the software-specific chapters also include exercises with step-by-step instructions, designed to take the reader through an introductory tour of the programs, as well as to apply some of the key concepts described in those chapters. The exercises include downloadable and/or online-accessible datasets that can be used as lab assignments for courses that include learning software within course objectives. For the practicing professional, the exercises can be used as tutorials that provide an introduction to the programs' user interfaces and basic capabilities for performing specific tasks.

Chapter 10, which delves into the technology of Geographic Information Systems (GIS), is designed to provide an overview of the key language and terminology, as well as some of its uses in healthcare and public health. In addition to the examples provided, the chapter includes an exercise in which the reader can create a free public account for an online GIS program, access epidemiological data, and create a basic thematic map displaying by zip code in Southern California deaths from respiratory disease.

The layout and content of this book are designed to address the needs of faculty teaching graduate or undergraduate courses integrating computer proficiency and health administration, public health, or clinical allied health programs. Additionally, the book is designed to be useful to the practicing professional needing to bolster his or her skills in the use of specific computer applications.

COURSE INSTRUCTORS

Assign chapters as reading assignments to provide context and conceptual understanding of key concepts. For introductory software training in a computer lab environment, use the exercises in chapters 5, 6, 7, and 10 as lab assignments that can be submitted electronically or on hard copy.

Refer to accompanying PowerPoint slides as an in-class lecture resource, and refer to sample exam questions to support student assessment.

Apply Your Knowledge questions can be used as online or face-to-face discussions, as well as the basis for short-answer homework assignments.

PRACTICING PROFESSIONALS

For those seeking to improve or develop specific skills with respect to computer applications, content and exercises in chapters 5, 6, 7, and 10 can be used as self-study tutorials. Also refer to discussions of Best Practices for the use of each of these tools in real-world environments.

1

COMPUTERS, HEALTH PROFESSIONS, AND LEGAL ISSUES

As the capabilities of technology advance at an ever-increasing rate, one trend that has become quite apparent is the rate at which the legal environment has failed to keep up with that technology. For instance, consider that copyright laws were originally written when the state-of-the-art in communication technology was the printing press. In many ways, the technology of today has outpaced changes in the legal system, resulting in a variety of potential situations to which we cannot always easily apply a legal test.

Within the healthcare industry, the use of computers produces a number of potential issues related to the unique nature of the information. In most industries (with the possible exception of financial services), businesses that provide a customer with a particular product or service generally collect little or no information about that customer. Healthcare providers, however, are required to collect, maintain, and protect sometimes large amounts of highly sensitive personal information about patients' medical histories, health behaviors, family environments, and insurance status. In fact, in order to provide the highest standard of care, it is necessary to collect that highly personal information for a healthcare provider to make the most appropriate treatment recommendations.

Although the protected and confidential nature of the relationship between physician and patient has long been established, the introduction of computer databases and electronic medical records into the healthcare industry has resulted in the ability to store tremendous amounts of information, including medical images, photographs, and video (in the form of echocardiograms, CT scans, etc.). In a digital form, the medical records for dozens, hundreds, or even thousands of patients can be copied and redistributed, intentionally or unintentionally, in mere seconds. An important consideration is that with great convenience and efficiency also comes significant vulnerability. While computer technology has provided a powerful tool in the treatment of patients and the administration of healthcare, it has also resulted in a number of very specific legal responsibilities for all who use the technology.

LEGAL RESPONSIBILITIES TO PROTECT DATA

In the healthcare industry, two of the factors that influence the legal obligations for healthcare providers to protect data are The Joint Commission (TJC), and the Health Insurance Portability and Accountability Act (HIPAA).

The Joint Commission: The Joint Commission (TJC) is an independent non-profit organization and certifies and accredits healthcare organizations throughout the United States.

To qualify for accreditation, along with other criteria, healthcare organizations must demonstrate that they have adopted appropriate disaster planning, including strategies for the protection of medical information, as reflected in the accreditation standards of The Joint Commission. Specifically, TJC standards require protection "against loss, destruction, tampering, and unauthorized access or use." Failure to comply with TJC standards can result in loss or suspension of accreditation, placing ongoing operations of the healthcare organization in jeopardy.

HIPAA: The Health Insurance Portability and Accountability Act (HIPAA) provides standards addressing the need to protect personal medical records from not only unauthorized access, but also loss and destruction. HIPAA requires that healthcare organizations covered by the law conduct a risk analysis. Specifically, the law requires that organizations *"Conduct an accurate and thorough assessment of the potential risks and vulnerabilities to the confidentiality, integrity, and availability of electronic protected health information held by the organization."*

Risk analysis is used to identify potential threats to data security. According to HIPAA, a threat is defined as being human, natural, or environmental in nature. Examples of threats in these categories:

- Natural threats such as floods, earthquakes, tornadoes, and landslides.
- Threats that are enabled or caused by humans and may include intentional (e.g., network and computer-based attacks, malicious software upload, and unauthorized access to Electronically Protected Health Records [e-PHI]) or unintentional (e.g., inadvertent data entry or deletion and inaccurate data entry) actions.
- Environmental threats such as power failures, pollution, chemicals, and liquid leakage.

The purpose of the risk analysis is to assess threats and vulnerabilities in order to properly inform the following:

1. Design appropriate personnel screening processes. (45 C.F.R. §164.308(a)(3)(ii)(B).)
2. Identify what data to back up and how. (45 C.F.R. ¡± 164.308(a)(7)(ii)(A).)
3. Decide whether and how to use encryption. (45 C.F.R. ¡±¡± 164.312(a)(2)(iv) and (e)(2)(ii).)
4. Address what data must be authenticated in particular situations to protect data integrity. (45 C.F.R. ¡± 164.312(c)(2).)
5. Determine the appropriate manner of protecting health information transmissions. (45 C.F.R. ¡± 164.312(e)(1).)

COMPONENTS OF A COMPUTER SYSTEM

Before delving further into the legal issues related to the use of computers, it is helpful to first review exactly what constitutes a computer system. Although many tend to use the term "computer system" or "system" as a blanket term pertaining to computer technology, it is important to recognize that there are specific components to any system. Each of those components has potentially different implications when discussing legal issues. For our purposes, there are four aspects to a computer in which we are interested. They are *hardware*, *software*, *data*, and *media*.

HARDWARE

Hardware is the tangible part of the computer that we can see and touch. Hardware components constitute the mechanical parts that we physically interact with. There are two sub-categories of hardware to consider:

Processor	This is the processing part of the computer based on the central processing unit or CPU. We can think of the processor as being the "thinking" part of the computer, which has the capability to interpret and execute software instructions, evaluate logical conditions, process data, crunch numbers, and do many other data-processing operations.
Peripheral Devices	Peripheral devices allow you to get information into or out of a computer. Consider that the job of a computer is to process data. In order for that to happen, a user must be able to get data into the computer so that it can be processed and then retrieve the data in its processed form when the operation is complete. Peripheral devices are often called *human interface devices*, and they can include things like the keyboard, monitor, mouse, and printer.

SOFTWARE

Software refers to the set of instructions that the computer processes or executes. Another phrase for software is *computer program*. Software is an intangible since, unlike hardware, it does not exist in a physical form. There are no moving parts to software and, as such, it tends to be more closely related to written work like a book. Legally, copyright laws apply to software in much the same way that they apply to written work, photographs, and other original or creative work. The legal term for this type of work is *intellectual property*. As intellectual property, software must be stored on a device or object capable of holding it, such as a computer disk, flash drive, CD-ROM, or paper.

DATA

The term *data* always refers to information of some kind. The word *data* is plural, although it is not generally used that way. So, the correct usage is "the data are available" as opposed to "the data is available." A single piece of information is referred to as a *datum*.

Computers are essentially input/output machines. You put some data into them, instruct the software to do something to process the data, and then the processed data are returned output back to you. The data that are output have been transformed in some way as a result of the data-processing operation. The processing that occurs might involve operations such as the addition of mathematical calculations, spellchecking of text, formatting of a word processor document, or sorting of a database.

Take the example of a word processor. As a user, you may start out with the data acquired from external sources like journal articles and books combined with your analysis and interpretation of that information, all residing in your brain. Using peripherals like the keyboard and mouse, you then input the information into the computer. Once input, you instruct a program such as a word processor to process the data by formatting, reorganizing, spell checking, etc. Once the processing is complete, the data are output using another peripheral device such as the printer.

MEDIA

The term *media* refers to the devices and objects that hold data and software. Media can include flash drives, CDs, tapes, paper, and external hard drives. It is important not to confuse software with media. If you purchase a program that is delivered on CD, the CD is just the media that holds the program—the software is the real item of value. Remember that software is intellectual property, consequently it must be stored on a media device in order to be transported.

PRIVACY VERSUS CONFIDENTIALITY

Now that we have reviewed the physical components of a computer system, we can move on to the specific legal issues related to the use of computers in a healthcare environment. The first legal issue we will explore relates to the sensitivity of personal health information. The two terms that are often used when considering the legal issues related to the use of computer technology in a healthcare environment are *privacy* and *confidentiality*. Although the terms *privacy* and *confidentiality* are often used interchangeably, there is a distinct difference between them both legally and practically.

PRIVACY

Privacy refers to information that you have control over whether to share it with anyone else. Any information that you keep to yourself is, by definition, private. Once you entrust that information to someone else, it is no longer private. The term *privacy* relates to an individual's right or ability to control access to his or her personal information. If someone attempts to gain access to your personal information without your permission, it is considered an intrusion into your privacy.

The distinction between privacy and confidentiality is important because the legal protections of privacy are subject to limitations. First of all, it is noteworthy that there is no right to privacy that appears explicitly in the U.S. Constitution or the Bill of Rights (the first ten amendments to the Constitution). In fact, the word *privacy* does not even appear in the Constitution. There are, however, two amendments to the United States Constitution that have an implied right to privacy:

The fifth amendment provides us with protection against self-incrimination, by providing that a citizen cannot be compelled to testify under oath if honest testimony will result in that person incriminating themselves legally. That protection implies that we have the right to keep certain types of information to ourselves.

The fourth amendment provides U.S. citizens with the protection against government search and seizure. The government cannot arbitrarily search a citizen's property unless it has some evidence that a crime has been committed. In the event that there is some probable cause that a crime has taken place or is taking place, the importance of the public's safety trumps an individual's right to privacy. Again, this suggests that law-abiding citizens have rights to keep some things to themselves by limiting access to their possessions.

The bottom line with respect to a constitutional right to privacy is that because the privacy rights in the Constitution are so specific, there is no single overriding constitutional right to privacy that guarantees every citizen protection in every situation. For that reason, it is very important to be aware of what specific protections are in place with regards to your personal information. Generally, those protections take the form of laws written to address specific situations.

Keep in mind that an individual is ultimately responsible for his or her own privacy, as we all control the information that we allow others to have access to. Once that information is released, in the strictest sense, it is no longer private, although it may be confidential.

In general, the best way to protect your privacy is by not giving out personal information in the first place. For example, making available your email address on a website is a fairly good way to ensure that you will begin receiving spam email faster than you can delete it, as your email address is harvested through a process called "screen-scraping" and sold to more and more marketing lists. As a general rule, once you provide private information, you lose control over what happens to it next.

CONFIDENTIALITY

In contrast to *privacy*, *confidentiality* relates to information that you have shared with another individual with the expectation that it will not be divulged to another person.

Once a person has given personal information to another, the information is no longer *private*, although it may be *confidential*, depending on the circumstances. If, for example, personal information is provided by a patient to a physician (or other healthcare provider), there is an expectation that the information will be used only for the purposes of delivering healthcare services, and that the information will not be provided to others who do not have a professional reason to have access to it. This expectation of confidentiality is typically associated with professional relationships where an individual must have personal information in order to provide a service.

The legal protections surrounding confidentiality are typically very specific in nature, depending on the circumstances, and tend to fall into three categories: contractual agreements, laws governing professional conduct, and specialized legislation (such as HIPAA) governing particular industries.

Protecting Confidentiality with Professional Ethics

Codes of ethics exist for virtually all professions. They are often written by governing bodies of professional trade associations that professionals belong to. The American Medical Association (AMA), for example, is the professional trade associations for physicians in the U.S. In order to be a member in good standing, physicians who belong to the association must promise to not violate the AMA's code of ethics.

State licensing requirements for health care professionals link licensing to standards of conduct that are aligned with industry codes of ethics. In California, for example, the Business and Professions Code Section 850–853 details what is considered to be unprofessional conduct by a healthcare professional. Violation of the code, in some cases, may be grounds for license revocation or suspension by the licensing agency.

Legally Binding Contractual Agreements

Contractual agreements (or contracts) can be a mechanism by which confidentiality is legally protected. Contractual agreements are simply agreements between two individuals, in which the agreement is considered to be legally binding. Based on contract law, a legally binding agreement typically requires five elements:

Common intent — Both parties to the agreement must have the same intent as to the terms of the agreement. This means that if someone agrees to a contract in which the terms were ambiguously or mistakenly stated, it is possible that the contract may not be valid or enforceable.

Offer — One party must provide an offer to another party in which the desired terms are clearly stated. The second party has the option to accept or decline the terms of the offer.

Acceptance — The second party must accept the terms of the agreement in order for the agreement to become legally binding. The acceptance must be clearly stated and within a reasonable amount of time from the offer. If, for example, the offer includes an expiration date, the acceptance must occur prior to that date.

Legal capacity — Both parties to an agreement must have legal capacity to enter into an agreement. That means that they must be legally and mentally competent to understand the terms of the agreement, and they must not be legal minors.

Consideration — The concept of consideration is one that ensures that a contract is really not a unilateral agreement, but that there is actually an exchange of goods, services, currency, or something else of value. For example, let's assume that a friend makes you the following offer: after purchasing a new car, he will give you his old car at no cost. As you are in need of a vehicle, you quickly accept his offer. Unfortunately, when he purchases his new car, he receives an attractive offer for his old car and decides to trade it in to the dealership rather than giving it to you. Was your agreement legally valid? Well, you had common intent, legal capacity, an offer, and acceptance. What you were missing, however, was legal consideration. Since the terms of the agreement did not include you paying anything for the car, it was not a legally binding contract. Instead, it was really just a promise. Had the terms of the agreement included you providing something of value in exchange for the car, your payment would have constituted consideration, potentially making the agreement legally binding.

In addition to these elements, an additional requirement is that the terms of the contract cannot call for an illegal action to be performed. If the contract is for unlawful purposes, the agreement can be found to be not legally binding and therefore not enforceable.

Non-Disclosure Agreements

Given that contractual agreements are legally binding contracts between two legal entities, one type of contract that specifically protects data is a non-disclosure agreement. Non-disclosure agreements can be contracts all by themselves, or they can be a part of a larger contract that requires confidentiality as a component. The purpose of a non-disclosure is to establish an agreement between two parties that sensitive information that is provided from one party to another will be protected and not disclosed intentionally or unintentionally to anyone else.

Let's take the example of a company called MegaTelco that hires a market research firm called Research Unlimited, Inc. On behalf of its client, Research Unlimited Inc. will survey the MegaTelco's customers and ask them questions about what they like and don't like about doing business with MegaTelco.

In order for Research Unlimited Inc. to do its job, MegaTelco will have to supply Research Unlimited Inc. with a database of its customers as well as their addresses and telephone numbers. To protect itself legally, MegaTelco will execute a non-disclosure agreement with Research Unlimited Inc. In that agreement Research Unlimited Inc. will promise to protect MegaTelco's data. That means that they will not intentionally give it to anyone who does not have a need for it other than for the completion of the research study. As part of the agreement, Research Unlimited Inc. also has to promise not to accidentally let the data fall into the wrong hands (for example, one of MegaTelco's competitors). That means they will employ proper security measures to ensure no one with unauthorized access will have the ability to see it (such as leaving it around on a conference table during a meeting with another client).

In a healthcare setting, many techniques can be used to make sure that unauthorized people with physical access to an office will not be able to access the data. For example, database password protection can be used to ensure that a computer technician working on an office computer would not be able to access medical records in a doctor's office.

SPECIALIZED LEGISLATION PROTECTING CONFIDENTIALITY: THE HEALTH INSURANCE PORTABILITY AND ACCOUNTABILITY ACT (HIPAA)

The Health Insurance Portability and Accountability Act (HIPAA) was originally passed in 1996. The legislation was designed to help protect individuals with preexisting conditions who were forced to change health insurers due to a job or other life change. The original legislation had four basic provisions:

- A limitation of exclusions for preexisting conditions;
- A prohibition of discrimination against employees and dependents based on their health status;
- Guaranteed renewability and availability of health coverage to certain employers and individuals; and
- Protection of workers who lose health coverage by providing better access to individual health insurance coverage.

In December 2000, one month prior to leaving office, President Clinton proposed the addition of medical records privacy provisions to HIPAA. In April 2001, President George W. Bush signed into law the provisions, which were phased in, taking effect in April 2003 and April 2004.

The medical privacy provisions (*The Standards for Privacy of Individually Identifiable Health Information*) of HIPAA are essentially designed to help ensure that a patient's medical records are distributed to others only for purposes of providing medical treatment. Prior to the enactment of the HIPAA medical privacy provisions, it was not uncommon for a situation to arise in which a company might approach a medical practice and, in exchange for payment, request a mailing list of patients, which would then be used for a promotional mailing. A company selling diabetes test strips, for example, might pay for access to a database of patients being treated for diabetes so that they could be sent marketing materials and a coupon for a discount on test strips.

With the enactment of the medical privacy provisions, medical records can no longer be used for marketing purposes, unless the patient agrees in writing. *"A major goal of the Privacy Rule is to assure that individuals' health information is properly protected while allowing the flow of health information needed to provide and promote high quality health care and to protect the public's health and well-being."*[2]

The privacy provisions protect all information that is "individually identifiable," meaning that the information can be related to a specific person, whose name can be determined. The provisions apply to information held by a healthcare provider or a business associate of a healthcare provider (such as a lab that processes blood draws or a company that does medical billing), and that can be held or communicated in any form, including electronic, paper, or oral.

Responsibilities of Healthcare Providers Under HIPAA

An important consideration for anyone working in the healthcare industry is that under HIPAA, virtually anyone who handles personal and/or medical information deemed to be confidential is held to the same level of responsibility as is a physician. In other words, the responsibility to maintain doctor–patient confidentiality extends not only to the physician, but to all working in the healthcare environment. In addition to employees other than the physician having responsibility to protect the data, those employees may also share in the liability should there be a breach of confidentiality.

Specifically, the *HIPAA Privacy Rule* specifies what type of information is protected under HIPAA. The Privacy Rule specifies that the rule applies to "health plans, health care clearinghouses, and to any health care provider who transmits health information in electronic form." HIPAA requires that healthcare organizations protect *"individually identifiable health information"* held or transmitted by a covered entity or its business associate, in any form or media, whether electronic, paper, or oral.[3]

Many of the security procedures related to HIPAA relate to non-technology issues, such as avoiding discussion of specific patients in public areas, making sure that patient charts are not left open and visible to others, and making sure to shred any documents to be discarded. Additionally, the presence of medical records in a digital format creates the need for specialized procedures to ensure that computer-based records also remain secure. This is particularly important given how quickly and easily multiple copies can be made of a digital document or database.

There are a number of methods commonly in use that can be employed to help protect computer systems and data. The methods vary based upon the specific type of situation. For example, a database that resides on a computer network to which many people in an organization have access requires different security measures than a database that resides on a CD that is being shipped across country to another location.

The following are technological methods often employed to help protect sensitive personal data.

AUTHENTICATION

Essentially all data security methods in use rely on the concept that access to sensitive data should be restricted to only those individuals who have a need to use it and who are therefore considered authorized users. Authentication is essentially the process of making sure that the person who is logging into a computer, attempting to access a secure database, or attempting to gain access to a secured mobile or media device is really who he or she claims to be. The most basic method for authentication generally relies upon a password or passphrase, which only the legitimate user has access to. In essence, the computer user is asked to provide a piece of information that only he or she knows in order to prove his or her identity.

There are three forms of authentication that are generally used, which can be described as:

- Something you know
- Something you are
- Something you have

The idea is that users are asked required to authenticate by one or more of these methods. Ideally, the more of these that are used in an authentication system, the more reliable the system will be at allowing access only to the individuals who are supposed to have that access. On a practical level, the three methods can be described as follows:

Something you know: This is an example of the traditional password system, where in theory only you know the password. Additionally, this can include answers to challenge questions, such as your high school mascot, your mother's birthday, and other facts that someone other than you would be unlikely to know.

Something you are: This form includes traditional biometric authentication methods that rely upon your physical characteristics, such as the shape of your face, the sound of your voice, your fingerprint, or the visual patterns found in your eyes.

Something you have: This method involves something being in your possession. In the non-digital world, the classic example is your possession of the key to your car. Without that key, someone is much less likely to have access to it. In a digital environment, this may include a computer hardware key that plugs into a computer, or an encryption key stored on a USB flash drive, which must be inserted into the computer. Another method that is sometimes used is a list of one-time passwords, where each password can be used only one time and in a particular order.

BIOMETRIC AUTHENTICATION

As described above, rather relying on words, phrases, or information (which can be guessed), biometric methods rely on physical characteristics of users to verify identify. The most common methods of biometric authentication include the following:

Fingerprint Scanning: Fingerprint scanning relies on a user's fingerprint to determine identity. When setting up access to a system, the user must provide a scan of his or her fingerprint, which is digitized and saved as part of their profile. When the user logs into a system, he or she is prompted to swipe their finger over a scanner, which then creates a digital image of their fingerprint and compares it to the fingerprint contained in the user's profile. Fingerprint scanning is a relatively popular method for biometric security, and is included on many consumer laptop computers. The primary limitation to fingerprint authentication is that scanners can sometimes be fooled by an image of a person's fingerprint.

FIGURE 1.1 Fingerprint Scanner.

Facial Recognition

As an authentication method, facial recognition works in much the same way as fingerprint scanning. Upon setting access to a system, a variety of photographs of the user's face are submitted to the user profile. This method requires that the computer used for login has a webcam focused on the user's face. Upon login, the user's picture is taken, analyzed, and statistically compared to the profile picture to determine whether the user is, in fact, the same individual as the one who set up the account. Since, like fingerprint scanning, facial recognition relies on the use of a camera to create a digital image of the user's face, it is entirely possible that it can be fooled with a picture of the user's face, rather than the actual user.

Retinal Scanning

This biometric method relies on the pattern of capillaries (small blood vessels) in the back of the eye. The method uses a specialized camera that aims a light through the pupil to illuminate the back of the eye. This method utilizes, but it requires specialized imaging equipment, and involves an image that is difficult to duplicate. It also requires that the eye be illuminated for several seconds up to a minute, while the person remains very still.

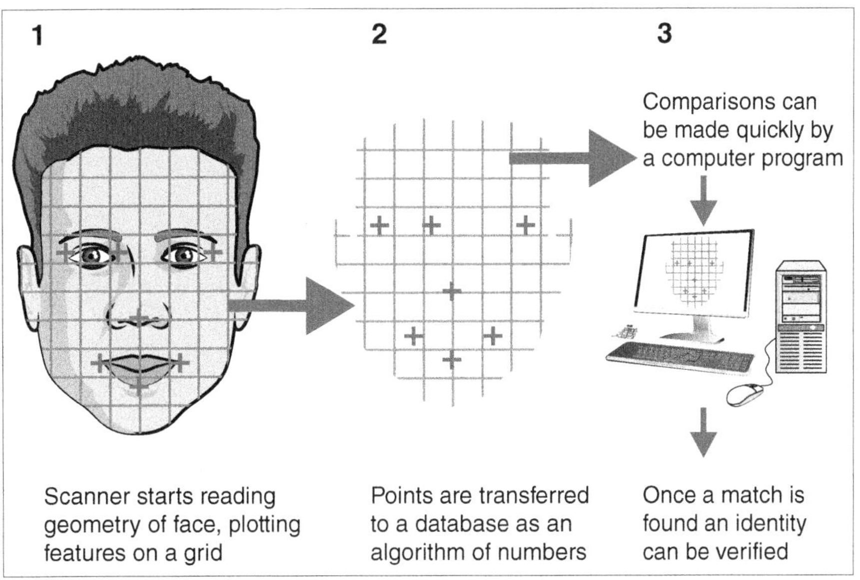

FIGURE 1.2 Facial Recognition Authentication.

Iris Scanning

Considered more functionally effective than retinal scanning, this method uses a camera to create an image of the user's iris (the colored ring surrounding the pupil). The advantage to the Iris scan is that it relies on over 200 specific points used for comparison, making it extremely difficult to fool. Although it is technologically advanced and quite effective, iris scanning is generally not used on a widespread basis, partly due to the cost of the technology.

ANONYMITY

The anonymity method is used to protect data in situations where certain individuals have a need to work with the data, but allowing them access to it will violate confidentiality. Take the example of a math teacher who has accumulated years of records on his students. For any given student, the database contains grades for assignments and exams, attendance, and other evaluative information. Let's assume that a researcher has decided to study the performance of math students and would like to use the teacher's data. If the teacher turns over the database to the researcher, the students' confidentiality will be breached, since student information is considered confidential. However, there is one way that the researcher can use the data without violating students' confidentiality. If the teacher first removes the names, addresses, and any other personal identifiers from the database, he will have made the database anonymous. Even though the information the researcher needs will still be there, the ability to connect the information to an individual will no longer exist.

Anonymity is often used with survey data and other information used for research, where the content may include sensitive and private information but the identities of the individuals are not relevant to the study. For more information about how anonymity can be applied using a relational database system, see the discussion in Chapter 7.

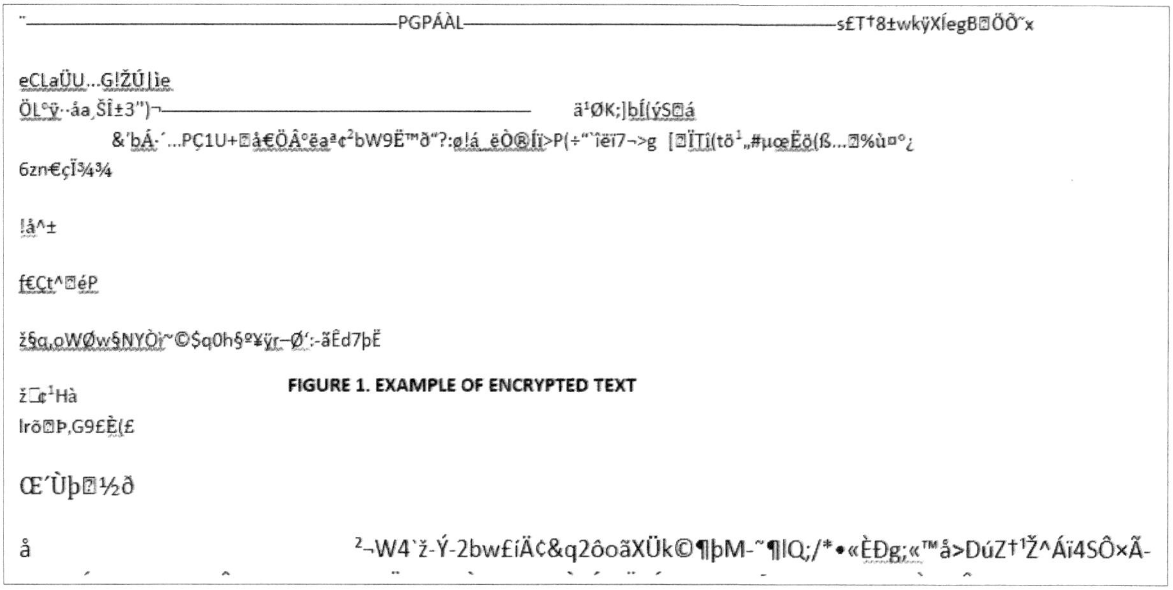

"——————————————PGPÁÀL——————————————s£T†8±wkÿXÍegB⍰ÕÕ˜x

eCLaÜU…G!ŽÚ]ìe
ÖL°ÿ··áa¸ŠÎ±3")¬——————————— ä¹ØK;]bÍ(ýS⍰á
&'bÁ·´…PÇ1U+⍰å€ÖÂ°ëa³¢²bW9Ë™ð"?:ø!á_ëÒ®Íï>P(÷"`îëï7¬>g [⍰ÏTi(tö¹„#µœËö(ß…⍰%ù¤°¿
6zn€çÏ¾¾

!å^±

f€Çt^⍰éP

ž§q,oWØw§NYÒì˜©$q0h§º¥ÿr–Ø':-ãÊd7þË

ž⍰¢¹Hà
Irõ⍰Þ,G9£È(£

FIGURE 1. EXAMPLE OF ENCRYPTED TEXT

Œ´Ùþ⍰½ð

å ²¬W4`ž-Ý-2bw£íÄ¢&q2ôoãXÜk©¶þM-˜¶lQ;/*•«ÈÐg;«™å>DúZ†¹Ž^Áï4SÔ×Ã-

FIGURE 1.3 Example of Encrypted Text.

ENCRYPTION

Encryption is a method that can be used to protect data that may leave an organization's possession, such as during transport, during offsite backup, or any other situation when a responsible individual is not physically there to ensure it is protected.

Let's assume that you are employed in a healthcare setting and need to email a patient's chart to another physician for a consultation. Your concern is that email is not the most secure medium to send the file since a number of events could result in the information being compromised.

For example, you could inadvertently send the email to the wrong address, or possibly send the email to the correct address but someone other than the intended recipient opens and reads the message.

For this particular situation, encryption is an appropriate tool for the job. Before sending the email, an encryption program would be used to convert the document into what is essentially a secret code. The only way to read the encrypted document is to know a password that will have been assigned to it and/or to have access to the encryption key needed to decrypt the file. After sending the document, the sender would call the other physician on the phone and tell him or her the password to unencrypt it (the password should never be emailed, since whoever intercepts the email would then have the password, as well). If the document is viewed without the password, it would appear as incomprehensible random characters. It should be noted that many email systems include the ability to automatically encrypt and decrypt messages and attachments between users.

Encryption is also useful when data is stored on a laptop or any other media, mobile device, or computer that may become lost or stolen. It is also often used when system backups are made (particularly when they are stored offsite) so that if the back-up media falls into the wrong hands, the data will not be compromised as easily.

For a more complete discussion of encryption and how it can be used, please refer to chapter 7.

SEGMENTATION OF DATABASES USING USER-LEVEL SECURITY

Sometimes called *data partitioning*, user-level security is a method that can be used to protect databases containing personal information. Databases that have been segmented are essentially split into two or more partitions. One segment of the database may contain the personal identifiers such as names, addresses, phone numbers, and social security numbers. The other segments of the database may contain other types of information such as medical histories, billing information, and test results. Users of the database can only gain access using individual user accounts, which provide them with permission to view or edit only certain portions of the database.

The approach is based on the concept that data access should be provided on a need-to-know basis. If an individual works in a clinical capacity, he or she may require access to certain portions of an electronic medical record and health history, although that person may potentially not need access to patients' insurance information. By limiting employees access to only the portions of a database needed to do their jobs, the potential security vulnerabilities can be minimized. This method requires that when employees' user accounts are first established, they are granted permissions, which specify exactly which data elements they will have access to and which elements they will not have access to. Each time an employee logs into the network, the permissions act as a filter to control what they can access.

TRANSACTION AUDITING

The transaction auditing method is generally used in situations where a large network exists that is accessible by many users. Transaction auditing is used mostly when a problem has already been found in a network environment. An example is a situation in which errors are consistently found in an accounting system that several individuals have access to.

A transaction auditing system essentially is used to examine users' interactions with a system after the fact. Each time an employee makes an entry into the system, the user's activities are recorded and examined to ensure that they are consistent with organizational policies. Transaction auditing systems are also often used in situations where employee fraud is suspected. Keep in mind that transaction auditing does not necessarily prevent security breaches from occurring; instead it is implemented after a problem has been identified as a way of resolving it.

WIRELESS NETWORKING AND SECURITY ISSUES

Wireless networking provides two basic benefits that have provided a new level of convenience and mobility in both homes and businesses. Those benefits include nearly ubiquitous access to the Internet, allowing for access to email, websites, and other web-enabled technologies. Another benefit relates to the capability to establish ad hoc peer-to-peer networking, meaning that two or more PCs can establish a connection and share and transfer files and folders between one another or between the PCs and a network file server. This capability is particularly useful in a large campus, such as a hospital or medical center, where staff members are not confined to working in specific offices, but must be able to move from one area to another throughout the workday.

FIGURE 1.4 Linksys Wireless Router.

Although wireless networking offers many conveniences and operational efficiencies, it also holds a number of potential vulnerabilities, such as the following:

- Unauthorized access to wireless-enabled computers and mobile devices
- Unauthorized access to fileservers having wireless network access
- Interception and unauthorized access to data being transferred to and from wireless networked computers

Unauthorized Access to Wireless-Enabled Computers, Laptops, and Mobile Devices

When a computer is on a wired or wireless network, it not only has the ability to connect to other personal computers, webservers, and fileservers, but other computers potentially also have the capability to connect to it. That connection may come in the form of an authorized login or unauthorized access resulting from a lack of proper security procedures.

Network Sharing

One of the most common vulnerabilities related to wireless networking results from computer users allowing unsecured shared access to files, folders, and disk drives on their computers without the benefit of a firewall. While shared access offers much convenience to others who need the ability to open or save files to or from a computer with shared access, it also allows almost anyone with access to a wireless network to be able to effectively view and open files on an unprotected computer. The issue arises primarily when a user of a computer on a network (either wired or wireless) enables "sharing" of one or more folders on his or her hard drive. This essentially allows other users on the network to open and/or modify files on the shared computer.

Most operating systems (Windows, Mac O/S, Linux, etc.) allow sharing of resources to be either enabled as *unsecured* (allowing anyone on a network to access a folder), or it may require a user name and password. Obviously, if sensitive data is stored on a computer, sharing should be enabled only using a secure password in order to avoid potential access by an unauthorized user.

The most basic level of protection involves simply avoiding the use of unprotected shared access altogether. Rather than allowing users to directly access each other's computers (called peer-to-peer access), a much better approach is for each user (called a "client") to transfer files to and from a secure fileserver, which can be accessed only using password authentication. In other words, rather than allowing users to directly access each other's computers, users are allowed authenticated access to a single computer called a fileserver as a central repository of files.

If peer-to-peer networking is required, shared access to an entire disk drive should never be given. Instead, shared access should be provided only to the specific folder to which access is required, with each folder requiring password access. Finally, the use of a network firewall (built into most operating systems) can provide users the capability of establishing rules for the types of network connections to be permitted to and from the computer.

Another vulnerability concerns the potential for unauthorized access to a wireless network. Although wired networks make it less convenient to connect to the network, they also make it impossible for an individual to gain access without physically connecting a network cable into his or her computer. Wireless networks, however, provide the capability of connecting to a network just by being within a physical proximity of a wireless access point. That means that access is not only possible within a work facility or home, but anywhere up to several hundred feet away, depending on the signal strength and placement of the access point. Once connected, an individual could have access to any computers on that network that have been configured for shared access.

The best protection against unauthorized access to a wireless network is the combination of a strong encryption method and password protection. While password protection provides a degree of security against unauthorized logins, the encryption provides protection if someone intercepts the radio transmissions between client computers and the network access point (although an encrypted transmission can still be intercepted, it will not be readable without an encryption key). There are several types of wireless network protection generally in use, including:

WEP (Wired Equivalent Privacy) is often the first option made available to individuals configuring a wireless router. Its name stems from the concept that it was originally designed to provide the same level of security on a wireless network as that of a wired network. In order for WEP security to work, an encryption key (a series of letters and numbers) is assigned to the wireless router, as well as to each of the computers on the network. The key can be in various lengths (10 characters, 26 characters, or 58 characters), with longer keys providing generally stronger protection than shorter keys. Although WEP security provides a degree of protection, it is also one of the older and more easily hacked of the wireless security methods.

WPA (Wi-Fi Protected Access) is a method designed to address the inadequacies of WEP security by improving the encryption technology. Two variants of WPA are WPA-PSK (Pre-Shared Key) and WPA-TKIP (Temporal Key Integrity Protocol). While PSK allows a static key to be assigned to the router and the various devices, TKIP uses a theoretically more secure approach of automatically changing the keys at preset time intervals, making it much more difficult for a hacker to determine and then continue using a single key. Unfortunately, a significant vulnerability was discovered in TKIP, making its use problematic.

WPA2 (Wi-Fi Protected Access 2) provides better security than WPA by addressing several known vulnerabilities, including the one found to exist in TKIP. On a practical basis, WPA2-TKIP works in essentially the same way as WPA-PSK, albeit with stronger encryption.

Given the three major wireless security methods (WEP, WPA, and WPA2), you may wonder why all three are included in wireless routers, even though WPA2 is a better method than WEP or WPA. The simple answer is that wireless-enabled devices, such as laptops, smartphones, and tablet devices, often have older hardware and/or operating systems, sometimes not compatible with WPA2, thus requiring WPA or WEP for compatibility. Keep in mind that all devices on a wireless network must use the same security method, effectively meaning that the device requiring the least secure method represents the lowest common denominator. Recognizing this limitation demonstrates the importance of setting organizational policies for hardware and software standards so that the highest level of security can be used with consistency and reliability.

Flash Drives and Other External Media Devices

Special attention should be given to the use of USB flash drives in a healthcare environment. The many advantages of flash drives include the fact that they offer a substantial amount of storage capacity, given their relatively small size and portability. Given their excellent performance and rugged durability, flash drives are an effective way to back up and transfer data. However, one risk associated with their use is the potential for a drive to be lost or stolen, particularly given their small size. Consider that one lost flash drive could easily contain thousands or millions of records that could be easily copied and distributed in just minutes.

In 2013, a dermatology practice in Concord, MA, agreed to a settlement with the United States Department of Health and Human Development for a HIPAA violation when a flash drive containing 2,200 patient medical records was stolen from an employee's vehicle. The medical practice was found to have performed an inadequate risk assessment and had not encrypted the flash drive, which was never recovered. As part of the settlement, the dermatology practice was fined $150,000 and was required to develop a risk analysis and risk management plan to address and mitigate any security risks and vulnerabilities.[4,3]

In this case, the majority of the risk could have been mitigated by simply requiring that external media devices containing patient data be encrypted and are not to be removed from the workplace.

Another risk associated with the use of flash drives relates to the potential for malware to be introduced. This can happen when an employee uses a flash drive for both personal and work-related tasks, and takes the drive from one computer to another. Plugging a flash drive into an unprotected home or public computer can result in a computer virus or other form of malware to infect the drive. The malware can then be transported to another computer when it is taken to the workplace. Once one computer on a network is infected, the possibility exists for the malware infection to spread to other computers throughout the network.

PROTECTING DATA FROM LOSS AND DESTRUCTION

In addition to protecting individuals' personal data from unauthorized access, one can argue that those in the healthcare professions entrusted to maintain electronic medical records also have a responsibility to ensure that those records are accessible and available when they are needed. In the case of electronic medical records, much of the clinical and diagnostic information in them is not typically held by healthcare consumers, themselves. Instead, those consumers trust that the healthcare providers who collect the information will safeguard it in order to protect that information from loss or destruction, and ensure that it will be available when needed.

For example, access to medical records can be critically important in the case of an acute medical event or accident, where physician must be able to quickly determine a medical history in order to assess and treat the individual. Even older data can sometimes be very important. For example, a patient who is found to have an unknown mass on a chest X-ray would benefit from having access to older X-rays in order to see whether the mass had been there all along or whether it appeared recently and seems to have grown. Additionally, important information about reactions to certain medications, allergies to medications, and other important aspects of a patient's medical history are critical to providing the highest clinical standard of care.

The approach used to protect data from loss and destruction is that of a comprehensive back-up strategy and policy. Before considering various approaches to back-up strategies, it is helpful to review the possible occurrences that can result in data loss:

Hardware failure This situation arises when a computer hardware component (usually a storage device, such as a hard drive) crashes, resulting in an inability to retrieve the information that it contains. Hardware failures can occur as a result of normal wear and tear, or as a result of an accident (dropped laptop, etc.), or a non-controllable event such as a power surge.

Physical Disaster A physical disaster is one in which the media upon which the data are stored (in addition to the facility) is physically destroyed or damaged beyond repair. The disaster could result from a fire, flood, lightning strike, earthquake, or any other event that produces physical destruction.

Accidental Deletion or Modification In the event of an accidental file deletion or modification, the data loss results from human error. This could occur as a result of user accidentally deleting the only copy of one or more files, formatting a media device, or modifying a database in a way that it no longer contains the required data elements.

BACK-UP STRATEGIES

The best way to protect against data loss is by copying the data to another device and/or location. Although there are many automated computer programs that provide for scheduling and automation of backups, there are three very important considerations that should be kept in mind when developing a back-up strategy:

Back-up devices should be geographically separated from the computer being backed up. Consider the following situation. Your computer has been backed up with a flash drive, which you keep in your computer at all times for convenience. Let's assume that disaster strikes in the form of an electrical fire, which produces smoke and heat damage to both the computer and the flash drive. In this situation, although pertinent information may have been backed up, it was still not safe. Unless there is physical separation between the computer and the flash drive, any disaster that can damage the computer can also damage the back-up device if they are stored together.

Backups should always be redundant. This essentially means that you should not trust a single back-up device with your data. Let's assume that your computer has been backed up using a flash drive or an external USB hard drive. Now assume that disaster strikes in the form of a hard drive failure, which results in all of the information on the computer being permanently lost. With the flash drive in hand, you proceed to another computer with the intention of restoring the data so that you can continue your work. However, when you insert the flash drive into the new computer, you discover that the flash drive malfunctions, making your backup completely inaccessible. Even though a backup is in place that contains all of the critical data on your computer, there is absolutely no guarantee that the back-up device will function when it is needed.

All back-up devices are ultimately stored on some sort of mechanical or electronic device, which is ultimately prone to failure, just like your computer. To protect your data, more than one redundant backup should exist on more than one device. One strategy employed by many organizations is to keep one backup onsite and near the computer, in order to provide convenient access in case of a computer failure or accidental file deletion. The second (or third) backup(s) can be kept offsite, in case of physical disaster that results in damage to the computer and/or onsite backup.

Backups should be regular and on a timely schedule. Backups that are done on an ad hoc basis run the risk of being available but out of date when they're needed. In order for a back-up strategy to be effective, backups should be scheduled on a timely basis that coincides with the business processes and workflow. For example, if an accounting department routinely pays bills and reconciles its accounts payable on the last day of each week, a backup should be regularly scheduled immediately following that process to ensure that the work performed during the day is recoverable in the event of data loss. A common approach is to back up all computers on a network using automated software that schedules the backup for a time period during which the computers are not likely to be used, such as late at night, or it can also be done on an on-going basis in real-time throughout the workday."

CURRENT TRENDS: ONLINE BACK-UP SOLUTIONS

Over the past twenty years, back-up technology has evolved from using stacks of floppy disks to tape cartridges and now to external hard drives and solid-state flash drives. One current approach involves the use of automated online backup and storage through the Internet. With this approach, software installed on a computer can be used to back up data either on a scheduled basis, or even continually (as the data changes) to an array of online servers (i.e., the *cloud*). This approach offers incredible convenience in that it eliminates the need to manage the physical media and to transport the back-up devices to and from onsite and offsite facilities.

Although online backups offer excellent convenience, the process is dependent on having a reasonably fast Internet connection in place. Another risk concerns the fact that a third party will effectively have access to the data being backed up on a computer. In the case of sensitive data (such as in a healthcare setting), the online back-up company must provide evidence that the systems they employ are HIPAA compliant. Ensuring compliance generally depends on the back-up service's ability to encrypt the data prior to its transfer, protecting it against:

1. Intrusion in the event the data is intercepted during the back-up process, and
2. Unauthorized access of the data while being stored by the back-up services.

The encryption system must be designed so that the information is encrypted in a way that the only person who can unencrypt the data is the user of the computer from which the data was backed up.

Another potential issue related to online back-up services is that a relatively fast Internet connection is required to retrieve the backed-up data. If the connection is either not available or if it is too slow to be usable (a potential issue with very large backups), relying on it may not be feasible. Many online back-up vendors now provide an option to deliver backups using media such as an external hard drive, if needed. Regardless of that option, another back-up method should be adopted in addition to the online method. This is especially important given that an online backup is entirely out of the control of the user.

DATA DISPOSAL: SECURELY DELETING DATA FROM MEDIA

The medical records privacy provisions under HIPAA require that Protected Health Information (PHI) be protected so as to ensure the privacy of healthcare consumers. In addition to the data protection methods used during the time that the data is being actively used to provide healthcare services, attention must be paid to PHI that is no longer needed (for example, when a patient changes to a new provider, or is deceased). Another issue concerns computer hardware that has been replaced with newer equipment and must now be disposed of. Once a data element is no longer of use, erasing the file from computer's hard drives must be done in a way so that it cannot be recovered.

> In a 2011 study of 56 computer hard drives that had either been sold or donated to charities the contents of the drives were examined in order to determine what data, if any, could be recovered. The researchers found that more than half of the drives contained full names, phone numbers, or addresses. A significant number of the drives contained social security numbers, bank account information, tax returns, credit and debit card information, PIN numbers, and one drive even contained a last will and testament. About half of the drives contained browser history, pictures, and browser cookies (which can contain automatic logins to secure websites).[4]
>
> Finally, about 27% of the drives in the study were also found to contain recoverable emails. In particular, one drive had been donated by a dentist and contained personal emails with the individual's spouse concerning their child. Additionally, that drive also contained recoverable emails between the dentist and other healthcare professionals concerning patients, as well as emails to and from patients themselves, making the non-secure disposal a HIPAA violation.

As many individuals, have discovered, simply deleting a file from a disc drive does not necessarily permanently delete that file. Contemporary operating systems maintain file systems using a master index, which contains the names of the files contained on a disc drive together with the locations of the various parts of those files. When a file is opened by a computer user, the operating system relies on the index as a map of where it can find the various portions of the file so that the complete file can be reassembled and opened for use.

When a user chooses to delete a file, the operating system does not actually delete the file, but it instead takes a shortcut. Instead of actually removing the file from the drive, it simply removes the *reference* to that file from the index and then pretends that the file does not exist. Over time, the space occupied by the file will eventually be over-written by new data. However, until that space is needed for a new file, the actual data is still on the drive, albeit with no reference to it in the index. Many programs exist that allow a user to methodically sift through the "empty space" of a hard drive in order to recover fragments of files or even entire files that have been deleted. Simply deleting the data on a hard drive and then disposing of the device or donating it to charity means that someone who finds or purchases the device can potentially access the deleted data.

DATA DESTRUCTION REQUIREMENTS UNDER HIPAA

Under the medical records privacy provisions of HIPAA, healthcare providers are required to protect the privacy of PHI, whether or not an individual is still a patient. *"This means that covered entities must implement reasonable safeguards to limit incidental, and avoid prohibited uses and disclosures of PHI, including in connection with the disposal of such information."*[5] Under provisions described in 45 CFR 164.306(a)(4), 164.308(a)(5), and 164.530(b) and (i), the law requires that employees (including volunteers) specifically receive training on the disposal of personally identifiable health information.

Disposal of paper records in dumpsters or recycling bins can result in those records being found by someone not authorized to access that information. For that reason, paper records must be destroyed by shredding, incineration, pulping or some other method that will ensure that they can no longer be read.

Media containing PHI in digital form must be securely cleaned using an effective method that ensures no parts of the data will be accessible. According to the U.S. Department of Health and Human Services, although no particular disposal method is required, proper methods of disposal include the following: *"For PHI on electronic media, clearing (using software or hardware products to overwrite media with non-sensitive data), purging (degaussing or exposing the media to a strong magnetic field in order to disrupt the recorded magnetic domains), or destroying the media (disintegration, pulverization, melting, incinerating, or shredding)."*[5]

Secure Digital Data Destruction Techniques

Given that computer hard drives are mechanical devices that rely on a magnetized disc to store information, there are a number of different methods that can be used to permanently destroy data that is contained on one:

Physical Destruction: Physically destroying a disc drive or damaging it beyond the ability to function by disassembling it and drilling holes through platters, whacking them with a hammer, or sawing through them is relatively effective at preventing all but the most determined and technologically sophisticated hacker from being able to recover any data since recovery would require specialized equipment and substantial technical expertise.

Degaussing: Hard drives are magnetic media that rely on a constant magnetic field to hold data, meaning that disruption of that magnetic field will lead to data loss. A degausser is high-intensity electro-magnet that can be used to permanently disrupt the drive's magnetic field, making it permanently unusable.

Secure Deletion: Secure deletion methods are based on the premise that even if a file is deleted and overwritten, some faint and recoverable magnetic trace of the data may still remain on the drive. Consider the example of writing something on paper with a pencil and then erasing it. In many cases, a faint image of the original writing is still visible. If you were to write something else over the same spot on the paper and then erase it a second time, the original writing becomes much more difficult to detect. The more times you write and erase, the less likely it is that any of the original writing will ever be recovered.

In order to ensure that the residual data is really deleted, a secure deletion process uses a very similar process by first erasing and then completely overwriting the drive with a single character– usually a one or a zero. Next, it will delete all of the characters and repeat the process using a different character several times over. The more times that the drive is over-written with different characters and then erased, the more difficult it will be to recover anything useful from it, so the number of iterations dictates the level of protection. For reference, the United States Department of Defense requires seven over-write passes (using alternating ones, zeros, and random characters) to be made before the drive is considered to have been securely erased.

Solid State Drives

Unlike traditional mechanical hard drives, Solid State Drives (SSD's) and USB flash drives do not contain any moving parts, but instead rely on silicon chips called *flash memory* to store data. It is important to note that SSD's and flash drives work very differently than do mechanical hard drives, therefore traditional write/overwrite programs are typically ineffective when used on an SSD. For that reason, software used to securely erase an SSD device must be specifically designed for SSD's in order to be effective. Many secure deletion programs will provide a specific version of the program to be used on SSDs and flash drives. If the program does not specifically indicate that it is for use on an SSD or flash drive, the assumption should be made that it will not provide secure deletion of the data.

DOCUMENTING THE DESTRUCTION

Regardless of the method chosen to securely destroy or delete sensitive PHI in a healthcare environment, the process used should be documented in the event of a future audit. The United States Health Resources and Services Administration (HRSA) protocol for the destruction of medical records specifically requires that a document destruction log be maintained in which a description of the specific documents and/or computer media and files be recorded[6]. In the case of shredding or physical destruction of paper-based records or physical computer media, many commercial vendors who provide the service will also provide certification that indicates the quantity of documents or the type of equipment that was destroyed together with the method that was used. Many vendors will also provide a video that can provide verification of the destruction process.

In the case of secure deletion of data from computer media, many commercially available programs for secure do-it-yourself deletion also provide the ability to produce and print a certification showing indicating the date, drives, folders, and files that were securely erased, the number of over-write passes performed, and descriptive information and/or serial numbers related to the computer equipment on which the deletion occurred.

Maintaining a destruction log together with the supporting certification is always a preferred practice when PHI is used within a facility. Not only do the log and certificates provide audit support, they also help the internal management of sensitive data by reducing the chances that digital or physical files that fall into disuse are forgotten and are assumed to have been destroyed when they have not been.

INTELLECTUAL PROPERTY

Intellectual property law relates to the use of creative works such as data, software, writings, music, artwork, etc. The intellectual property laws that currently exist can be grouped into the following:

Copyright law—Copyright law addresses original written material. Copyright law can apply to books, periodicals, and electronic publications on the Internet.

Patent law—Patent law addresses inventions and the processes used to create them. Patents could apply to machines, drugs, or manufacturing processes.

Trademark law—Trademark law applies to logos, company names, and product names used by companies as a part of their organizational identity or branding.

Trade secret law—Trade secret law tends to apply to information that companies and individuals use in the course of conducting business that provide them with a competitive advantage. The ingredients of a fast food company's secret sauce could be considered a trade secret. Another example is a software company's programming method that enables its database software to process data much faster than competitors.

Most of the issues we will discuss in this section are related to copyright law, which protects authors from having other individuals illegally use and redistribute their original work without the author receiving compensation.

SOFTWARE LICENSING METHODS

Computer software is similar to other forms of intellectual property in that purchasers do not actually purchase the property, only the right to use it. For example, purchasing a music album gives the purchaser the right to listen to and enjoy the recording, but does not give them the right to do as they please with it. For example, the purchaser cannot make copies of the disc and begin selling them, as they do not own the legal rights to the album. In a similar fashion, someone who purchases software is not actually purchasing the legal rights to the software, but instead is purchasing the right to *use* the software, but with certain conditions attached. When the legal right to use computer software is extended to someone, it is known as a software license. It should be noted that there are a number of methods that are used to license software. Since the methods can vary considerably as to how they work, it is useful to understand their similarities and differences to ensure that software is being used in a way that is compliant with the type of license.

The terms and conditions associated with the right to use software are typically contained in a document called a software license agreement (SLA), also sometimes called an End-User License

Agreement (EULA). The software license agreement represents a legally binding contract between the purchaser and the software developer. In essence, it specifies the conditions by which the end-user is allowed to use the program. Usually during the installation process, the end-user is asked to review the terms and conditions of the agreement and to accept or reject those terms. Acceptance of the terms means that the end-user has accepted the offer to enter into a legally binding contract with the software company.

COMMERCIAL LICENSING

Commercial licensing is the method most often used when software is purchased directly or indirectly from a software developer. After the purchase, the purchaser is essentially given the opportunity to review and decide whether to abide by the software license agreement (SLA). The conditions typically relate to what a user can and can't do with the program. For example, most license agreements prohibit the user (licensee) from installing the program on more than one computer at a time. This means that someone who loans an installation disc and/or license key for a downloaded program to someone else has effectively violated the agreement. Some license agreements will allow use on multiple computers if the software is in use on only one computer at a time. For convenience, larger organizations with many computers in use will often purchase software using a site license agreement, which grants them the right to use the software on larger numbers of computers.

Since different software developers have different restrictions, it is important to read the terms of the software license agreement to really know what is and is not considered a violation of that agreement. Use of the software that not consistent with the conditions is considered a breach of the legally binding contract and is grounds to terminate the purchaser's right to use the software. This is a particular problem in organizations that poorly manage the software that is in use by not keeping track of what computer programs are in use and the terms of those programs' EULAs.

SaaS – SOFTWARE AS A SERVICE

The concept of Software as a Service (SaaS) is one that has become part of a somewhat more recent trend in the licensing and delivery of commercial software throughout the world. SaaS relies on cloud computing as a way for software developers to deliver software to end-users by making it web-based and accessed through a web browser, rather than software that is traditionally downloaded and installed directly on the end-user's computer. In the case of SaaS-based programs, the software resides on a cloud server maintained by the software company. Access is provided to paid users by providing each user with an individual account and login allowing them to run the program using a web browser (A well-known example of SaaS would be the various Google applications, such as Google Docs, which users can access through a web browser without the need to install software on their own computers).

SaaS software is often licensed on a subscription basis by which users pay for the right to use the program for some time period (typically for one year), after which the license either expires or is renewed for another term.

Advantages to SaaS programs include the fact that once a user has subscribed to the service, the software is immediately available without the need to install anything new on his or her computer. Additionally, since the software actually runs on cloud servers rather than a user's computers, the performance of the software will be relatively uniform from user to user.

It is important to consider that in organizations that are legally required to provide security for confidential data (such banking, healthcare, and education), the use of SaaS software may require that confidential data be stored or accessible to a software vendor's cloud servers, placing it in the hands of a third-party entity over which the company using the software has no direct control. Although contractual agreements and data security methods can be designed to reduce the chances of a data breach, many organizations' IT directors often make the decision to implement policies forbidding the transfer of confidential data to cloud servers in order to eliminate the chances of a data breach. The key limitation associated with SaaS software is the need for a constant, fast, and reliable Internet connection.

A 2011 survey of IT executives found that the factors found by IT executives to be significant opportunities associated with SaaS software included cost effectiveness, strategic flexibility, and an organization's improved ability to focus on its core competencies by adopting a SaaS solution. Two significant perceived problems associated with SaaS products influenced those who chose not to adopt the technology. The first was the potential for financial risk associated with a SaaS solution that exceed the costs that were initially budgeted, while the second concern focused on the potential security risks associated with SaaS.[7]

SHAREWARE LICENSING

Another older but sometimes still-used method used to license software is called *shareware*. The shareware approach can be illustrated by the following example. Let's assume that a small software developer has written a program but does not have the resources to have it mass marketed and stocked on the shelves of large software stores.

The developer makes the program available on a website as a free download. Accompanying the program is a shareware license agreement that is written differently than a standard commercial agreement (see above). Shareware license agreements typically state that the user is granted a free trial period to use the program. After the trial period, the user can either remove the program and stop using it or, to continue using it, register the program by paying the fee to the developer. The benefit of shareware is that it is typically much lower priced than commercial software and you have the ability to try it before spending money on it.

It is important to note that shareware is not the same thing as a limited functionality trial version of the program. The shareware program that can be installed for free is exactly the same version that a paying user receives. From the developer's perspective, he or she does not need to invest heavily in marketing and advertising. The developer is, however, relying on users who like the program to pay for it. Since the developer has no way to know who has tried the program, as more and more copies are distributed, the process is based entirely on the honor system. As an incentive to register the software, most developers will send users an updated version, documentation, and provide technical support to those customers who register by sending in their money.

PUBLIC DOMAIN SOFTWARE

Public domain software is software that has few or no conditions for use and distribution and where there is no cost involved. Software is often placed into the public domain by developers who have programs that are outdated or have limited or no commercial potential. Some programs have limited use to a very small number of users and are not commercially viable. Developers, in that situation, may choose to place the program in the public domain, meaning that it can be freely used, duplicated, and redistributed by anyone. Software that is developed by agencies of the federal government is typically public domain since it was funded by tax dollars. For example, the U.S. Centers for Disease Control and Prevention (CDC) has developed a number of sophisticated programs that are freely available to anyone who would like to use them.

FREEWARE

Software licensed as freeware is sometimes produced by developers who use it as a promotional item to attract users. Although both freeware and public domain software are free, the major distinction between freeware and public domain software is that developers of freeware reserve some rights to place conditions on the use of the software. Freeware is often accompanied by a freeware license agreement that spells out the conditions of use.

OPEN SOURCE LICENSING

Open Source software is a somewhat more recent development in the area of intellectual property. This method of licensing is based on the premise that software licensed under the Open Source method is developed by a global community of programmers, and is free for anyone to use. Another distinction of Open Source software is that in addition to the compiled version of a program, the programming source code is also distributed. Distribution of the source code allows anyone to customize the program for their own needs, as well as to contribute to the global development effort. As of this writing, a number of very popular and widely used programs have been distributed as Open Source. A few of the numerous examples: Moodle, Open Office, the Linux operating system. More information about Open Source licensing can be found at the Open Source Initiative website at http://opensource.org.[5,8]

A NOTE ABOUT DATA

An important consideration is that databases, written work, illustrations, and photographs can be also covered under similar license agreements as software.

Let's look at a hypothetical example. Medi-Research, Inc. goes out and collects information from all of the major pharmacies in a state regarding the sales volume of various drugs. It then compiles a database and reports that show how each pharmacy stacks up against its competition. Medi-Research, Inc. offers the database for sale to the pharmacies for use in their marketing planning. That database can be copyrighted by Medi-Research, meaning that users of the database must abide by a similar license agreement as for software. Users can be prohibited from reselling or distributing the database in any way. Even though the data in the database are readily available to anyone who wants to collect it from the pharmacies, Medi-Research has invested time and money in collecting the information and is entitled to receive compensation from anyone using their database.

As with public domain software, data that have been collected by the federal government are generally placed in the public domain since the collection was funded with tax dollars. As an example, the CDC collects survey data on a variety of public health-related topics throughout the U.S. Virtually all of the datasets are available for download at no cost since their cost was paid for through taxpayer funding.

BEST PRACTICES

Prior to using any form of intellectual property, it is important to understand the possible legal consequences of its use. The following guidelines should be considered when making the decision to use intellectual property, whether or not it carries a copyright notice.

- Before using any software, data, photographs, video clips, music, or written work that you will redistribute, you should always look for a copyright notice. If there is a copyright notice, permission must be sought from the author before using it.
- Whenever using any photos or graphic images found on the Internet, users should always confirm that the image is either in the public domain or that that they have permission to use it. If uncertain about an image's copyright status, make sure to ask the owner of the image whether it can be redistributed. For example, if you would like to put a photograph found on the Internet on your web page or in a brochure that is to be redistributed, the owner of the intellectual property may ask that you first pay a royalty for use of the image, ask you to cite the source, or have some other condition for its use.
- Always read the software license agreements (although they are generally long and difficult to read, it is worthwhile to at least skim the entire piece) for any program you use. The agreement will spell out the conditions under which you can use the program.
- Never loan a program to another person to install on their computer. Not only will you be violating the license agreement, you will also cause a potential problem if the other person calls for technical support using your registration number, serial number, installation key, or other identifier that can be used to determine who originally purchased the program.
- Organizations should always have in place a policy requiring any software purchased on behalf of the organization (or software is installed on a computer owned by the organization) be tracked. This generally means that an information technology and/or accounting department maintains records of who is using the programs, which computer(s) they are installed to, and what the terms are of the software license agreements. In the absence of such a policy, a problem can arise as employees bring in personal software and/or make illegal copies or installations of software, potentially exposing the organization to widespread legal liability.

SUMMARY

The legal issues related to the use of computer technology in a healthcare environment encompass a large variety of issues ranging from data protection to copyright issues. In the U.S., the medical privacy provisions of HIPAA describe the security requirements uses must consider when maintaining medical records in a digital format. Those working with health information in a technological environment should be familiar with current data security methods and should be able to select the appropriate data security method for a particular task. Intellectual property issues arise when data, software, and other non-physical products are used and/or redistributed. Technology users must be familiar with the various forms of intellectual property licensing and with the rights and limitations associated with each form.

APPLY YOUR KNOWLEDGE

Please note that some of the software interfaces and example screenshots have changed since publication. Errata, revisions to instructions, and updated images can be found at http://drspinello.com/cohs.

Consider the following situations in answering the discussion questions:

1. You are an administrator in a healthcare organization and have been asked to provide an independent researcher with medical records of several thousand patients. Discuss why or why not each of the following data security methods would be appropriate under HIPAA: Data segmentation, Encryption, Anonymity, and Transaction Auditing.
2. The healthcare organization for which you work maintains backups of employees' computers at an offsite storage facility. Discuss why or why not each of the following data security methods would be appropriate under HIPAA: Data segmentation, Encryption, Anonymity, and Transaction Auditing.
3. Describe three common limitations found to the use or installation of software under a commercial licensing agreement.
4. Using your own workplace or other organization, assess the data security practices by identifying some of the following: data protection methods for sensitive information, secure data destruction policies and practices, policies related to the use of personal media devices, such as flash drives.

IMAGE CREDITS

Fig. 1.1: Copyright © Mariko GODA (CC BY-SA 3.0) at https://commons.wikimedia.org/wiki/File:Reading_Fingerprint.jpg.
Fig. 1.2: Adapted from: http://rst.gsfc.nasa.gov.
Fig. 1.4: Evan-Amos, "Linksys Wireless Router," http://commons.wikimedia.org/wiki/File:Linksys-Wireless-G-Router.jpg. Copyright in the Public Domain.

2

COMPUTER MALWARE AND SECURITY THREATS

Immediately following the introduction of the personal computer in the early 1980s, computer viruses almost immediately became a factor that resulted in major changes to the way that computers are used today. The modern computer virus and other malware have evolved considerably, as have the motivations of the individuals who produce them.

In today's environment, computer malware poses a significant threat, particularly to any organization that makes use of personal data. Given the sensitivity of the data maintained by healthcare organizations and the legal requirements to protect those records, the issue of malware is of particular concern in healthcare. In this chapter we will explore some of the basic concepts related to computer malware, along with some of the best practices for maintaining security in the workplace.

MALWARE

Short for *malicious software*, the term *malware* essentially describes all computer programs, including viruses, which are designed to perform an unwanted action to the user's computer. Malware can be broken down into a number of different categories such as viruses, Trojan horses, worms, adware, spyware, ransomware, and scareware.

VIRUSES

Computer viruses can be best described as small computer programs that are written specifically to do two things:

1. Replicate themselves. In other words, they make copies of themselves with the intent of infecting as many computers as possible.
2. Deliver a payload. After some period of time, a virus will generally to perform an unwanted action to the computer, data, or software.

In recent years computer viruses have evolved considerably both in terms of how they work and what they do. In the early days of personal computing, the earliest viruses were often somewhat less malicious but were more or less designed to make a statement. The motivation for writing a virus was often bragging rights for the hacker who was able to claim that a given number of computers in as many countries as possible were infected. Once infected, the effects of the virus ranged from playful to destructive. In one example, the *Pong* virus, prevalent in the mid- to late 1980s, resulted in the periods contained in text falling to the bottom of the screen and then bouncing around, leaving trails of dots behind them.

Over time, the payloads of computer viruses became somewhat more destructive, with the motivation being to cause as much technological havoc and mayhem as possible. Viruses during this period were often likely to cause data destruction and in some cases, hardware damage.

With the advent of the Internet and the reliance on the web by many home computers, the motivation of hackers shifted from the desire to cause destruction to the desire to generate profits. In many cases today, the viruses that are found tend to be of the variety that harvest personal information such as account numbers, passwords, and other information useful for identity theft. Another typical payload of contemporary viruses is to plant a Trojan horse, which is often used by the hacker to control the computer and use it for illicit purposes, such as sending out spam emails from the user's email account without his or her knowledge.

WORMS AND TROJAN HORSES

Although worms and Trojan horses describe two different types of malware, the types of damage they can inflict tend to be similar, so they will be discussed together in this section.

Trojan Horses

The historical tale of the Greek war with Troy describes how the Greeks hid a number of men inside a large wooden horse that they left behind just outside the city gates of Troy, as the Greek troops pretended to sail away in defeat. The Trojans then pulled the horse into the city as a symbol of their victory. During the night, the Greek men let themselves out of the horse and opened the gates for the returning Greeks to invade the city. Much like this tale, Trojan horse malware consists of a computer program that is intentionally installed to a computer, but it unknowingly contains programming that allows access via the Internet to the computer by a hacker.

Worms

Although computer worms technically have the same definition as viruses, there is one important difference in that they do not spread by attaching themselves to legitimate programs. Worms tend to spread through wide area and local area network connections. Many worms do not have a payload, meaning that they do not necessarily cause a specific and intentional problem (such as destruction of data); however, in almost every case, worms will increase network traffic, occupy computer memory, and reduce the performance of the computer.

Worms and Trojan horses that contain payloads can delete or corrupt data, or open backdoor access to a computer, rendering it a "zombie" and making it vulnerable to a large number of hackers who may take it over to send spam email or

Author's note: *Several years ago, I was reviewing a website that had been experiencing problems. In doing so, I found some very deeply nested and undocumented folders that were not officially part of their website. Looking into those folders, I discovered that the server had been infected with a worm, allowing access to a hacker who had created and was operating a pornographic website from that server, without the knowledge of the server's owner.*

Had it not been found, the porn site could have continued to operate for quite some time using a legitimate company's webserver and URL.

even use the computer as a server for an illicit website.

Another common payload is to take over a computer as part of a Denial of Service (DoS) attack. In a DoS attack, hundreds or thousands of computers are coordinated so that they all simultaneously generate many rapid-fire "hits" to a given website. Although modern webservers are designed to be able to support thousands of simultaneous visits, DoS attacks are designed to overwhelm a webserver and essentially shut down service for legitimate users.

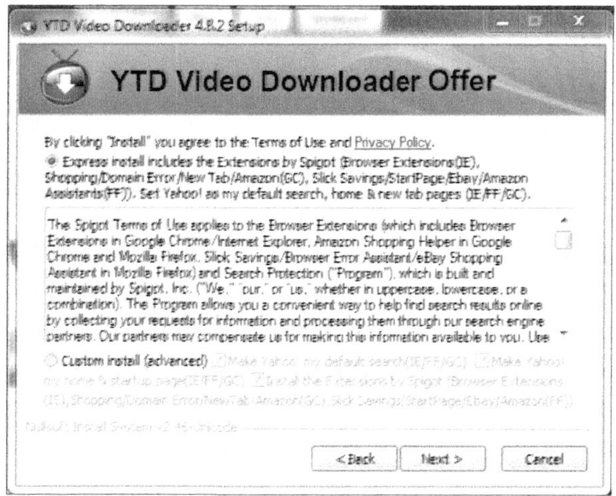

FIGURE 2.1 YTD Video Downloader Offer.

ADWARE

Adware is essentially software that is sometimes included with a program that a user intentionally downloads and installs, which presents advertisements to the user. Although some types of adware may be considered a form of malware, adware is not by definition considered to be a virus.

Some software developers see adware as a way to defray the cost of software development. By including adware with a program, they are essentially selling advertising to another vendor. The concept of adware is similar to the use of television commercials during a show. Although the viewer gets essentially free access to the TV program, he or she must deal with the commercials that are included with the program. Although not destructive, adware can be seen as an occasional annoyance and may monopolize network bandwidth, slowing down access to websites and email.

The issue with many adware programs is that they are sometimes installed without the user's knowledge. For example, installing a free program that is found on a website may often include adware that the user is not aware of. In some cases, the set-up program may include checkboxes allowing the user to uncheck the option to install the adware; however, these can often go easily unnoticed and result in the user essentially agreeing to the adware installation.

Note the example in Figure 2.1, which is the installation program for a free program called *YTD Video Downloader*, which used to download YouTube videos. On this screen of the set-up program, the option has been automatically selected by default for an *Express Install*. Note that the Express Install option will also install a number of adware programs, and it will automatically change the user's browser homepage and default search engines. Although the *Custom Install* option at the bottom of the screen allows each of the adware items to be unselected, it could easily be missed by someone who quickly clicks the *Next* button to complete the installation, especially since the Custom Install options are presented in a light gray font, making it appear as though they are not even active.

SPYWARE

The term *spyware* describes several different types of threats that vary considerably in terms of how they work and their potential to cause a disruption to use of the computer. In many cases, spyware can be essentially the same as adware, which is discussed in the section above. "The term 'spyware' generally refers to software programs that act as data sensors that illicitly collect and transmit information about end-users, and then send it back to a third party."[6,9] Spyware generally refers to software or technology that does one of the following without the user's consent:

1. Presents advertising
2. Collects personal information
3. Changes the configuration of your computer

Some of the more common approaches used for spyware include the following:

Tracking cookies: Many computer users are familiar with the concept of *cookies*, which are very small text files often left behind when a user visits a website. Cookies can be very useful, for example, by keeping track of when a user logs into a website so that the user does not have to log in again after each click to a different link.

> **Author's note:** *A few years ago I was explaining the concept of tracking cookies to a class of undergraduate students when one student suddenly realized that was what was happening to her. She had recently become engaged and had begun looking online for wedding dresses. Within a few days, she noticed that almost every website she visited seemed to contain an ad for wedding dresses.*
>
> *The ad-supported websites had detected the tracking cookies left behind from the websites she had shopped, and then began presenting related advertising to her.*

Some websites, however, will take a much more aggressive approach of tracking events such as specific mouse-clicks and other actions while on a website. The tracking cookies left behind can then be used by the same website (or other spyware) to see what websites the user has explored on the Internet and then to present advertising based upon that information.

Unauthorized configuration changes: This spyware approach works by changing the configuration of a user's computer or web browser without their knowledge and/or approval. In the case of *adware*, this can happen when a user downloads and installs a free program and is then presented with an opt-out option that may not be immediately obvious to them. Although that approach may be a bit devious, a user who carefully reads the terms and conditions and who pays attention to the set-up screens does have the opportunity to avoid the changes.

However, in the case of *spyware*, the opportunity to opt out is typically not provided. The changes may occur when a user downloads and installs a program, or simply visits a webpage containing embedded code that executes without the user's knowledge. That code may alter the security settings of the browser, change the default search engine, or sometimes install an unwanted "helpful" toolbar. In most cases, the changes made to a browser will result in reduced performance and some degree of user confusion as they try to understand what has changed.

Access to personal data: Some spyware can effectively pose as either a legitimate program that was intentionally downloaded, or as a "drive-by" download that was unintentionally initiated by visiting a website. Once the program is installed to the unsuspecting user's computer, it can begin to locate personal files and relay that information to a third party for purposes ranging from advertising to identity theft.

BROWSER HIJACKERS

Browser hijacking malware is software that takes control of a web browser and controls what can be displayed. Browser hijackers are generally installed without the user's knowledge either through code that is executed when a user visits an infected website or they can be installed through trickery.

In one very common ploy, a user visits a website and discovers a window that has opened alerting them to a virus present on the user's computer. The user is then instructed to press a button to remove the virus. Unknown to the user, pressing the button actually installs the virus in the form of a browser hijacker. In the case of the fake virus alert, the browser hijacker takes control of the browser and in response to any action by the user, it simply presents a message saying that the webpage the user is trying to visit is infected by a virus and has been blocked, regardless of which website the user chooses. In order to "clean" the virus, the user is instructed to purchase a virus removal tool; otherwise any action on the part of the user simply leads back to the same message. Keep in mind that in this case the only virus on the computer is the malware that is masquarading as a virus scanner of some sort.

Other browser hijackers work by changing the default home page and search engine used by the browser in a way that cannot be easily altered. Many browser hijackers also have the ability to disable a computer's legitimate virus protection, making removal of the malware a time-consuming task. Removal procedures typically vary from hijacker to hijacker and involve a fairly technical process. In most cases, a relatively non-technical user will find him- or herself taking the computer to a technician for repair.

PHISHING

Phishing is a form of malware that relies on essentially fooling users into willingly giving up their user names and passwords. A typical phishing email contains a message from what appears to be an organization that the recipient is familiar with, such as an employer, bank, or school. The message will usually indicate that some sort of immediate action is required and it will also contain a link for the recipient to click on to be taken to a website so that he or she can log in. In all cases, the website will appear to be legitimate, including the correct logos, colors, and webpage layout, but in reality it is a fake site that was simply created to fool the recipient into entering his or her user name and password. Once the login information has been entered, the hacker may use it to access a bank account online, perform some other type of fraud, or possibly to send out spam emails from that person's email account.

The example in Figure 2.2 shows an actual phishing email appearing as though it was sent by Apple Computer, and designed to fool recipients into clicking the link to a fake website and then entering their user names and passwords.

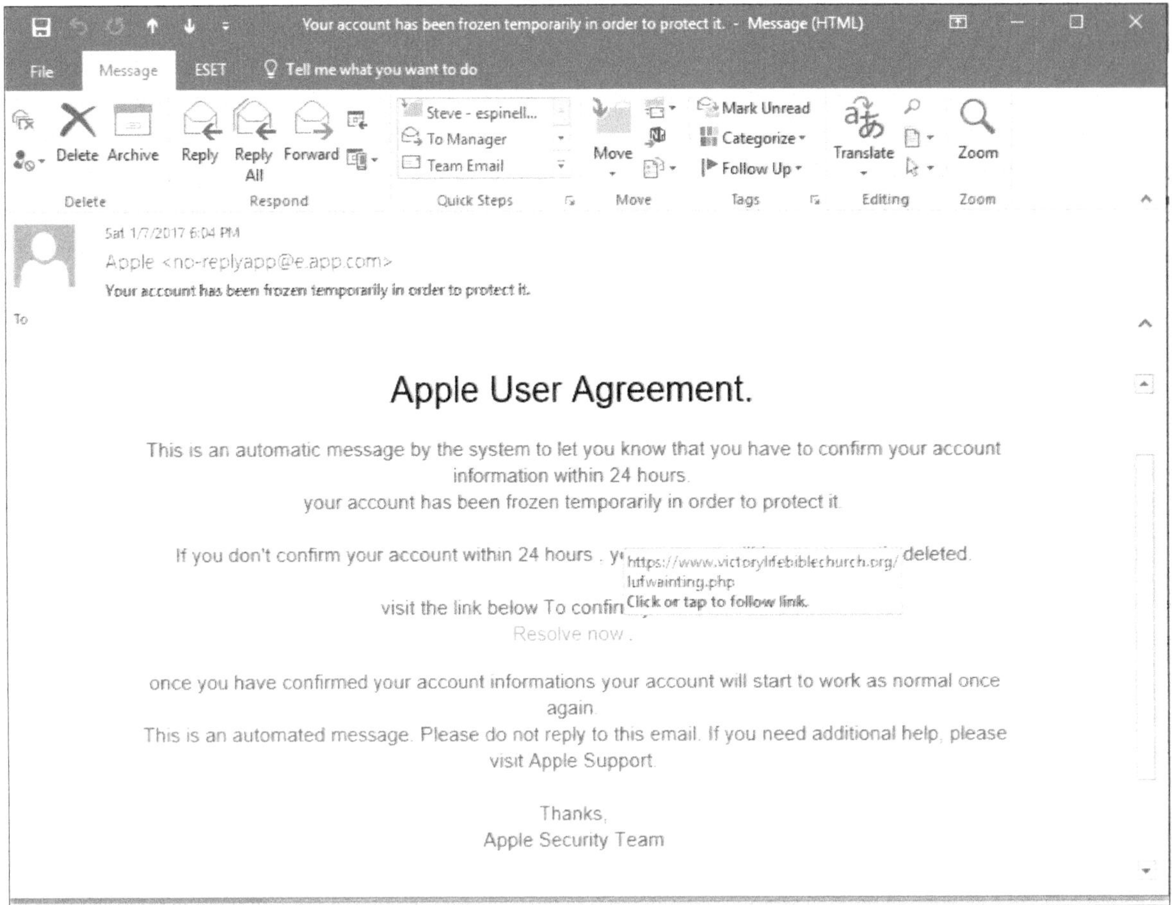

FIGURE 2.2 Example of a Phishing Email.

HOW VIRUSES TRAVEL

Many of the current computer viruses that cause the majority of the damage make use of the Internet. Before the Internet, a computer user had to share an infected diskette with another user in order for a virus to infect that computer. The typical scenario consisted of the following events:

1. A computer user inadvertently infected his or her computer by using a diskette infected by another computer.
2. Once the person's computer was infected, they would then copy a file to a diskette to share with another person.
3. That person would then infect their own computer, thus continuing the process.
4. After some time, the virus would cause some type of damage to the infected computers.

Today's viruses work much the same way with the exception that they travel through the Internet. Here is a typical scenario:

1. The creator of the virus unleashes it by emailing it randomly to individuals under an assumed name.
2. The recipient of the infected email opens the email and the attachment containing the virus.
3. Once the attachment is opened, the virus infects the computer. Without the user knowing that his or her computer has been infected, the virus goes to work by emailing itself to addresses found in the user's email address book and in web pages that the user has visited.
4. Recipients of the emails recognize the name of the person they are receiving the email from, assume it is a legitimate message, and open the attachment, thus infecting their computers.

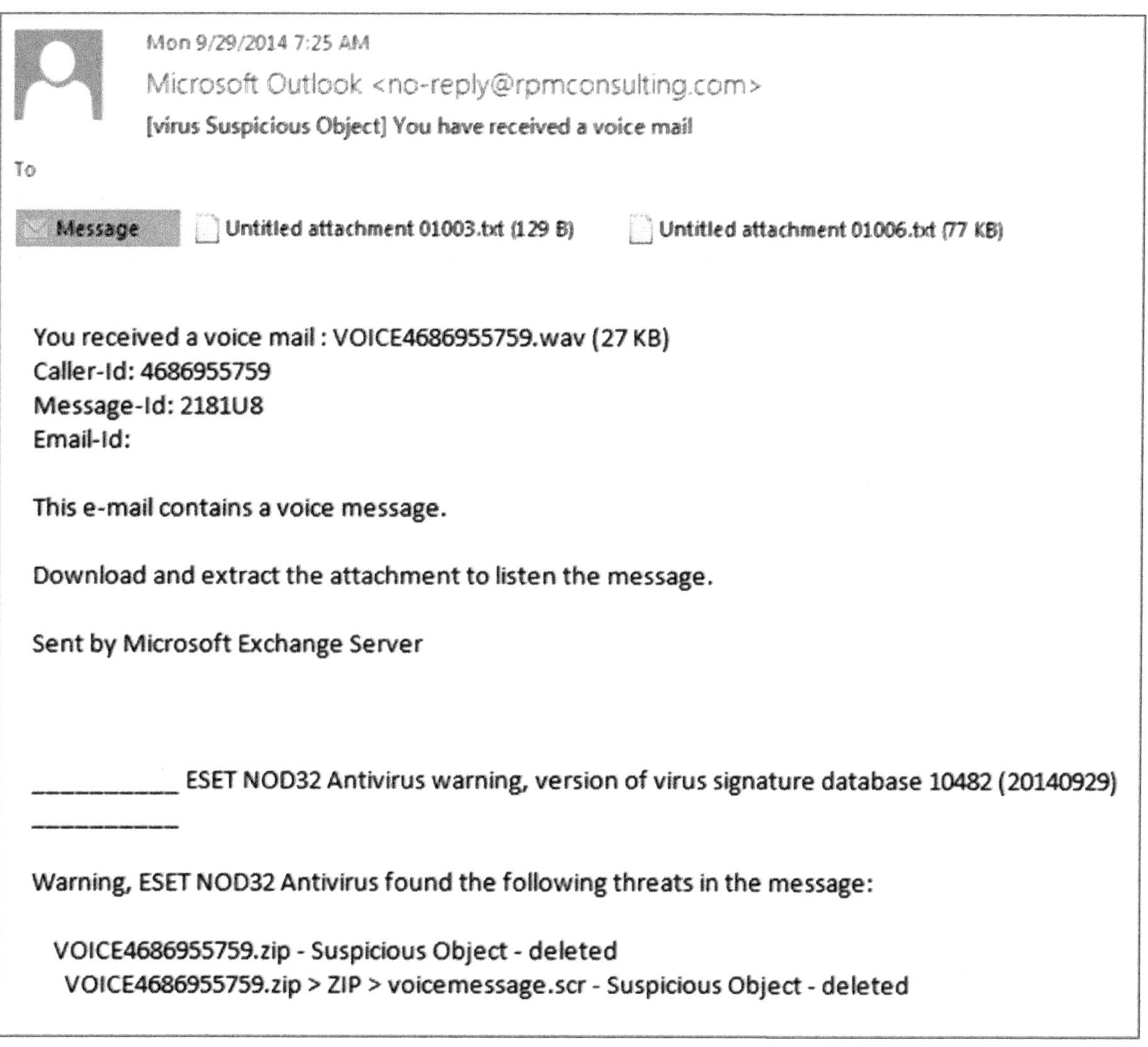

FIGURE 2.3 Example of a virus-infected email.

5. After some period of time, after it has emailed itself, the virus damages or destroys the data on the user's hard drive, or begins some other activity, such as using the computer to send out spam emails from the user's email account.

Another scenario involves an unknowing computer user inadvertently visiting a website containing a virus, which is activated once the webpage is opened. The infected website could either have been created expressly for purposes of spreading a virus, or it could have been a legitimate website that was hacked in order to spread the virus.

FIgure 2.3 is an example of an email virus. Note that the computer's email scanner (ESET NOD32) identified the attachment as a virus and attached a warning at the bottom of the email. In this example, there are a few telltale signs that the email is not legitimate:

Spotting an Email Virus

- Although the content of the email sounds important, it does not really make a lot of sense and is not something that would be expected from the sender. Some examples of the contents of mail viruses include passwords, virus inoculation programs, and pictures of an attractive female celebrity. Some viruses, like the w32.magistr virus, will randomly pick a file from your hard disk and email it to the recipients.
- The virus will almost always have an attachment.
- Some viruses can infect your computer when you click on the email to read the contents, even without opening the attachment.

WEB-BASED MALWARE

While the earliest forms of malware were generally spread when a user executed an infected program from a disk that was either given to them or purchased, a large number of computer virus infections in today's environment are transmitted by visiting websites. Millions of websites are estimated to be the distribution channels used to propagate malware throughout the web. Once infected, computers can be controlled by attackers who can utilize them to steal login credentials, generate spam emails, and attack other computers. Traditional security measures typically have limited effectiveness against this threat.[7,10]

RANSOMWARE

The concept of *ransomware* is one that has gained notoriety in recent years as hackers have attempted to leverage malware attacks as a way blocking access of legitimate organizations to their information systems and then extracting payments from them in exchange for providing them access.

Traditionally, much of the illicit money made from healthcare hacking has come from the theft and black-market sale of Electronic Health Records (EHRs), which would then be typically sold on the *dark web (see sidebar)* and then used for identity theft. With the transition from paper-based records to EHRs combined with system vulnerabilities, the availability of hacked EHRs has increased, resulting in black market cost of stolen EHRs having dropped. As reported by HealthCareIT News, James Scott, senior fellow at the Institute for Critical Infrastructure Technology estimated that in 2016 the price of EHRs on the dark web dropped from a high of $100 in 2015 to as low as $20 to $50 in 2016.[11] With the drop in income that can be made from the sale of stolen EHRs, hackers have begun to rely more on *ransomware* as an income source.

As estimated by Symantec Corporation, there were 2,400 complaints reported to the FBI in 2015 (increased from 1,800 in 2014), with a total demand for ransoms of approximately $24 million. In July

2016, the average ransom demand was estimated to be $679, which was more than double the average of $294 at the end of 2015. In January 2016, a relatively new ransomware threat called "7ev3n-HONE$T" was discovered, which demands a ransom of just over $5,000, paid in Bitcoins.[12]

A common scenario consists of an employee unknowingly triggering a malware attack by opening an infected email attachment or providing company login information on a phishing website.* Once the hacker gains access to the organization's computer network, the hacker will often encrypt an operationally important database, such as an electronic medical records system, which effectively blocking the organization from access to their own data. This, in turn prevents the healthcare organization from conducting business as usual. In many cases, the hacker can also encrypt the drives of multiple computers connected to the network, in addition to network storage devices and connected backup devices.[13] In the case of a healthcare organization, the sense of urgency is compounded by the fact that many of healthcare consumers require critical care, which may be impossible to deliver without real-time access to medical records. Given the potential for physical harm to patients combined with the potential legal liability and lost revenue, healthcare organizations are faced with immense pressure to comply with hackers rather facing the possible consequences.

The Dark Web

The Dark Web is often used as a term to describe websites and forums that are not indexed by search engines, not visible to the general public, provide anonymity to users who visit them, and are often associated with illegal activities. In a study conducted at the University of Portsmouth, researchers attempted to determine the contents of hidden sites available on The Onion Router (TOR), which is a portal that provides anonymous access to a variety of sites on the dark web[1].

The majority of the sites found on TOR were used to control botnets, which are home computers owned by unsuspecting users who had become the targets of malware attacks and whose computers were being used by the hackers. The most frequently visited dark web sites involved child pornography, black market sales of illegal drugs and weapons, Bitcoin money laundering, and sites offering counterfeit items for sale.

It should be noted that a number of legitimate sites also exist on TOR, such as discussion forums used by whistleblowers, political dissidents living in repressive regimes, and journalists communicating with individuals seeking anonymity.

MEDSTAR HEALTH

One high-profile example of a ransomware attack against a healthcare organization involved Medstar Health. In March 2016, Medstar Health's 10 hospital system based in Baltimore, MD was attacked by a hacker who was able to essentially block access to 370 programs in use by the health

* Phishing is a hacking technique by which the hacker fools an individual into logging into a website that appears to be legitimate but is in fact an identical replica designed to steal the user's user name and password. Spear-phishing takes the approach a step farther by targeting specific individuals about whom information is already known, making the login request seem much more legitimate.

system. Users discovered the problem as they attempted to open files and perform other routine tasks. Attempting to access those files triggered a "ransom note" to appear that instructed them to visit a website where they could pay the ransom using Bitcoin. The hacker essentially blocked access to the data by encrypting the individual databases and then offering to sell Medstar the encryption keys in exchange for the ransom demand. In fact, the hackers requested a ransom payment for each individual database, as well as offering a bulk discount to unlock all of them at once.

In the case of Medstar, the attack was the result of the healthcare organization's use of a particular network server program called JBoss. JBoss contained a known vulnerability that had been identified in 2010, and a software update patch had been made available by the software vendor in the same year to repair the vulnerability, Medstar's IT staff had never applied the patch to the server, which rendered the server vulnerable to an attack. The hackers simply searched the Internet for un-patched JBoss servers that still contained the vulnerability. When Medstar's server was found, they were able to exploit the vulnerability, allowing them access to the server where they then encrypted all of the key clinical and administrative databases.[14]

As a result of the attack, the Medstar healthcare system had to begin turning away patients and rescheduling existing appointments. Delays were also encountered in the communication of various diagnostic test results, which further impacted patient treatment.[15]

By reviewing the impact and response to the attack, several important lessons can be learned:[16]

1. The speed of a cyberattack can be much faster than most organizations might anticipate, leading to delays as the problem is identified and protection is put into place.
2. Although many organizations practice disaster recovery drills, many do not consider what would happen if all of its systems were to become suddenly unavailable simultaneously.
3. Response plans should be rehearsed in order to identify all of the possible issues that might arise in trying to recover from a cyberattack or natural disaster.
4. Employees should be trained to work using alternate technologies. In the case of Medstar, they found that many of their younger employees had only experienced using electronic record-keeping and had not used paper charts before.
5. Software security updates should be consistently applied as they are made available, and must be kept up to date.
6. Basic malware protection practices must be employed, such as rotating passwords, anti-malware software, and employee training designed to reduce help them recognize phishing and other hacker attacks.

BEST PRACTICES FOR MALWARE PROTECTION

Although different types of malware require specific precautions, the security procedures used to help protect against malware are typically common to all malware and should always be employed for both personal and workplace computing.

Malware Protection Software

One of the most basic things that a computer user can do is to install and use a virus protection program (although many of these programs refer to themselves as *antivirus programs*, they typically protect against many types of malware). These programs rely on a database of viruses that they use to compare against the contents of a hard disk. If a file is found on the drive that matches the description of a virus in the program's database, it can then delete the infected file or try to remove the virus from it. In order for the antivirus program to work, however, it must have an up-to-date virus database, since new viruses are found constantly. The more sophisticated programs are often marketed as being *security suites*, which include antivirus capabilities, as well as phishing detection, network firewalls, and other forms of protection.

A very common myth is that only Windows-based PCs require malware protection but that Macs and computers using other operating systems are not vulnerable to malware. The reality is that since the majority of personal computers are Windows-based, most viruses are specifically designed to attack Windows PCs; however, there are many types of malware designed to attack Mac and Linux computers, as well. In one recent case, a computer virus targeted Mac computers of employees at Facebook, and the same virus also targeted computers used by employees at Apple.[8,17]

Additionally, it is very important to note that mobile devices, such as smartphones and tablets, are also vulnerable to malware. Consider that whenever a mobile device is connected to a Wi-Fi network, that device is then exposed to any network worms, Trojan horses, viruses, and other malware that can pose a threat.

There is a huge variety of antivirus software available, ranging from very basic programs that are offered for free, to much more sophisticated security programs appropriate for large-scale corporate environments. Given the sensitivity of data maintained by the healthcare profession (and the legal obligations for workers to protect that data), no healthcare organization relying on computers should ever have unprotected devices of any type in use.

Network Firewalls

Network firewalls are a type of rules-based software or firmware (firmware is essentially software that is built into a hardware device) that acts as the gatekeeper to a wide area network (WAN) connection. For purposes of this discussion, a WAN connection is generally the same thing as an Internet connection. For this discussion we will use the term *local* computer to mean a computer that is within an organization, and the term *remote* computer to mean one that is outside of the organization. The importance of a firewall is that while anti-malware programs work to find and remove malware that has already infected a computer, the job of the firewall is to help prevent malware from infecting a computer in the first place.

When a connection is attempted from a local computer to a remote computer (such as a user trying to open a website), the connection is referred to as an outgoing connection. In the case of an outgoing connection attempt, the firewall first checks to see that the connection is in compliance with its specified rules and, if in compliance, it then allows the connection. An example of a non-compliant request is an automated connection attempt that was generated by a program, Trojan horse, or other malware that should not have access to the Internet, or simply a user attempting to connect to a website that an organization has blocked in the firewall.

Connections from remote computers to a local computer through the Internet connection are similarly tested by the firewall before the connection is allowed to be made. When a remote computer attempts a connection to a local computer, which is referred to as an *incoming* connection, the firewall's rules are used to determine whether the connection is be allowed. Since the majority of Internet connections to other computers are typically initiated from local computers to remote computers (for example, someone using a browser to access a website on a remote server), incoming connections are generally scrutinized somewhat more carefully than *outgoing* connections (a web server would be much less likely to try to access your local computer). Prior to allowing an incoming connection to be made, the firewall will determine whether the incoming connection is one that has been explicitly allowed in the connection rules that have been established. If the rules indicate that the incoming connection is allowed, it will then allow the connection to be made. It is important to note that the end-user has control over the creation and maintenance of the firewall connection rules.

There are two types of network firewalls typically available, consisting of either hardware or software firewalls. Hardware firewalls are contained in an organization's (or household's) network router, and are accessible through a secure webpage that connects the user directly to his or her router's configuration screens. Through that screen, a user can establish the rules for the firewall to specifically allow or disallow connections to either certain websites or certain types of connections. The main advantage to a hardware firewall is that every computer connected to the network (either by Wi-Fi or through a cable) is protected by the hardware firewall.

Connection through WANs typically relies on port numbers as a way of classifying the type of connection to be made. One can think of port numbers as being different entry points into the computer through the network connection. Certain types of programs, such as email and FTP transfers, rely on specific port numbers when making connections. For example, FTP programs typically rely on ports 20 and 21 in order to transfer data, while connections to websites typically use port 80. Firewall rules can be established to allow or disallow either incoming or outgoing connections by port number based upon the IP address of the local or remote computer being connected, the time of day, the logged-in user, or any number of other criteria.

Software firewalls work exactly the same way as hardware firewalls except that they are based on computer programs installed locally on a computer, rather than on the router, as is the case with a hardware firewall. As opposed to a firewall in a router, which protects all computers connected to that router, a software firewall will protect only the computer to which it has been installed and configured. Both the Windows and Mac operating systems have built-in firewalls that can be configured and enabled on most computers.

Given the large and growing number of network security threats, it is not unusual in some organizations to rely upon *both* hardware and software firewalls.

Strong Password Protection

Since passwords are the frontline security protection, the use of passwords that are difficult to guess is an important step toward ensuring cybersecurity. Healthcare organizations should encourage use of a standardized procedure for password creation, such as the Password Checklist found at the end of this chapter.[9,18]

Commonsense Email Practices

Common sense is an important tool when working with email. Although fraudulent and/or malware-infected emails can often be cleverly disguised as legitimate messages, some basic precautions can help most users detect the vast majority of them before damage is done. For example, emails containing attachments should *always* be treated as being suspect unless the user can confirm that an attachment was expected, or that the attachment was intentionally sent by the sender (many viruses will send mail with an attached virus to contacts in the email program without the user knowing it is happening). Even if the sender is someone known to you, there is always a possibility that the attachment contains a virus. This is particularly true if the contents of the message appear to be out of context or something one would not normally expect from the sender.

Verify links before clicking on them. Phishing emails and many viruses work by tricking an email recipient into clicking on a legitimate-looking link that actually goes to either a fraudulent or an infected website. The way that hyperlinks are created in emails is through the use of HTML code. HTML stands for Hypertext Markup Language, which is the computer language used to create many websites. Using HTML code, any text can be turned into a hyperlink, even text that appears to be a different hyperlink. For example, the text string www.cdc.gov is a URL that will take a user to the U.S. Centers for Disease Control and Prevention website. However, that text string can be turned into a hyperlink that takes the user to an entirely different website, even though it appears to say www.cdc.gov.

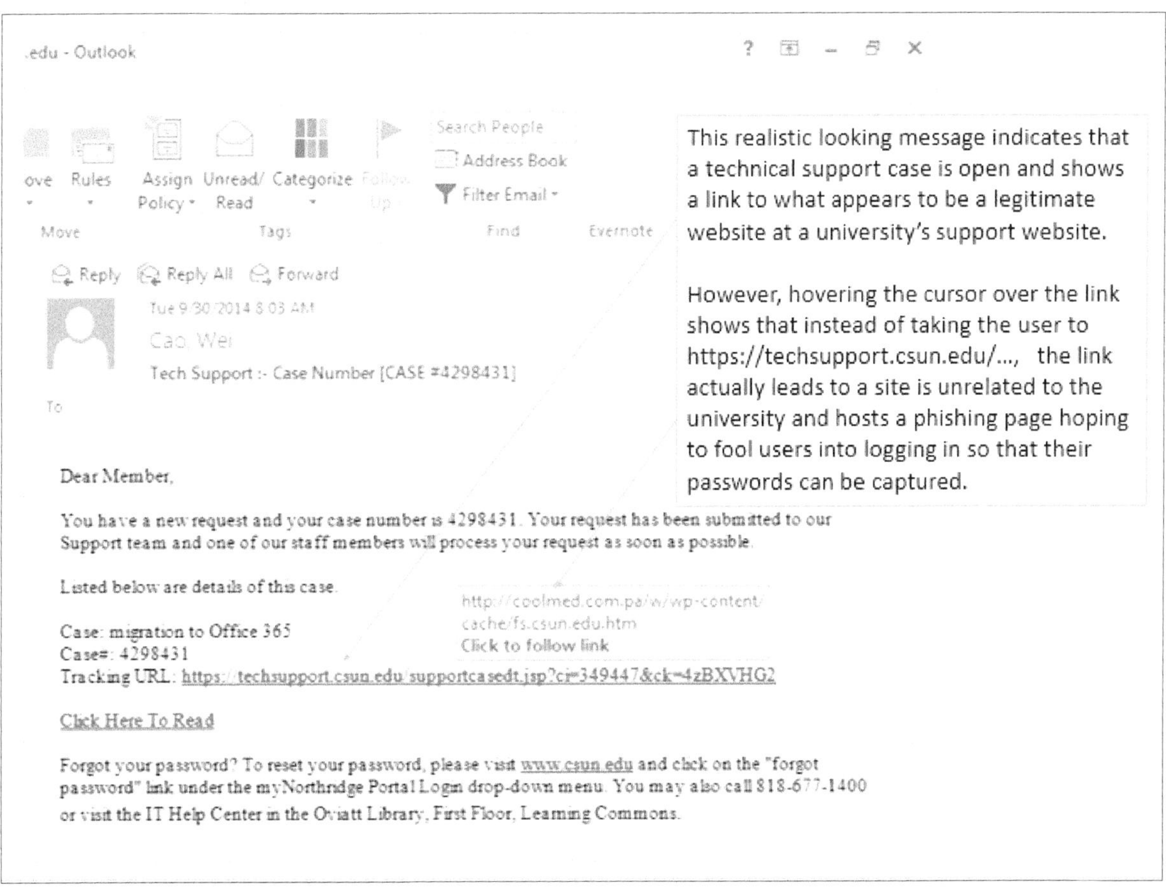

FIGURE 2.4 Example of a Phishing Email (small).

Note that in the example below of a fraudulent email, the text "http://techsupport.csun.edu... does not actually lead to that location. By hovering the mouse over the hyperlink (without clicking on it), the actual destination of the link can be viewed and verified that it is legitimate. In this case, hovering over the link *should* show a URL of "http://techsupport.csun.edu... but instead, it is

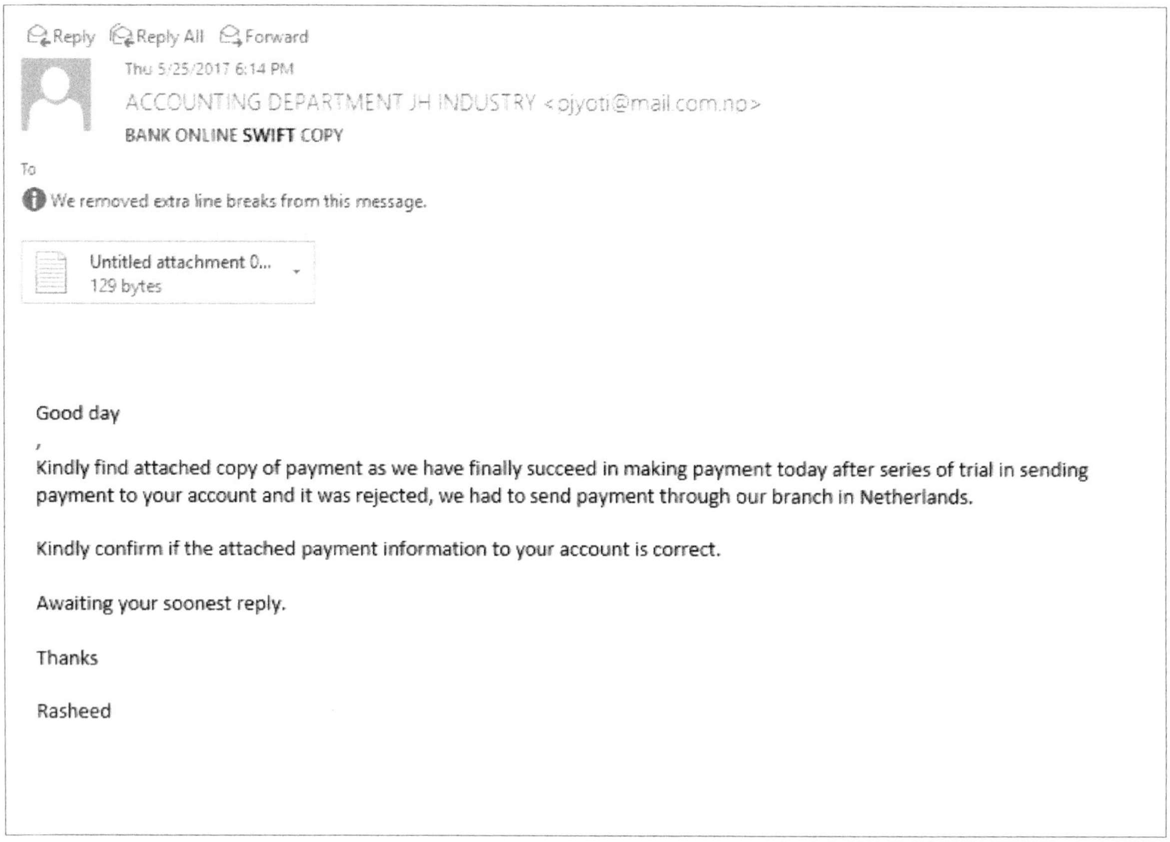

Reply Reply All Forward

Thu 5/25/2017 6:14 PM

ACCOUNTING DEPARTMENT JH INDUSTRY <ojyoti@mail.com.no>

BANK ONLINE SWIFT COPY

To

We removed extra line breaks from this message.

Untitled attachment 0...
129 bytes

Good day

,

Kindly find attached copy of payment as we have finally succeed in making payment today after series of trial in sending payment to your account and it was rejected, we had to send payment through our branch in Netherlands.

Kindly confirm if the attached payment information to your account is correct.

Awaiting your soonest reply.

Thanks

Rasheed

FIGURE 2.5 Example of an Email with a Malware Attachment.

apparent that the link really leads to a URL at http://coolmed.com.pa..., which is a realistic-looking fake website designed to fool someone into to entering their user name and password.

Avoid opening unverified attachments. Email attachments are one of the most common ways for computer malware to spread. In many cases, a virus will infect a user's computer and begin covertly sending out emails to recipients in that user's contact list. In many cases, the email may contain a vague reference to an important-sounding attachment, such as an invoice, court summons, order confirmation, or other official document. Even attachments that appear to be harmless, such as PDF or word processing documents, may contain malware code that is executed when the attachment is opened. One should always make certain that the attachment is expected and from a legitimate source. Keep in mind that since some viruses will send attachments from someone who is known to the user, it is very possible to receive an email from a legitimate and recognized address containing attached malware.

In the example pictured, note that the attachment is vague in terms of the type of file and content. The rather vague message, "Kindly confirm if the attached payment information to your account is correct" is often enough to induce someone to open the attachment. Also consider if the sender is not one who is known to the recipient. In the worst-case scenario, the email could contain an attachment infected with a virus, or it could consist of a scam designed to swindle money from the recipient.

Keep operating systems up to date. In addition to keeping virus scanner updates current, computer operating systems updates must also be kept current. As hackers identify vulnerabilities associated with various operating systems, developers such as Microsoft and Apple create updates designed to fix those vulnerabilities. However, if a computer does not have the most current operating system updates downloaded and installed, those vulnerabilities will still exist, leaving it open for a malware attack that is designed to exploit the particular weakness. Most operating systems offer the option for the automated download and installation of those updates, making it important that workplace computers always be configured in this way.

Flash Drive Policies

In 2008, the United States military experienced the worst cybersecurity breach in its history when a malware-infected flash drive was inserted into a single laptop computer at a U.S. base in the Mideast. The malware, planted by a foreign intelligence agency, allowed sensitive intelligence data to be transferred to servers outside of the U.S.[10,19] Since 2008, federal agencies have prohibited the use of flash drives on worksite computers in order to avoid a repeat of that incident.

This incident illustrates the risk of how a single employee, using his or her own flash drive, can intentionally or unintentionally introduce malware into a network at their workplace. This can easily happen unintentionally when an individual carelessly uses a flash drive on an unprotected computer, resulting in the flash drive becoming infected. Using the same flash drive on a workplace computer can then infect the workplace computer with a virus, which can then spread throughout the entire local area network.

In addition to the threat of malware, the additional risk associated with the loss or theft of a flash drive should also be considered. Once again, removing a flash drive from the workplace not only opens the door to a potential malware infection, but it also creates the possibility that the drive can be lost or stolen. If a lost or stolen flash drive is unencrypted, the risk of a potential security breach associated with the incident is much higher.

Given the speed, convenience, and low cost associated with flash drives, a full ban on their use is not necessarily in the best interest of many organizations. However, the risk should be recognized and appropriate security procedures should be established to minimize the risks. Following are some of the basic security procedures that can help lower the risks of flash drives:

1. Ensure that all flash drives used in the workplace have a common strong encryption program to make a lost or stolen drive less likely to be accessible by an unauthorized individual.
2. Flash drives containing sensitive data should not leave the work environment, such as being taken home or transported in employees' personal vehicles, unless it is for a necessary purpose.
3. Although virus-protection software is not foolproof, workplace computers should be equipped with up-to-date virus protection software that is configured to automatically scan any external storage devices connected to the computer.
4. Personal storage devices, such as flash drives, smart phones, and other flash memory-equipped items should not be connected to a workplace computer, whether for charging batteries or for data transfer.
5. Operating system updates should always be kept up to date in order to minimize vulnerabilities.

SUMMARY

Cybersecurity threats are a very real and prevalent threat to network computing. Given the unique requirements associated with the sensitivity of health information, computer users in a healthcare environment must be extremely vigilant with respect to security issues. Cybersecurity threats in the form of malware can be introduced through network connections, web browsing, and email. Effective security precautions include the use of network firewalls, antivirus software, strong passwords, and the vigilant use of email.

APPLY YOUR KNOWLEDGE

Please note that some of the software interfaces and example screenshots have changed since publication. Errata, revisions to instructions, and updated images can be found at http://drspinello.com/cohs.

1. Using a web search engine, identify three commercially available antivirus programs. Using information provided by the antivirus programs' websites, identify the following for each of the programs:

a. How many virus definitions are contained in each program's database?
b. How often do program updates to virus definitions occur?
c. How has each program performed in independent testing against other antivirus programs? (This may require some online research using a search engine.)

2. Using the computer that you most often rely upon for personal use, determine what type of malware protection program is present. Using a web search engine to conduct some research about that program, compare it to the three that you researched in Question 1, above.

3. Using the computer that you most often rely upon for personal use, determine how to access the firewall on that computer. To do so, you will most likely need to search the help system for topics related to *network connections*. Once you have found the firewall, determine the following.

a. Whether the firewall is turned on or off
b. What rules are in effect controlling incoming connections
c. What rules are in effect controlling outgoing connections

Note: do not make any changes to the firewall unless you have an understanding of how it works. If you have any doubts, locate a technical support resource for assistance. Making inappropriate changes may reduce your level of protection or can cause some programs to stop functioning properly.

As provided the by *The Office of the National Coordinator for Health Information Technology,* the following password checklist is recommended for use in healthcare organizations.

SECURITY CHECKLIST

Practice 1: Password Checklist

- Policies are in place prescribing password practices for the organization.
- All staff understand and agree to abide by password policies.
- Each staff member has a unique username and password.
- Passwords are not revealed or shared with others.
- Passwords are not written down or displayed on screen.
- Passwords are hard to guess, but easy to remember.
- Passwords are changed routinely.
- Passwords are not re-used.
- Any default passwords that come with a product are changed during product installation.
- Any devices or programs that allow optional password protection have password protection turned on and in use.

Strong passwords should:

- Be at least 8 characters in length.
- Include a combination of upper case and lower case letters, at least one number and at least one special character, such as a punctuation mark.
- Be changed often, at least quarterly.

FIGURE 2.6 Health Information Password Checklist.

IMAGE CREDITS

Fig. 2.2: Copyright © Microsoft.
Fig. 2.3: Copyright © Microsoft.
Fig. 2.4: Copyright © Microsoft.
Fig. 2.5: Copyright © Microsoft.
Figure 2.6: Source: HealthIT.gov.

3

COMPUTER HARDWARE

This chapter addresses the topic of computer hardware, or the physical and tangible components of computer systems. The objective of this chapter is to provide an understanding of the key components of computer hardware with respect to each component's function and significance so that an intelligent decision can be made with respect to a computer purchase or a component upgrade. The chapter is designed to provide an understanding of how each component can be measured and compared in terms of performance and/or capacity. Given the sometimes bewildering terminology related to computing, key terms are presented with explanations.

Consider that the modern personal computer system is composed of a series of components that all work together to perform the required tasks. First of all, it is useful to break the computer system down into four basic components:

Hardware — The physical, tangible devices that you can see and touch. We can further break down hardware into two sub-components: the computer processor (the brain of the computer) and peripheral devices, which allow you to transfer data to and from the processor (keyboard, monitor, mouse, speakers, etc.).

Software — Computer programs, or the set of instructions that the computer hardware executes.

Data — The information that computers do something to. Think of computers as input-output devices. You put data into a computer, the software tells the hardware what to do to that data, and it is then returned to you in some altered (hopefully improved) fashion.

Media — Storage devices that are able to hold software and data. Because software and data are intangible (you can't see or touch them), they exist in a binary (1's and 0's) format. Those 1's and 0's must be stored on a form of media, such as a flash drive, diskette, hard disk, or paper.

MEASURING INFORMATION

Before an in-depth discussion of hardware components can be started, it is important to have an understanding of how information is measured in computer terms. This is the section that discusses bits, bytes, etc. Although there is quite a bit of technical nuance to the definitions, the truth is that the basic concept is quite simple. In fact, for most purposes, the exact numbers are not really quite as important as is the ability to simply approximate the amount of information being dealt with.

Understanding how to measure an amount of information relative to a computer is based on the fact that computers operate as *binary* devices. In other words, every piece of information on a computer can be ultimately reduced to a series of 1's and 0's. That applies to every sophisticated computer program, every piece of clipart, and every photograph, video clip, and digital audio clip that is stored on a computer. Given this approach, the smallest piece of information that a computer can deal with is either a "1" or a "0." A binary "1" or "0" is referred to as a *Binary Digit*, more commonly referred to as a *Bit*.

Bits are relevant to a computer only when they are in a series with other bits. In fact, it takes a series of eight bits in a series to form a complete character. A string of eight bits meaningfully assembled into a character is referred to as a *byte*. Although bits are obviously an important factor in the technical design of hardware and software, bytes are generally the unit of measure referred to in most end-user applications. Because bytes are related to actual characters (such as letters and numbers), for purposes of most practical applications, the byte is often the important measure to focus on.

Now that we have an understanding of bits and bytes, we can move on to the other measures. Fortunately, once you understand bytes, everything else is really quite simple. As the speeds and capacities of various computer components have increased over time, the numbers used to measure them have increased, as well. For example, the first IBM Personal Computer, sold in the early 1980s, contained memory whose capacity could be measured in thousands of bytes. Today's computers contain memory with capacities measured in the billions of bytes. In order to keep the numbers being used relatively smaller, a sort of rounding shorthand is used. As the numbers get bigger, we use different units of measure. This is a similar concept to the concept of fluid measurements using pints. If you were to fill up your car with gasoline, instead of saying you purchased 136 pints of gasoline, it would be easier to say that you purchased 17 gallons. The smaller number for gallons, rather than the larger number for pints, is easier to state and grasp. In much the same way, we can use the following larger units of measure for bytes, as quantities increase:

TABLE 3.1. BINARY UNITS OF MEASURE

UNIT OF MEASURE	HOW MANY BYTES (CHARACTERS)	ABBREVIATION
Byte	1	
Kilobyte	1,024 (approximately 1 thousand characters)	KB
Megabyte	1,0240,000 (approximately 1 million characters)	MB
Gigabyte	1,024,000,000 (approximately 1 billion characters)	GB
Terabyte	1,024,000,000,000 (approximately 1 trillion characters)	TB

OVERVIEW

The mainboard (sometimes called the motherboard), is the central component of a modern computer, in that it physically connects the central processing unit (CPU) to every peripheral device in use. In most computers, the mainboard is, in effect, just a very large circuit board that often takes up a rather large portion of the inside of the computer. Mainboards include connectors allowing for devices such as the monitor, USB flash drives, speakers, keyboard, and other devices to be connected using a wired or possibly a wireless connection. The mainboard also contains the socket where the central processing unit (CPU) chip is plugged into.

PERFORMANCE

The performance of a mainboard is really based on two basic factors: the speed at which it can transfer data between components and the amount of data that can be transferred at one time. A good analogy for mainboard performance is that of a school bus transporting students to and from school by making multiple trips until all of the students have been transported. If you consider the factors that can influence the performance/efficiency of a school bus, they will generally fall into one of two categories:

1. The "speed" category (how fast the bus can move the children from school to home), given factors such as traffic, weather conditions, lack of breakdowns, and horsepower. The faster the bus can travel, the faster it can transport students to their correct destinations and complete the task.
2. The size category (how many children can be transported in one trip). The idea is that the more children you can fit on the bus, the fewer the trips that will be needed.

On a computer, information travels in much the same way as students travel to school—on a bus. The word *bus* is actually the term used to describe the mechanism by which information is transported from one peripheral device to or from the CPU. Although it does not quite appear like a little yellow vehicle driving around the mainboard, it can be thought of in those terms. The mainboard's bus carries information (which can be data or software instructions) between components. The bus is able to carry a certain amount of information at one time, and it can transfer the data at a certain speed. Just like a school bus, the faster the computer bus and the more information it can carry, the faster the computer will perform.

FIGURE 3.1 A Computer's Mainboard.

On most contemporary personal computers, the bus is formally referred to as the Front-Side Bus (or FSB). Consequently, many computer systems will list among their specifications an FSB speed. The FSB speed is similar to the concept of miles per hour for a motor vehicle. However, instead of miles, the measure is based on how many cycles per second information can be transferred by the bus. Using this approach, one transfer cycle per second is roughly equivalent to one *hertz*. The following prefixes are used as a way of dealing with very large numbers.

- Hertz = 1 cycle per second
- Kilohertz = 1 thousand hertz
- Megahertz (Mhz) = 1 million hertz
- Gigahertz (Ghz) = 1 billion hertz

Based on this measure, a mainboard that can cycle data 200 times per second has an FSB speed of 200 hertz, while one that can cycle at 200 *million* times per second has an FSB speed of 200 megahertz (abbreviated Mhz). The convention is to try to use the unit of measure that produces the smallest whole number possible. For that reason, once the number reaches 1,000 kiliohertz, one would refer to it as 1 megahertz. Likewise, 1,000 megahertz would be referred to as 1 gigahertz.

As an alternative to the use of hertz as a measurement of bus speed, many newer systems measure the performance of the bus as the number of actual *transfers per second*, which is a more accurate estimate of a mainboard's ability to move data quickly. As with the *hertz* measurement, the numbers can be simplified by using the prefixes *mega* and *giga*, and abbreviated as follows:

GT/s = 1 gigatransfer per second, equivalent to 1 billion data transfers per second

MT/s = 1 megatransfer per second, equivalent to 1 million data transfers per second

One advantage in using *transfers per second* as a measurement is that the transfer rate can more easily be multiplied by the data bandwidth (the size of the bus) to determine how much data is actually transferred per second, rather than just how many times it is transferred.

PRACTICAL APPLICATION

Comparing the mainboards of two different computer systems can be accomplished by comparing the FSB size and speed, with the speed being measured in either *hertz* or using *transfers per second*. At 64 bits, the size of the buses is typically the same on most computers, although the CPU installed on the mainboard and the operating system installed on the computer will typically determine two what extent the full 64-bit capacity of the bus is utilized.

FIGURE 3.2 A CPU that has been plugged into a Socket on a Mainboard.

CPU: CENTRAL PROCESSING UNIT

The CPU is composed of a single silicone chip, which plugs into the mainboard. The CPU is essentially the brain of the computer. It is responsible for a number of very specific tasks in the computer system, including the following:

Interpreting and executing instructions: This means that it determines what the software requires to be done and then physically makes that happen.

Performing mathematical calculations: The CPU essentially functions as a very fast calculator, with the ability to perform mathematical calculations to a very high precision. The term floating point calculations essentially refers to this process with respect to the fact that CPUs can deal not only with integers, but also with real numbers.

FIGURE 3.3 CPU Fan.

Managing the movement of data: The CPU also directs traffic with respect to the data moving around in the computer system. At any given point in time, data is coming and going from a variety of peripheral devices. For example, as an individual is typing on the keyboard, the incoming data is potentially saved in RAM, routed to the monitor, or possibly entered into an email about to be sent.

CPU PERFORMANCE

The performance of a CPU is primarily measured by how many times per second it can execute instructions, which is referred to as *clock speed*. The processing of a set of instructions is called a CPU *cycle*, meaning that in every CPU cycle one or more instructions is executed by the CPU. The processing speed of a CPU is measured by how many cycles per second it is capable of processing. Similar to the FSB speed of mainboards, the unit of measurement used to assess a CPUs clock speed is also a *hertz*. One hertz is the equivalent of one cycle per second. The following prefixes are used as a sort of shorthand:

- Kilohertz = 1 thousand hertz
- Megahertz (Mhz) = 1 million hertz
- Gigahertz (Ghz) = 1 billion hertz

Using this terminology, a processor operating at 2 gigahertz could be described as one that processes instructions at a rate of 2 billion times per second, 2.5 gigahertz would be processing at 2.5 billion times per second, etc.

PROCESSING CORES

Another factor affecting the performance of a CPU concerns the number of processing *cores* in the CPU. As the designs of CPU chips changed over time in order to operate under faster and faster speeds, one of the issues that arose was that the faster they processed, the more heat they generated. Consequently, battery-powered laptops suffered from poor battery performance due to the fans required to cool the CPU chip, as well as from the high power consumption of faster CPUs.

The engineering approach used to solve this problem was that of a multi-core chip. In other words, a single CPU chip could contain multiple processors, all working side-by-side. A multi-core CPU chip consists of a single silicon chip, which actually contains two or more processing cores. Processing cores can be described as being independent CPUs housed on the same chip. Since a multi-core CPU effectively has multiple CPUs working together, a multi-core CPU can process at the same speed as a single-core CPU, but can do a greater amount of work.

Consider the example of having the task of producing fifty-page report containing a variety of different sections. Assume that working alone, it would normally take one individual about 100 hours to complete the report. However, if a second person were to help by doing half of the sections, the report could be completed in about half the time without the first individual having to work any faster. The concept of a multi-core processor is based on the same idea by having multiple processing cores working side by side to complete a task in less time.

Contemporary chip manufacturers now produce CPU chips with anywhere from two to sixteen cores, although most consumer PCs contain between two and eight cores.

Practical Information: How to Determine CPU Performance

The best measure of CPU performance has traditionally been by determining a CPUs MIPS, or Millions of Instructions per Second. Since this number can vary, depending on the task at hand, it may not always be the easiest piece of information to determine for a CPU. In the absence of knowing the CPUs MIPS, a comparison between the clock speed of multiple CPUs and the numbers of cores can provide a quick determination of which CPU is likely to be faster.

For example, if two CPUs are being evaluated, both of which operate at 2 Ghz, but one has two cores and the other has four cores, the four-core processer will be significantly faster. A 3 Ghz four-core processor is faster still.

COMPUTER MEMORY

Like people computers have two distinct types of memory, which can loosely be categorized as long-term and short-term memory. For us humans, short-term memory consists of the part of our brains that stores information to be used for a specific task at hand. Once the task is complete, the memories of the information needed to perform the task are not necessarily kept around. As an example, let's assume you are asked by your dining partner to pass the salt during your meal. There are a number of discrete pieces of information required for you to complete the task, such as the location of the salt, the direction in which you must pass it, and the location of possible barriers such as water glasses. Once the task is completed, you tend to most likely forget that information since it is of no further use to you. If someone asks you a week later what action you performed at that particular date and time, you would likely be hard-pressed to do so, since the information associated with it was stored in your short-term memory (unless something about the action made it memorable—maybe knocking over a glass of red wine into your partner's lap as you passed the salt).

On the other hand, long-term memory is for information that will be relied upon over and over again. Information such as your name, address, and names of your family members are all stored in a part of your brain reserved for long-term memory. If someone asks you for your middle name, you can say it before you even really think about it. Computers are similar in that information is stored in different locations based on whether it is needed for an immediate task or it has a requirement to be kept around for a longer period of time.

RANDOM ACCESS MEMORY

Short-term memory for a computer is in the form of silicon chips called Random Access Memory (RAM) modules. RAM modules consist of small circuit boards, each containing a number of silicon memory chips. The modules are plugged directly into slots in the computer's mainboard. There are three characteristics of RAM that are noteworthy:

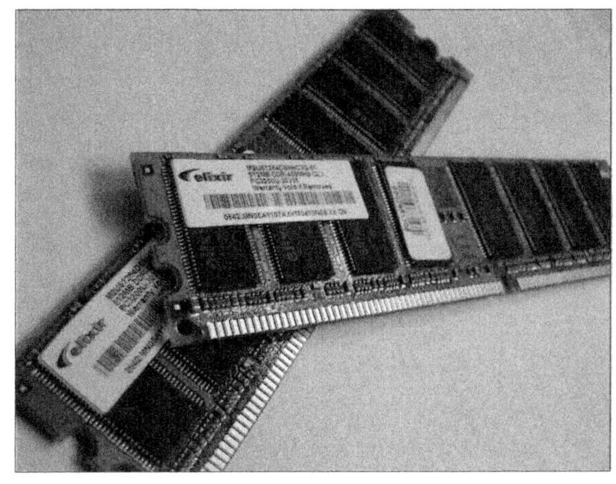

FIGURE 3.4 Ram Modules.

RAM modules are very fast at storing and delivering data to the CPU. This is because RAM is entirely made of silicon chips, in which there are no moving parts.

RAM modules are considered to be volatile memory. This means that RAM modules can store data only while they are receiving an electrical current (the computer is turned on). Any information contained in RAM modules is immediately lost if the computer is powered down, or interrupted (such as during a reboot).

Compared to long-term memory devices like hard drives and flash drives, **RAM has a relatively smaller and limited storage capacity.**

HOW RAM IS USED BY A CPU

Computers use RAM much the same way that people use their short-term memory. Information that is needed to complete a task at hand is stored in RAM in order to complete the execution of that task, and then replaced with new information for the next task after the first one is completed. So why use a limited capacity, volatile device like RAM to store data?

On most typical computer systems, the operating system, applications software, and data are stored on the computer's hard drive. Although modern hard drives are quite fast and hold a tremendous amount of information, they are still mechanical devices with many moving parts. Compared to the silicon chip-based RAM modules, hard disks are actually quite slow at retrieving and delivering data. Since millions of information transfers per second are typically required to process information, the computer's CPU can end up spending much of its time waiting for information to be delivered to it from the hard drive. The solution to this problem is that the CPU transfers the information needed (and anticipated to be needed) from the relatively slower hard drive to the much faster RAM modules. Once the information has been transferred to RAM, the CPU is able to work with it much more efficiently, given the speed at which the information can be made available.

As an analogy, consider the following situation: you have been asked to prepare an analytical report discussing a particular health problem and the current research related to treatment options. Working from your home, you realize that the journal you would like to quote from is on your desk at your office. In order to gain access to the information stored in the journal, you must walk to your car, drive to your office location, park, climb the stairs, enter your office, and pick up and read the article section. After reading the quote, you return the journal to your desk, drive home, and then write about that particular quote. After doing so, you remember another paragraph in the article that was pertinent. In order to read it, you must again walk to your car, drive to the office. ... You see where this is all going. Each trip to the office to retrieve a piece of information requires much physical effort. This is functionally similar to the situation faced by the CPU, which experiences a delay each time it requests information from the hard drive. It is not difficult to find a much more efficient alternative to the dilemma you face in our hypothetical scenario. The easiest thing to do (assuming the article can't leave the office) is to simply make a copy of it and take that copy home with you. Once at home, you place the article on your desk for easy reference as you write about it. In much the same way, the CPU utilizes RAM as sort of a desk, where it can place information it needs for easy and fast access. Once the CPU completes the task, the information in RAM is removed and replaced with information for the next task at hand, the same way you would clear off your desk once you complete the paper and are ready to work on another project.

Computers that do not have sufficient RAM generally suffer from the same problems—they are excessively slow. Anyone who has ever worked on a computer that takes seemingly forever to respond to a command—while the hard drive LED is on constantly, and the sound of the hard drive can be heard, struggling to keep up—has had this experience. When that situation arises, the amount of information needed by the CPU exceeds the capacity of the RAM, so the CPU must transfer the data a little at a time from the hard drive, which falls further and further behind. Such a computer would benefit from additional RAM, upgraded either by adding more RAM modules to the mainboard, or by substituting the existing modules with higher capacity modules. Every mainboard is different with regard to the type and capacity of RAM that it can use.

In essence, RAM makes the computer's CPU more efficient. Given the fast processing speeds of modern CPUs, adding RAM to a poorly performing computer can be the quickest and least expensive way to improve its performance.

PRACTICAL GUIDE

There are a number of different types of RAM modules on the market today. Different types and manufacturers of computers will vary with regard to the type of RAM that they require, so it is always important before purchasing new RAM modules to confirm the specific type required by your computer's mainboard.

RAM Modules typically have three characteristics that are useful to know about:

Capacity	The amount of information each module can hold. This can vary from typically 512MB up to about 4GB.

Type	Common types include DDR2 (*DDR stands for Double Data Rate*) and DDR3.
Configuration	Referring to the chips physically on the RAM Module (e.g., DIMM = Double Inline Memory Module, SIM).

FIGURE 3.5 A Computer Hard Drive Containing Two Platters.

HARD DRIVES

Hard drives are the internal non-portable storage devices built into computers, which allow them to store and quickly deliver tremendous amounts of information. Although hard drives owe their evolution from the lowly diskette drive, modern hard drives have advanced in recent years to the point of having both incredible speed and storage capacity.

Hard disks are really not just a single disk, but a series of disks, called platters, which are stacked in a series. Using multiple read/write heads, all of the platters can work together in tandem to split up the work and move data at very fast transfer rates. In the example above, the inside of a hard disk drive is shown. In this example, there are two platters visible, each with a separate read/write head.

Along with the multiple platters, another characteristic of hard drives that makes them perform so well is the fast speed at which the platters spin. Measured in RPMs, or *revolutions per minute*, the rate at which the platters spin can be used to assess the approximate speed at which a drive can transfer information. Most hard drives on the market today spin at speeds ranging from 4,800 RPM to approximately 12,000 RPM, with most consumer drives being in the 5,400 to 7,200 RPM range.

Given the extremely fast speeds at which the drive spins and the very close tolerances to which they must be constructed, hard drives must be assembled in dust-free clean rooms. In a clean-room environment, specialized air filtration systems remove particles from the air and assembly technicians wear spacesuit-like garments to avoid introducing contaminants into the environment. Once assembled, hard drives are sealed to avoid any possibility of dust entering the drive and causing damage to the platters.

RAID TECHNOLOGY

RAID (Redundant Array of Inexpensive Devices) is a method used to expand the storage capacity and performance of hard drives by linking multiple drives together in various configurations. In essence, there are three advantages that can be gained from a RAID, depending on the configuration:

1. Improvement in data transfer speed
2. Improvement in storage capacity
3. Improvement in drive reliability

Although there are a number of possible RAID configurations, the most common are typically the following:

RAID 0 – Striping

RAID 0 arrays are designed to maximize the transfer speed of the drives without regard for reliability. In a RAID 0 configuration, two (or more) drives are linked together in a way that essentially splits the data being saved across the drives, a process referred to as striping, helping to reduce bottlenecks in the movement of data. In the case of two drives being used, a RAID 0 configuration results in half of the data being written to one drive and half being written to the second drive, effectively cutting the amount of time needed for the transfer in half, and making the two drives together approximately twice as fast as just one drive alone.

A key limitation to a RAID 0 configuration is that although the combined drives are very fast, if either of the two drives were to encounter a hardware failure, it would result in complete data loss since both drives together are needed to access *any* of the files. For this reason, RAID 0 configurations are generally not recommended for environments in which the drives are being used to store critical data.

RAID 1

A RAID 1 configuration consists of multiple drives that are usually paired, so that each disk drive in the system also has another drive containing a mirror image. The purpose of a RAID 1 configuration is to ensure data reliability. Since a complete copy of each data file is stored on two separate drives, if either of the two drives was to fail, the second drive would serve as a real-time backup that would be able to take the place of the failed drive. Most RAID controllers are designed to provide immediate failover so that if one of the two drives fails, the second drive would immediately and transparently

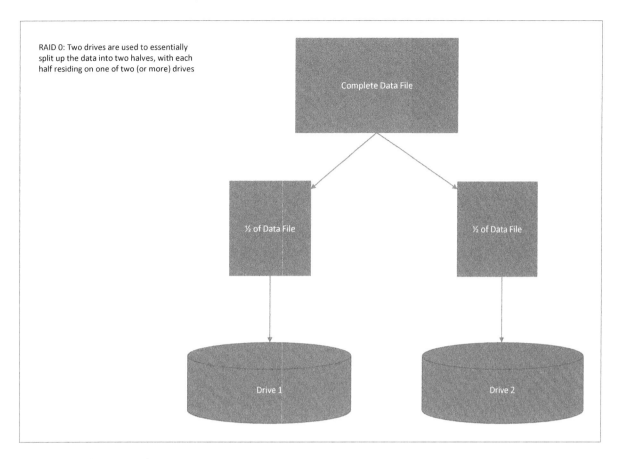

RAID 0: Two drives are used to essentially split up the data into two halves, with each half residing on one of two (or more) drives
Complete Data File
½ of Data File
½ of Data File
Drive 1
Drive 2

FIGURE 3.6 Illustration of a RAID 0 Array.

take over, without causing in loss in data or loss in the ability for the user to continue working on the system. In many RAID 1 systems, a failed drive can be *hot-swapped*, meaning that while the computer is still operating, the bad drive can be removed and replaced with a new one. Once replaced, the remaining good drive will then be used to automatically create a new mirror image on the replacement drive. Because there are two drives containing exactly the same data, there is typically some improvement in read speed. Since the files can be accessed

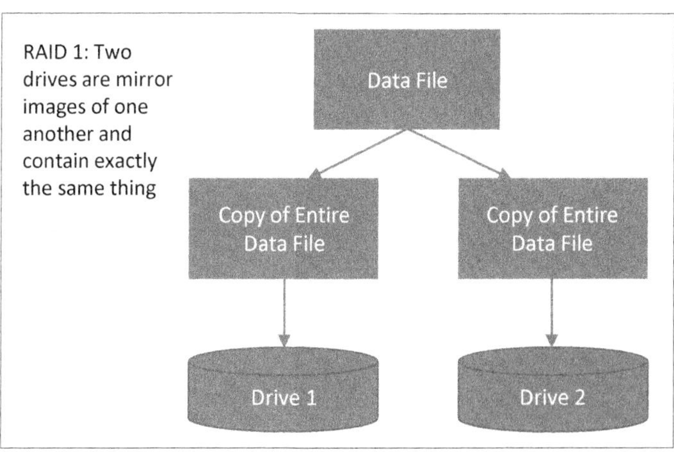

RAID 1: Two drives are mirror images of one another and contain exactly the same thing
Data File
Copy of Entire Data File
Copy of Entire Data File
Drive 1
Drive 2

FIGURE 3.7 Illustration of a RAID 1 Array.

from two different places the computer can read and write two different files simultaneously from two different locations.

RAID 5 – Striping with Parity

RAID 5 configurations are one of the most frequently used on servers to maximize both performance and reliability. The technical description of a RAID 5 array is that it is designed to be both a high performance striped array with parity, meaning that the array has the reliability of a mirrored array. Rather than relying on a mirrored drive that contains a duplicate copy of all data, RAID 5 relies on the use of parity data. The array requires at least three drives and a maximum of 16 drives. The data drive contents are split up among the drives in the array, much like a RAID 0 configuration. In the case of a 3-drive array, each drive would contain about 1/3 of the total data.

The key difference from a RAID 0 is that each drive also contains a portion of the data stored on the other two drives, which is called *parity data*. In the case of the 3-drive array, if any one of the drives were to fail, the remaining two drives would have the data that was contained on the failed drive and the computer would seamless continue operating normally, although more slowly than with all of the drives in operation. RAID 5 arrays are often configured using hardware controllers that allow a failed drive to be *hot-swapped*, meaning that it can be replaced without needing to power

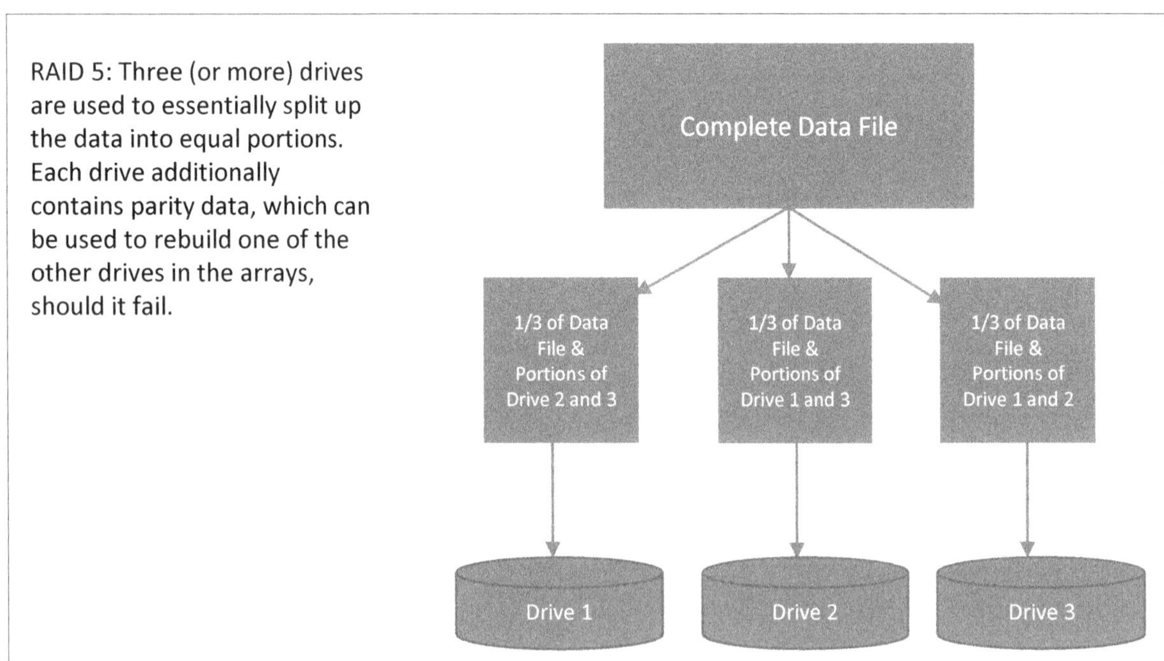

FIGURE 3.8 Illustration of a RAID 5 Array.

down the computer and taking it out of use during the replacement of the failed drive. The RAID controller hardware and software can often be configured so that replacement of the failed drive will authomatically begin rebuilding the array so that full performance can be restored.

RAID 6 – Striping with Dual Parity

RAID 6 arrays are created with essentially the same approach as RAID 5 in that the data is split up across multiple drives, with each drive containing parity data. The difference is that a minimum of four drives is required for a RAID 6 array and that the parity data maintained on each drive is doubled. The result is that the array can survive the simultaneous failure of two drives without data loss. It should be noted that although data will not be lost, there would be a slowing in the array's performance until the faulty drive(s) are replaced.

As with a RAID 5 array, the RAID hardware and software can often be configured so that replacement of the failed drives will result in the array being automatically rebuilt to its proper configuration, after which the normal performance levels will return.

RAID Drives and the Need for Backups

It should be noted that although RAID 1, RAID 5 and RAID 6 arrays offer strong reliability in the event of a drive failure, RAID technology is not a replacement for a comprehensive backup strategy. Although protection is offered in the event of a drive failure, there is no protection for physical damage to the entire computer, such as in the event of a natural disaster or a significant power surge. To protect against catastrophic damage, all individual workstations and computer should be protected though redundant on-site and off-site backups.

SELECTING A HARD DRIVE

Hard drives are typically compared on the basis of their storage capacity and their speed. Storage capacity, measured in gigabytes or terabytes, is relatively easy to determine from the specifications of most hard drive manufacturers.

Speed, on the other hand, can be somewhat more difficult to determine, particularly since there are a number of different measures that can be used. Although a drive's RPMs influence the speed at which it can transfer information, the following characteristics are good indicators of drive performance:

RPMs	The revolutions per minute at which the platters spin are related to the overall performance of the drive. In general, the faster it can spin, the faster it can transfer information.
Seek time	Measured in milliseconds (one millisecond is 1/1000 of a second), a drive's seek time is the amount of time that it takes for a piece of information to be physically located on the drive. Although seek time is not always advertised, it can often be found on a drive manufacturer's specifications. Typically, a smaller seek-time number indicates better performance than a larger number. For example, a drive with a seek time of .08 milliseconds performs better than one at .10 milliseconds.
Transfer rate	A transfer rate is simply the amount of information that can be transferred to or from the drive per second. This measure is generally expressed in the numbers of megabytes per second that can be transferred. A larger number is more desirable with respect to transfer rates.

Burst speed The burst speed is a drive's transfer rate for a very short period of time. Modern hard drives contain a certain amount of RAM, which allows them to read ahead (that is, cache) information, so that when it is requested, it can be delivered from RAM rather than the platters. For short bursts of data transfers, the result is that very fast data rates can be achieved.

Buffer size A hard drive's buffer is actually a series of RAM modules built into the drive itself. The hard drive utilizes the RAM modules by "reading ahead" and storing information in its buffer, so that it is more readily available when needed. Conversely, a hard drive can also use a *write-behind* buffer to store information that needs to be saved to the drive. Since the information can be saved to the buffer much more quickly than to the mechanical disk, the hard drive is able to save information to the buffer first, freeing up time for the computer to do other tasks, while the drive then transfers the information from the buffer to the actual disk at its leisure.

RELIABILITY

An important consideration for both internal hard drives and external removable hard drives is the reliability of a drive. Reliability of hard drives is measured by manufactures using two different methods. Annualized Failure Rate (AFR) is a measure of the probable percent of drives of a given model that will fail per year. For example, if a particular drive has an AFR of 3.5%, it is an indication that approximately 3.5% of those drives are likely to fail in a given year.

Another measure is the Mean Time Between Failures (MTBF). The MTBF is a measure of the average number of hours that a drive would be expected to be in constant use before failure. Although most drive manufacturers estimate both measures, many have begun to move toward using the AFR with the belief that it is a more accurate measure than MTBF.

It is important to note that although both of these measures are quantitative indicators of a disk drive's reliability, neither one can be used to actually predict the life of an individual drive. However, when selecting a hard drive from a number of alternatives, both the MTBF and AFR estimates are useful for comparison. Identifying the drive with the lowest AFR and/or the highest MTBF of the alternatives will help ensure that the drive being selected has a stronger likelihood of having the longest usable life and the lowest likelihood of unexpected failure.

MONITORS

Computer monitors have changed quite dramatically over the past several years. Monitors of the early 2000s and prior relied on cathode ray tube (CRT) technology, producing very large, very heavy devices that required much energy consumption and generated quite a bit of heat.

Today's monitors are almost exclusively based on *liquid crystal display* (LCD) technology, which results in much smaller, lighter, energy-efficient, and cost-effective devices. LCD monitors also have some significant advantages compared to their CRT counterparts. Since the entire screen of an LCD monitor is flat (unlike a CRT, which requires a curvature at the edges), there is no image distortion around the edge of the monitor, making the screen 100% usable.

Selecting a monitor is partly based upon what looks best to the user. However, there are some general characteristics that can be referred to when comparing the various options:

Screen size: The size of the screen is the diagonal measurement from one corner of the actual screen (not the frame surrounding it) to the opposing corner. Most standalone LCD monitors typically range from approximately 15" to 22", and many are larger. As the industry has begun to adopt LCD as a standard, manufacturing costs have dropped (as have retail prices), making larger monitors more and more affordable.

Backlighting: Although LCD monitors have been traditionally backlit using incandescent or fluorescent lighting, monitor manufacturers have more recently adopted *light-emitting diode* (LED) backlighting as an alternative. The benefits are LED backlighting include more vivid images due to the higher contrast ratio and lower power consumption, important for notebooks and other battery-powered mobile devices.

Dot Pitch: All computer monitors work in one similar way in that they produce complex images by assembling a set of very tiny dots together. The dots, each of which carries one of the primary colors, are assembled in combination to produce images and many different colors. The basic rule is that the smaller the dot, the better the image. Smaller dots can be used to produce sharper, crisper images. Additionally, the smaller size of a dot means that more dots can be placed in combination to produce a greater array of colors. Technically speaking, *dot pitch*, generally measured in fractions of a millimeter, is a measurement between two dots of the same color. However, the *really* important thing to remember is that the smaller the dot pitch, the smaller the dot, and the better the image. Consequently, a smaller dot pitch number is better than a larger one. Dot pitch (sometimes abbreviated "DP") for most LCD monitors can range from approximately .20 mm to approximately .40 mm.

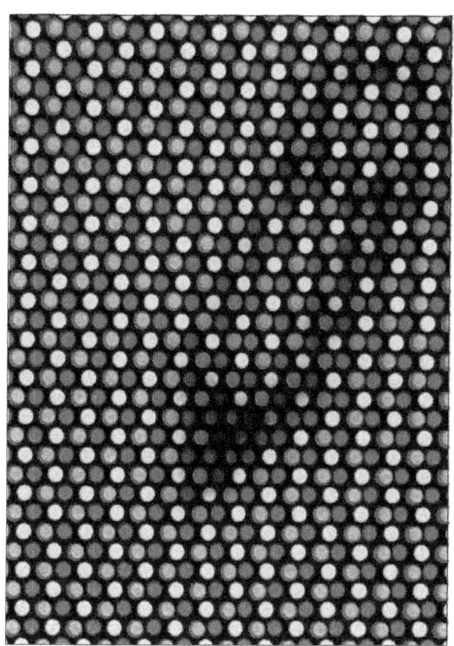

FIGURE 3.9 Closeup of Monitor Dots.

PRINTERS

As a general rule, printers fall into three general categories: dot matrix, inkjet, and laser. Although they are in some ways interchangeable, there are specific applications for which one type may work better than the others. The following is an overview of the types of printers and their uses:

DOT MATRIX PRINTERS

Many computer users remember dot matrix printers as noisy machines, requiring boxes of fanfolded paper and inked ribbons. Dot matrix printers work using a series of pins arranged in a matrix. In order to form a printed character, certain pins selectively and rapidly protrude and poke through a ribbon to form an image on the paper behind the ribbon, much like a typewriter.

Although dot matrix printers are not the most commonly used type of printer today, they still do serve one useful purpose. They are the only types of printers that can be used effectively to print on multi-copy carbon or carbonless forms. For that reason, dot matrix printers are typically best used in situations where multiple copies of a document must be produced in one pass, and where high resolution quality is not required, such as for receipts.

Advantages	Can print multiple copies in a single pass using carbonless forms, using inexpensive ribbon ink
Disadvantages	Noisy, relatively slow, low-quality printing, can typically only print black and white

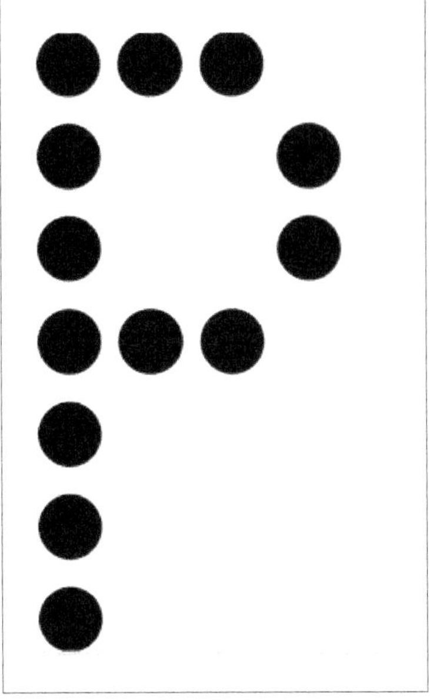

FIGURE 3.10 Example of a Letter Formed Using A Dot Matrix Printer Head.

INKJET PRINTERS

Inkjet printers utilize a liquid ink. They form characters on the screen by spraying the ink in small precise dots. Much like monitors, each dot is a single color (cyan, yellow, magenta, or black), but millions of different colors can be produced by arranging the color dots together in combinations. Although each microscopic dot is too small to discern an individual color, the combinations of the dot colors next to one another can fool the brain into seeing different colors (this is in contrast to the continuous color technique utilized by film cameras and dye sublimation printers).

Inkjet printers have the distinction of producing very high-quality output (particularly for photographs and other graphic images) and for having a relatively low cost, making them quite attractive for home use. Although the cost of inkjet printers is often low, the cost of their ink is generally quite high, making the cost per page higher than non-inkjet printers.

Another key characteristic of inkjet printers is that in general, they are designed for relatively low printing duty cycles (a duty cycle is how many pages per month can be printed). Printers that are used beyond the duty cycle specified by the manufacturer will wear out faster, and will most likely suffer some sort of failure (such as page jams and poor print quality). For this reason, most consumer inkjet printers are not the best choice for large office environments where multiple people must share the same printer and where many pages per day must be printed on a continual basis. However, they can work out quite well for less constant use in a small office or home environment.

Advantages	Low initial cost to purchase, outstanding color print quality, fast printing
Disadvantages	Lower duty cycles, high ink cost per page printed, not designed for heavy duty or constant use

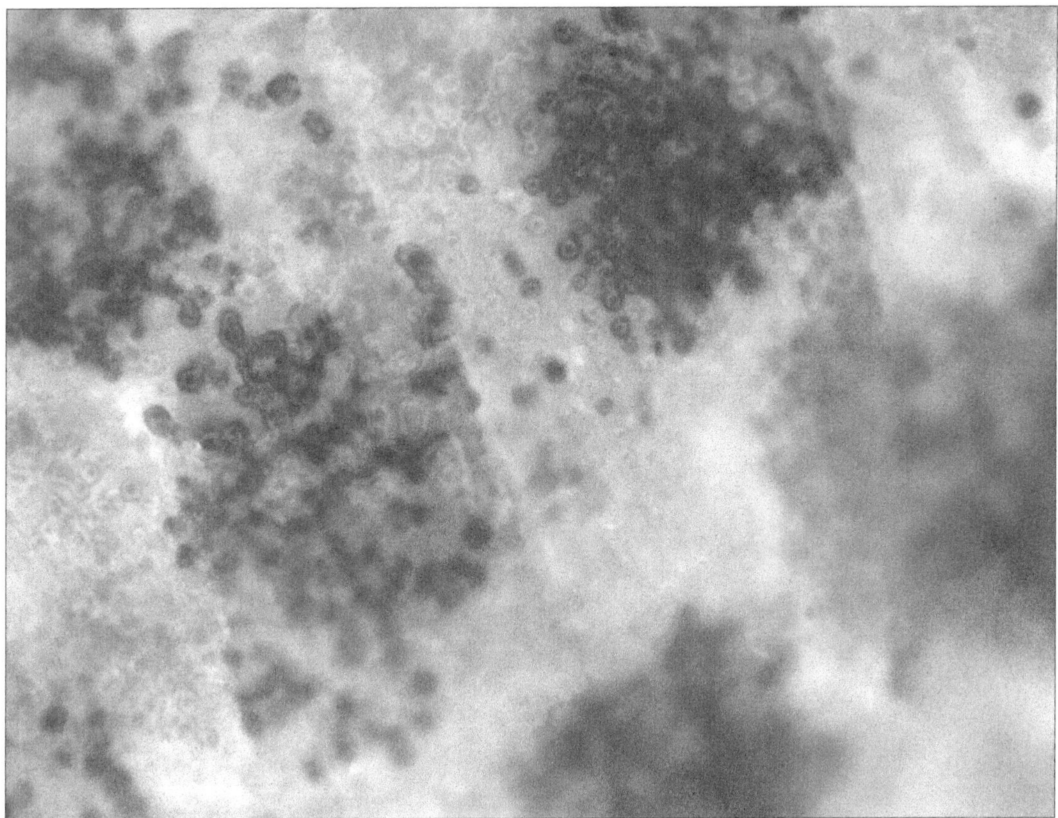

FIGURE 3.11 Color Laser Print Magnified.

LASER PRINTERS

Laser printers are distinguished as being designed quite differently than inkjet and dot matrix printers. Instead of using liquid ink or a ribbon, laser printers use a dry toner, which is a very fine powder.

How Laser Printers Work

Laser printers utilize a photoelectric drum, which is a long cylinder upon which the image to be printed is etched using a laser beam. The drum, which is in constant rotation while printing, passes through a reservoir of toner, which sticks to the etched image. After the excess toner is scraped off with a blade similar to a windshield wiper, the sheet of paper is pressed against the drum, transferring the toner from the drum to the paper. After the toner has been transferred to the paper, it passes over a fusing roller (another cylinder heated to a high temperature), which essentially melts the toner and makes it stick to the paper.

One of the key characteristics of laser printers is that toner is generally purchased in the form of a cartridge, which along with the toner, also contains the photoelectric drum, one of the key components. Since the photoelectric drum is replaced each time the printer runs out of toner, laser printers tend to have very high reliability, even under high usage. Although laser toner cartridges tend to be much more expensive than ink jet cartridges (toner cartridges typically cost $100 or more, compared to $20 to $30 for an inkjet cartridge), laser printers can print thousands of pages, compared to well under a thousand pages for an inkjet cartridge. An important note with respect to ink cartridges is that the number of pages that can be printed with a cartridge varies greatly depending on what is being printed. A photograph, for example, will use up substantially more ink than will a page of plain text.

FIGURE 3.12 Hewlett-Packard Laser Printer.

Advantages	Very high duty cycles, excellent reliability in demanding environments, low cost per page, very fast printing
Disadvantages	Relatively high cost, high cost of toner cartridges, large footprint, and heavier weight of printer unit

Practical Knowledge: Selecting a Printer

When shopping for any type of printer, the factors are essentially the same and include the following:

Duty Cycle: The duty cycle is generally stated as the maximum number of pages per month that should be printed. Office environments where many pages per month must be printed will generally require a laser printer, while home or small office environments may do well with an inkjet printer.

Speed: The speed of a printer is measured in the number of pages per minute (PPM) that it can print. The higher the pages per minute, the faster the printer.

Print quality: All types of printers (except for dye sublimation) produce images by generating tiny dots. As with monitors, the smaller the dots, the better the image. Print quality is measured in dots per inch (DPI) that can be printed. The higher the DPI, the better the quality of the printed image.

OPTICAL STORAGE MEDIA

Optical storage devices include Compact Discs (CDs) and Digital Video Discs (DVDs). Unlike magnetic media, such as hard drives and diskettes, optical media utilizes laser beams to store and retrieve information from a disk.

How Optical Devices Work

To store information on a disk, CD and DVD drives work by burning a series of microscopic indentations (sometimes called *pits*) into the surface of the disc (for historical reasons, CDs and DVDs are referred to with the British spelling of *disc*, rather than the American spelling of *disk*). The presence or absence of an indentation corresponds to a binary 1 or 0. The pits are detected and read from the disk using a low-power laser.

Although CDs were originally created in the early 1980s to store music in a digital format, they were quickly adapted for computer use, due to their large storage capacity and low cost, compared to other types of media at that time. Most CDs can store approximately 640 megabytes of data, and modern drives can read and write the data at acceptable speeds, although far slower than hard disks or flash drives.

DVDs, originally designed to store digital video as a replacement for VHS tapes, are also commonly used in computers, due to their low cost and storage capacity, which ranges from 4.7GB to 9GB, depending on the type of disk.

TYPES OF DISCS

There are three types of discs generally available for CD and DVD drives:

Read-Only Memory (ROM) discs can be read from but not burned. These are typically discs that are packaged to deliver commercial software, audio, or video to the end-user. Any type of drive can generally be read from a ROM disc.

Recordable Discs are usually designated as CD-R and DVD-R (sometimes DVD+R) for CDs and DVDs, respectively. Recordable disks can be burned to capacity only once. After they are filled, they cannot be erased and overwritten with new information.

Rewriteable Discs are designated as either CD-RW or DVD-RW for CDs and DVDs, respectively. RW discs have the distinction of being able to be erased and rewritten multiple times. Although RW discs can be rewritten, there is a limit to the number of times it can be rewritten and still reliably hold data. Although some estimates of the number of times a disc can be rewritten are close to a thousand, the actual number can vary depending on a variety of factors.

There has been a bit of debate in recent years regarding the appropriateness of optical discs for long-term archival. Since the technology has only been in use for the past 20 to 25 years, there is insufficient historical experience to know just how long optical discs can reliably hold information. For that reason, care should be taken when storing information for long-term archival. As with any other media, if optical discs are used, the information should also be redundantly stored on another form of media for safekeeping.

SELECTING AN OPTICAL DISK DRIVE

Over the years, the differences between various types of optical disc drives have diminished as prices have dropped and manufacturers have adopted the best available technology. Currently, the following factors are key to selecting an optical drive:

DVD, CD, or Both	Although in the recent past, CD drives were produced that could only read and/or write CDs, the majority of drives on the market today can typically accept both CDs and DVDs. However, to ensure that a future compatibility problem does not occur, the type of disk that can be used should be verified.

Read-Only or Read-Write

Some drives may be designated as ROM drives, which means that they can read from a disc but not "burn" a new disc. A drive that can burn a disc is generally designated as R/W, indicating that it can both read and write to a disc.

Speed

The speed of an optical drive is based on a somewhat unusual measure. For CDs, the speed is based on how many times faster than an original audio CD the drive can read information. The standard for audio CDs is 150KB per second. Therefore, a CD drive that is advertised as having a speed of 30X would be able to read a disk at 30 times the speed of 150KB per second (or 4.5MB per second). Keep in mind that it is not important to do the math! Just knowing whether a drive is 20X or 40X will tell you that the 40X drive is twice as fast as the 20X drive. The same thing holds true for DVDs. Although the "X" numbers are based on the DVD standard (1.32MB per second), the higher the X number, the faster the drive.

In many cases, optical drives will advertise three different "X" numbers; for example, 20X 30X 40X. In this case each of the numbers relates to a different drive function. The first number indicates the drive's speed when burning a recordable disc, the second number indicates the drive's speed when burning a rewriteable disc, and the third number indicates the speed when reading a disc.

UNINTERRUPTABLE POWER SUPPLIES

In addition to the processing components, peripheral devices, and media devices, another component worthy of discussion is the *Uninterruptable Power Supply* (UPS). A UPS device essentially consists of a large external battery into which the computer is plugged in. The purpose of a UPS is to provide emergency power in the event of a power failure. Although the amount of power is generally limited to several minutes to an hour, the purpose of the power supply is to provide time for all files to be closed and saved in an orderly fashion and to allow the computer to be safely powered down. Many UPS devices include firmware and software that communicate with the computer via USB interface. In the event of a power failure (or severe power fluctuations), the UPS can initiate an orderly shutdown by the computer, while the battery allows it to safely remain powered with regulated voltage. UPS devices are generally considered mandatory on fileservers, webservers and other systems in which many users rely on access to those computers and where down-time would result in significant disruption to many users.

UPS devices not only provide protection against data loss from unexpected power loss, but also protection from hardware failure. Many computer components are particularly sensitive to fluctuations in voltage and amperage, and can be physically damaged to the point of failure as a result of a power surge.

There is also a risk of damage related to power that is restored following a power failure. Initial power restoration can often be accompanied by a power surge that can be detrimental to electronic components. The use of a UPS device acts as a buffer between the computer components and the power outlet, and can protect computers and other electronic devices from those fluctuations.

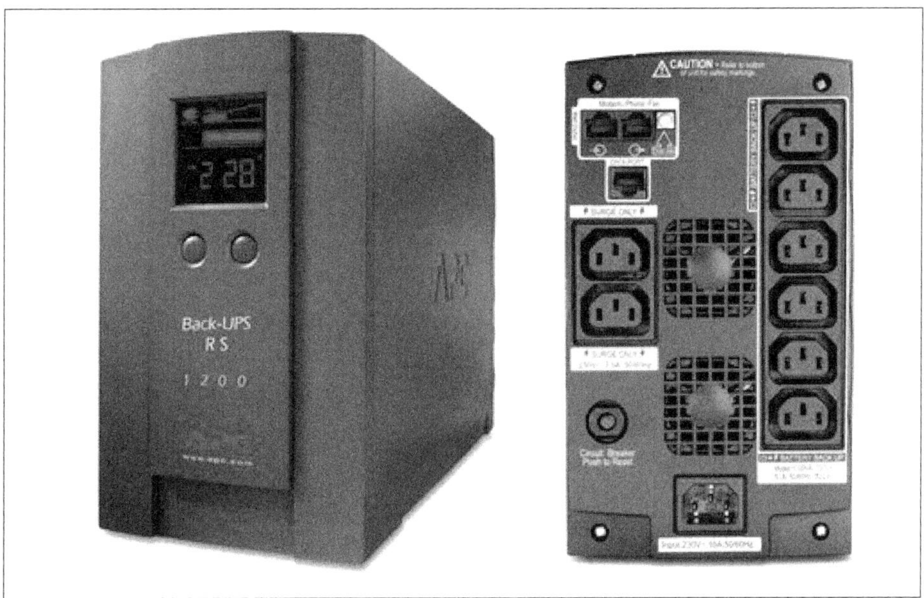

FIGURE 3.13 Uninterruptible Power Supply.

BACKUP TECHNOLOGIES

Technology for backing up computers can range from the simple to the complex, depending on needs. One can argue that given the degree to which most individual rely on computers for everyday tasks, virtually all computer users should incorporate a backup strategy of some kind into their practices. At the very least, the use of flash drives to copy folders containing important or valuable files, photos, and even music libraries, can be a quick and inexpensive way to avoid the time-consuming process of reconstructing the state of a computer following a hardware failure, malware attack, theft, loss, or accidental damage.

When viewed from the perspective of an organization having a legal responsibility to protect consumer data from loss and destruction, a sound backup strategy based upon reliable and efficient technology is mandatory. The backup strategy and associated technology should be considered as part of a comprehensive business continuity plan, which considers the technological vulnerabilities and recovery methods in the event of a disaster, hardware failure, or malware attack.

NETWORK ATTACHED STORAGE

Network Attached Storage, commonly referred to as NAS devices are essentially very large hard drives that are connected directly to a network router, allowing multiple computers on a local area network to access them. While in use, NAS devices offer expansion beyond the capacities of the individual computers' hard drives, and additionally offer the capability of allowing for collaborative shared access to the same folders by multiple users. In the case of database, documents, or other work files that must be accessed by more than one user, NAS devices can be selectively shared to other users by assigning user-level permissions to individual files and folders.

Technologically, NAS devices generally accommodate multiple hard drives that can be configured as a RAID array in order to optimize performance and to provide a degree of redundancy. As an example, a RAID drive can be assigned a mirror, which contains exactly the same information. If either of the drives were to fail, the other mirror would automatically take over, without a loss in data.

NAS Devices as Backup Media

As a backup technology, NAS devices allow for routine scheduled backups of computers on the same network. Since NAS devices are not typically designed to be removable media (like a flash drive), an NAS-based backup strategy may offer good protection against a computer hard drive failure, malware attack, accidental file deletion, or other events resulting in lost or corrupted data.

Due to the large drive capacity, a single NAS device could be used to back up multiple computers on the same network on a regularly scheduled basis that could range from weekly, daily, or even hourly. Using incremental backups of only the files that have changed since the last backup, an NAS device can provide historical snapshots of all backed up files, making it possible to roll back a computer's status to an earlier historical point in time. This approach is extremely useful in the event of an accidental file deletion or other data loss, in that the files can be recovered as they were at an earlier point in time.

The most significant limitation to NAS as a backup technology is that, although there may be internal redundancy in the form of mirrored RAID drives, there is no geographic separation between the computer and the backup media. If a natural disaster, such as a fire or earthquake were to occur, both the computer and the NAS device would be vulnerable to damage or destruction. The issue is that the location of the computer would represent a single point of failure meaning that something happening at that location would result in a complete data loss.

To avoid having a single point of failure, If one or more NAS devices are used as backup media, an additional form of removable backup media should be used in addition to the NAS so that it is possible to store one of the backups at an offsite location. In some cases, another alternative to ensuring an offsite backup would be to combine the use of an NAS device together with a cloud backup so that computers on the local area network are backed up to two places, to the NAS device and also to a cloud server.

CLOUD SERVER BACKUPS

The concept of the "cloud" is one that is often misunderstood by many consumers. The concept of the "cloud" refers to the idea that using the Internet, it is possible to assemble multiple computers in a way that an individual has access to them as a collective, rather than individually. Companies that offer cloud services are often referred to as *cloud service providers* (CSP) do so by making available a variety of servers, potentially in various locations around the globe. One of the key characteristics is that when an individual saves a file to the "cloud," that user has no way to specifically identify the location or identity of the computer to which that file has been saved.

Cloud based backups offer the convenience of off-site storage, often using software that can back up a computer's files in real time as they are modified or created. Since most backups are done incrementally, there is a history of the files that have been backed up with respect to the various versions that were saved over time. This approach makes it very convenient to access an older version of a file that was accidentally deleted, modified incorrectly, or has become corrupted.

Backed up files can generally be accessed online from either the same computer or any other computer that has Internet access, making it easy to get immediate access to a needed files, although larger files will take time to back up and restore through a slower Internet connection. Another advantage is that cloud backups do not require the user to purchase or manage any of the media devices, since they are maintained by a third-party vendor.

Considerations for Cloud Backups

Although cloud backups offer much convenience and flexibility, there are some limitations to be considered:

1. Availability of an Internet connection is required. The loss of an Internet connection due to service provider problems, power failure, or natural disaster will result in the inability to both back up data and also the ability restore from an existing backup. If an Internet connection is available and a large-scale data recovery is needed, the data transfer will likely be relatively slow over an Internet connection and could require many hours to complete, depending on the amount of data. This can be particularly problematic in the event that a fire or natural disaster results in data loss, as well as a loss in an Internet connection. In that situation, a cloud backup would not be accessible via the Internet. Many CSPs offer overnight delivery of physical media (such as one or more external hard drives) containing the backup so that recovery can proceed quickly and without the need for an Internet connection.
2. Confidential and/or proprietary data is in the hands of a 3rd party. When cloud backups are performed, sensitive data (for example, electronic medical records) included in the backup are essentially being given to another company for safe-keeping. In the case of EMR data, that transfer to another entity without consent of the patient could represent a violation of laws such as HIPAA. Careful attention must be paid to the standards to which the CSP promises to adhere in protecting the data, and to the possible legal implications. Establishing a service agreement with a CSP requires a very specific agreement in which the CSP details specifically how the data will be stored and protected in compliance with HIPAA. CSPs should also be willing to undergo a security audit and provide a report of the audit findings to potential customers.
3. Encryption of the data is mandatory. If the cloud server(s) on which the backup is stored are compromised, the last line of defense is a strong key-exchange encryption of that backup data. If properly used, the encryption can help prevent someone with access to the server from being able to view any of the actual files. In the interest of security, databases can sometimes be encrypted twice, first on the computers upon which they reside, and again by the backup software prior to being uploaded to a cloud server. This approach requires that two sets of encryption keys are needed to completely decrypt the data.
4. Selecting a reputable and reliable CSP is mandatory. Access to a backup is ultimately dependent on the reliability of the CSP. Deciding on a cloud backup solution requires a thorough due-diligence analysis of the CSP vendor with respect to factors such as service reliability, access to customer support, financial viability of the firm, and experiences of other existing users.

Ideally, a cloud backup solution would also be accompanied by an onsite backup using physical media that can be managed in-house. By maintaining an in-house backup, the risks associated with a CSP vendor can be at least partially mitigated.

DIGITAL TAPE CARTRIDGES

Although magnetic tape technology has been largely supplanted in many organizations by external removable hard drives, tape drive technology remains as one that has continued to advance technologically and is still often used to address large-scale enterprise level backup needs. The attraction to tape cartridges as a backup media is based on their relatively low cost, combined with the ability to store vast amounts of data on a single device at a relatively low cost and with low power consumption.

FIGURE 3.14 LTO-5 Ultrium 3 TB Rewritable Tape Cartridge.

The most common tape-backup format is called LTO (Linear Tape-Open), with the most current version being LTO-6, which is capable of storing up to 6.25 terabytes of data on a single cartridge (with full data compression). LTO was developed as an open standard by the LTO Consortium, led by Hewlett Packard, IBM, and Quantum. When referring to tape formats, the *format standard* refers to the software algorithms used to compress data in order to allow more of it to be fit onto a tape. *Open standards* are standards in which the compression algorithms are made available freely (similar to the concept of open-source software).

As an open standard, LTO was created to offer an alternative to the proprietary tape format standards used by tape drive manufactures. Using the LTO standard allows the software to be offered at a reduced price compared to proprietary software. Additionally, it offers the ability for that standard to be used by a variety of tape drive manufacturers, allowing for improved compatibility.

Other advantages to the use of tapes include very low power consumption and much improved performance and reliability in comparison to older tape drive technology. Additionally, tape drives do not require any power when not in use and generate very little heat, resulting in reduced need for cooling fans compared to hard drives.

In large-scale enterprise level environments, automated tape libraries with the capacities to hold dozens of tape cartridges are often used to manage the backups of many computers throughout a facility. Tape library systems often utilize robotic technology able to mount, dismount, and store

FIGURE 3.15 IBM 3584 tape library with LTO-1 (Ultrium) tapes visible.

tape cartridges as needed throughout the backup cycles, making the management of backups a highly automated and reliable process.

EXTERNAL HARD DRIVES

External hard drives are essentially the same technology as the permanent fixed disk drives that are installed inside of a computer. External hard drives are connected to a computer using a cable and can be easily disconnected and removed for storage or for use on another computer.

There are typically two interfaces used for external storage devices. The most common is usually a USB interface, which is ubiquitous for a variety of external devices. Although the cables for USB devices typically all look similar, there are different forms of USB interfaces available, including USB 2, USB 3, and USB 3.1, with each respectively providing faster data transfer than its predecessors. In order for the highest data transfer rate to be achieved, the computer and the device must both have USB 3.1 ports and a USB 3.1 cable must be used to connect the external hard drive and the computer.

In addition to USB interfaces, some external hard drives also offer an IEEE 1394 interface, commonly referred to as a *Firewire* interface. Variations include IEEE 1394a, which is referred to as Firewire 400 and capable of transferring data at 400 Mbps,** and IEEE 1394b, which is called Firewire 800 and capable of transferring at 800 Mbps.

Security Considerations of External Hard Drives

Despite the convenience and flexibility associated with removable hard drives, there are also data security risks associated with them. Because they are removable, there is always a risk of loss or theft during transport. Several documented cases of data loss have been associated with the theft of backup drives from delivery vehicles and in some cases, even from the cars of employees who were transporting the drives and in some cases from the facilities in which the backups were performed. In one case, 57 hard drives were stolen from a storage closet at a Blue Cross facility.[20] The theft resulted in Blue Cross having to notify over one million patients of the potential theft of their data, and in payment of a $1. 5 million fine due to the breach.[21]

Given that a removable drive can be easily taken to another location for off-site storage (where it may be outside of the direct control of an administrator), a good practice is to routinely encrypt the contents of removable hard drives using a strong encryption method so that in the event of a theft of loss, the contents will have a degree of protection.

** Mbps stands for megabits per second. Since a byte is composed of 8 bits, megabits per second can be converted to megabytes per second by dividing by 8.

SUMMARY

The term *hardware* refers to the tangible components of a computer that can be physically handled. Computer hardware components can be classified into two basic categories. The peripheral devices are the human interface and other types of devices that facilitate data and software being transferred to and from a computer's processor, while the processor refers to the collection of components responsible for interpreting the instructions of the software, modifying the data, and producing the output.

Data in a digital format can be measured in bytes, which represent characters. Due to the large numbers associated with contemporary computer systems, bytes are often described in terms of thousands, million, billions or trillions, which equate to kilobytes, megabytes, gigabytes, and terabytes, respectively. Most hardware components can generally be measured in terms of either data capacity or processing speed. Understanding those measurements is key to being able to make an informed purchase or upgrade decision.

Given the legal requirement to protect healthcare data, there is a need to select and use appropriate technology to prevent data loss. These technologies can include devices such as RAID arrays and uninterruptble power supplies, as well as comprehensive backup strategies.

APPLY YOUR KNOWLEDGE

Please note that some of the software interfaces and example screenshots have changed since publication. Errata, revisions to instructions, and updated images can be found at http://drspinello.com/cohs.

1. Using online computer hardware vendors' websites, identify three computers for comparison. For each of the three computers, identify the following specifications for comparison:

a. CPU (Manufacturer, model, numbers of cores, and clock speed)
b. Hard disk (locate the size of the drive and its speed measured by seek time and RPMs)
c. The amount of RAM physically on the computer, and the amount of total capacity
d. Monitor (located the size and dot pitch)
e. Printer type (inkjet or laser), quality (DPI), and speed (PPM)
f. Price

2. Based upon the computers you researched in Question 1, and given what you have learned with respect to the performance and capacity measures of various hardware components, answer the following questions:

a. Which computer has the CPU with the fastest processing speed?
b. Which computer has the most powerful processor, overall?
c. Which computer has the most unused capacity for RAM?
d. Which computer has the largest capacity hard disk drive?
e. Which computer has the fastest hard disk drive?

IMAGE CREDITS

Fig. 3.1: Al-CaPoNe85, "A Computer's Mainboard," http://commons.wikimedia.org/wiki/File:ASUS_Motherboard.JPG. Copyright in the Public Domain.

Fig. 3.2: Copyright © Nayu Kim (CC by 2.0) at http://www.flickr.com/photos/nayukim/3826877775/.

Fig. 3.3: Copyright © Metoc (CC BY-SA 2.5) at http://commons.wikimedia.org/wiki/File:CPU-Cooler-Intel.jpg.

Fig. 3.4: Cyberdex, "Ram Modules," http://commons.wikimedia.org/wiki/File:Memory_module_DDRAM_20-03-2006.jpg. Copyright in the Public Domain.

Fig. 3.5: Copyright © 2007 by SPBer (CC BY-SA 3.0) at http://commons.wikimedia.org/wiki/File:Innansicht_Festplatte_512_MB_von_Quantum.jpg.

Fig. 3.9: Copyright © Prateek Karandikar (CC BY-SA 4.0) at http://commons.wikimedia.org/wiki/File:CRT_pixels_close-up_crop.JPG.

Fig. 3.10: Pluke, "CPT Outputs Printers Impact," http://commons.wikimedia.org/wiki/File:CPT-Outputs-Printers-Impact-P.svg. Copyright in the Public Domain.

Fig. 3.11: Copyright © MrCrackers (CC BY-SA 3.0) at http://commons.wikimedia.org/wiki/File:Color_Laser_Printer_Magnified.jpg.

Fig. 3.12: Copyright © diskdepot.co.uk (CC BY-SA 3.0) at http://commons.wikimedia.org/wiki/File:Hp-laserjet-printer.png.

Fig. 3.13: Copyright © AnthDaniel (CC BY-SA 3.0) at https://commons.wikimedia.org/wiki/File:UPSAPC.jpg.

Fig. 3.14: Copyright © Andrew Dodd (CC BY-SA 3.0) at https://commons.wikimedia.org/wiki/File:LTO-5_Ultrium_Data_Cartridge.png.

Fig. 3.15: Copyright © Raven (CC BY-SA 3.0) at https://commons.wikimedia.org/wiki/File:Ibm3584.PNG.

4

RESEARCH, HEALTH, INFORMATION, AND THE INTERNET

Although the Internet represents a vast repository of potentially interesting and useful information, a number of barriers exist with respect to the access and use of that information. One barrier concerns the difficulties encountered with respect to just locating the one key piece of information that is needed from the huge sea of data that exists. The sheer amount of information available on the Internet can make answering even a simple question the technological equivalent of trying to find a needle in a haystack.

Another potential barrier is that once the needed information is found, there is a need to determine whether that information holds scientific validity or not. Despite the huge amount of information related to health and medicine that exists on the Internet, current research has found significant amounts of that information to be lacking in scientific validity and represents potential *misinformation*.

This chapter describes some of the issues related to health information found on the Internet, along with strategies to help ensure that the information you choose to rely upon is scientifically sound. Additionally, this chapter describes a basic strategy that can be used to help locate needed information more quickly and directly, while minimizing the distractions and chasing down unrelated or irrelevant sources.

ANECDOTAL VERSUS EMPIRICAL DATA

Determining whether information is scientifically valid requires an understanding of the scientific method and the concept of empirical data. Empirical data consists of data collected using a rigorous scientific method to ensure that any bias or inaccuracy is minimized. It is then further tested using specially designed procedures to ensure that conclusions drawn from the data are valid to a statistically quantifiable degree of certainty. Once empirical data is collected and analyzed, the findings and conclusions are generally published in peer-reviewed journals, in which the results are scrutinized by other researchers prior to publication. Although the information published in a medical, academic, or scientific journal is generally of high quality, one of the limitations encountered by the layperson is that the results are often read, interpreted, and disseminated to the public by newspaper reporters, TV commentators, magazine editors, and bloggers, who may or may not have the appropriate training to properly interpret the findings.

To further compound the problem, consider that newspapers, magazines, TV news shows, and blogs are motivated primarily to maximize their readership and/or viewership. This means that there is generally some incentive to make the results of research sound a bit more dramatic than they may actually be. Let's face it, many of the studies published in medical journals are not exactly the most exciting things to read about. Additionally, many published articles about scientific studies often seem to contradict one another. How many times you have you read a dramatic news story telling you about the latest study showing that a particular food or behavior has been found to be bad for you, only to be followed by a story months later about a study finding that it is actually "good" for you?

THE ROLE OF INFORMATION IN EVIDENCE-BASED MEDICINE

The concept of evidence-based medicine (also referred to more generically as *evidence-based practice*) suggests that optimal healthcare decisions are best made when they are based upon the best available empirical research and combined with patient preferences and clinical experience.[11,22] In other words, healthcare decisions should be based upon solid research that supports the use of a particular medical intervention for a particular problem. Although the definition of EBM (evidence-based medicine) applies to the practice of clinical medicine, the concept can be extended to related fields outside of clinical practice such as public health promotion, which relies on an appropriate behavioral, environmental, or policy intervention being implemented for purposes of addressing a particular public health issue within a population.

EBM is considered a 'best practice' in the field of medicine, in that medical interventions are guided by the most valid and reliable information available, rather than untested opinion or anecdotes. It is valuable to keep this concept in mind when searching for health-related information by asking yourself, is this information valid evidence for a healthcare decision?

THE COST OF INVALID DATA

It is important to consider that we are all consumers of information. The basic reasons that any of us seek out information may be to make a personal decision regarding our own lifestyles or health choices. For example, information may be needed to recommend a personal decision to someone else, or possibly to include as a reference in an academic paper being submitted for course work or publication. Regardless of the reason that the information is needed, it is extremely important to be aware there is always a cost associated with relying on data that turns out to be invalid. For example, if a person is looking for information upon which to base a personal health decision for him- or herself, the use of invalid information could result in:

- The financial cost of purchasing an ineffective product
- The opportunity cost of not effectively treating or preventing a problem while allowing it to worsen
- The possible physical harm related to engaging in a behavior or using a product that is contraindicated

From the perspective of a healthcare provider, recommending inaccurate or invalid information to another while in a professional capacity could result in legal liability resulting from a scientifically unsound course of action. And, of course, in an academic environment, citing inaccurate or invalid information in an academic or scholarly work could result in a low grade, loss of credibility, or being found guilty of scientific misconduct.

Given the potential costs associated with the use of questionable data, it is particularly important to verify the quality of any health information that will be used upon which to base a decision. This chapter addresses some of the specific ways in which online health information may be presented inappropriately, as well as some strategies that can be used to help assess the quality of health information found on the Internet.

THE QUALITY OF INTERNET-BASED HEALTH INFORMATION

In recent years, a significant amount of research has been conducted, examining the accuracy of health information found on the Internet. Most of the research has focused on trying to better understand the extent to which health information tends to be inaccurate, and what indicators can be identified that may help to predict the scientific validity of information found online.

In one early study, the characteristics of websites that tended to contain scientifically valid data were examined in order to determine what factors are consistent with accurate websites. The authors of the study reviewed each of the websites to determine what indicators of scientific validity were present, and to what extent the content presented was actually valid from a scientific perspective. Each website was assessed as to its accuracy and then categorized accordingly.

The researchers found that almost 65% of the websites examined contain incomplete information, suggesting that some significant information was missing from the content. A key requirement for evidence-based information is that reliable sources are referenced. The researchers found that only 24% contained references to reliable sources, making it impossible for the average consumer to know whether information on the remaining 76% of websites came from scientific sources.[12,23]

The characteristics of websites that tended to contain scientifically valid data were examined in a 2002 study by Fallis and Fricke.[13,24] In order to determine what characteristics are associated with accurate websites, the authors of this study chose to study one hundred websites providing information about children's fevers by examining the websites using a panel of content experts. The websites determined to be most accurate were then categorized by their degree of accuracy, and then analyzed to determine what characteristics they have in common.

The authors found that three website characteristics were the best indicators of medical accuracy:

1. Display of the Health on the Net (HON) logo
2. Display of a copyright notice
3. Having a .ORG (non-profit organization) domain

Yet another study that examined the quality of websites containing information about thyroid disorders found that the quality of the information contained in the websites tended to vary considerably from website to website. Based on a review of 103 websites, the authors concluded, "The quality of Internet health information regarding thyroidectomy is variable. High ranking and popularity are not good indicators of website quality."[14,25]

WEBSITES THAT SELL

It is very common to find websites that purport to provide health information and advice but that also sell a variety of nutritional supplements. One key study published in 2011 examined the quality of information found on fifty-four websites that sell the popular herbal supplement St. John's Wort. The authors scored each website using DISCERN, which is a validated instrument for assessing the quality of health-related websites. Of the websites examined, 96% scored at close to the two lowest possible levels (a score of 1 or 2), while none of the websites received the highest possible score of 5. Of the websites that scored lowest, the most common deficiency was a failure to document what sources of information were used to support the website. Additional deficiencies related to the lack of information concerning contraindications and potential risks.

Although St. John's Wort has been found to be an effective antidepressant in some cases, there are risks associated with its use, which were not disclosed in many websites. The authors of the studies concluded, "Failing to inform consumers about these safety concerns can be potentially serious, or even fatal. The need for minimum safety standards for e-commerce websites selling St John's wort is therefore a matter of necessity and urgency."[15,26]

ISSUES AFFECTING WEBSITE ACCURACY

Health-related websites that are not scientifically accurate may have inaccuracies for a number of different reasons:

Reliance on invalid information	Although the author of a website may be well meaning, it is not unusual for a website to contain an unintentional inaccuracy. The inaccuracy may be due to poor research or simply a result of the author relying upon information that was anecdotal in nature and not having evidence-based supporting research.
Bias	A biased website is one in which the author intentionally (or sometimes unintentionally) cherry-picks the research they use to support a particular argument or recommendation. In this case, the author overlooks research that may refute his or her contention.
Fraud	A fraudulent website is one in which the recommendation being made is based upon an intentional lie or inaccuracy. Research that is cited may be taken out of context in an attempt to mislead the person reading the website to believe something that is not true. Authors of these websites may attempt to mislead readers by claiming degrees from non-accredited diploma mills, as well as work experience they do not really have.

Poor Reporting

Although scientific research may exist to support a particular claim, one of the issues affecting website accuracy concerns poor reporting of scientific research. For example, although an empirical study may exist and has produced certain findings, an individual reporting about that study may misinterpret the importance or meaning of those findings. Just before the fourth of July in 2008, a researcher at the Texas A&M Fruit and Vegetable Improvement Center was interviewed about his finding that watermelons contain the amino acid citrulline, which is converted by the body into another amino acid, arginine, which is considered a precursor to nitric oxide, which in turn can help dilate blood vessels. As a result of the interview, at least one news story written about the interview carried the title, "Watermelon may have Viagra-like effect"[16,27]—in spite of the fact that no research had ever been conducted on the effects of watermelon on male erectile dysfunction. It is unclear, however, what effects the article may have had on watermelon sales for July 4th events.

MEDIA REPORTING OF SCIENTIFIC RESEARCH

Consider the following example. In this case, a 2010 study was conducted to determine whether automated external defibrillators (AED) are effective in saving lives. AEDs are similar to the devices used in hospitals when a patient's heart stops or begins beating in an irregular rhythm. AEDs have electrodes that are placed on the patient's chest. The device detects the heart rhythm, determines whether it can be corrected with an electric shock, and then if necessary, administers the shock. AEDs are designed to be placed in airports, airplanes, schools, and other public locations where they may be needed.

In this particular case, an article was published in *The New England Journal of Medicine* in which researchers collected and evaluated the medical records of people who had suffered a heart attack, cardiac arrest, or other coronary emergency, and then tracked what happened to them. The researchers found that in cases where an AED device was present and used, they were in fact effective in helping to save the lives of patients. However, the researchers also found that in cases where AEDs were not used but where CPR was administered, the survival rates of patients were similar to those where AEDs were used. The general conclusion of the study was that although AEDs are effective, it is probably more cost effective to provide CPR training to individuals than to mass-purchase AEDs.

Here is the first page of the article and its abstract:

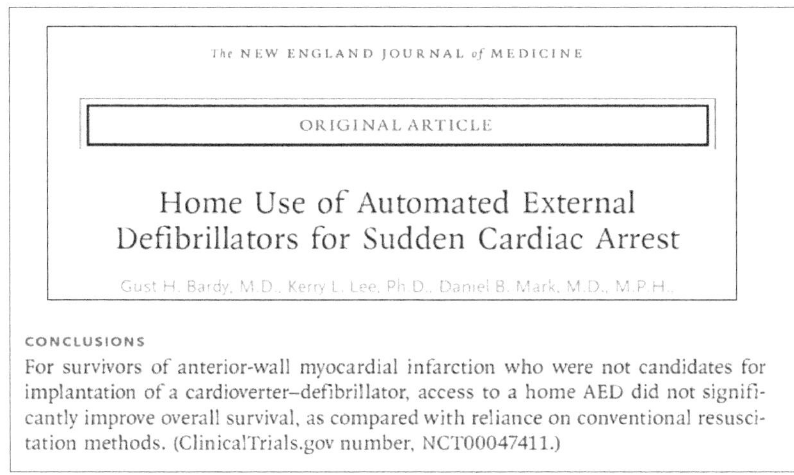

The NEW ENGLAND JOURNAL of MEDICINE

ORIGINAL ARTICLE

Home Use of Automated External Defibrillators for Sudden Cardiac Arrest

Gust H. Bardy, M.D., Kerry L. Lee, Ph.D., Daniel B. Mark, M.D., M.P.H.,

CONCLUSIONS

For survivors of anterior-wall myocardial infarction who were not candidates for implantation of a cardioverter–defibrillator, access to a home AED did not significantly improve overall survival, as compared with reliance on conventional resuscitation methods. (ClinicalTrials.gov number, NCT00047411.)

FIGURE 4.1 Screenshot of First Page from: "Home Use of Automated External Defibrillators for Sudden Cardiac Arrest."

Now, let's take a look at two of the articles that were written about this study—both written by newspaper reporters at two different news services: Reuters and Associated Press. Both articles appeared on the Yahoo News website in April 2010:

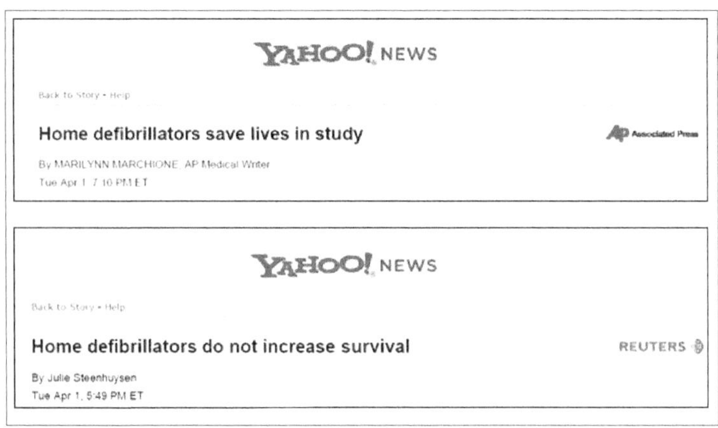

YAHOO! NEWS

Back to Story • Help

Home defibrillators save lives in study

AP Associated Press

By MARILYNN MARCHIONE, AP Medical Writer

Tue Apr 1, 7:10 PM ET

YAHOO! NEWS

Back to Story • Help

Home defibrillators do not increase survival

REUTERS

By Julie Steenhuysen

Tue Apr 1, 5:49 PM ET

FIGURE 4.2 Screenshots from Yahoo! News Website.

Both articles make dramatic, definitive statements regarding the effectiveness of home defribrillators, and both statements appear to completely contradict one another. In fact, based on the titles one would almost have to assume that the news articles must have been written about two different studies.

It is very important to recognize that news articles written about scientific studies are not necessarily accurate, even if they are reported by reputable news sources. The dramatic difference between the two titles begs the question of how and why this could happen. In this particular instance, the research study produced findings that were not actually very dramatic. Home AED units *did* help to improve survivability of a cardiac arrest, but survivability with CPR was a close second to that of the AED. The authors concluded that while AEDs are effective, encouraging CPR training may be more cost effective, especially given the cost to purchase and maintain AEDs. The goal of most newspaper reports is not to report the subtle findings of nuanced studies; it is generally to report on the big important stories of the day that readers will want to read. In this case, both reporters made the mistake of creating drama through their headlines where there was none. Interestingly, both stories were written somewhat accurately, although the titles were at least somewhat misleading.

THE ANXIETY OF THE WEEK

Another perspective on this issue is articulated by Dr. Walter Willett, an epidemiologist at the Harvard School of Public Health. In a 2008 interview, Willett was asked, *"The science of risk-factor epidemiology is controversial these days because of what people call the 'carcinogen-' or 'anxiety-of-the-week syndrome.' It seems that every week the newspapers carry a new and usually contradictory study telling us what we should or should not eat. Is this our imagination, or is there really a problem?"*[17,28]

Willett: "It's true; there is a problem. Part of it is this very direct link between ongoing work and what comes out in *The New York Times*. The natural course of science is that people do studies and report finding something, but nobody believes it too much—and, hopefully, neither do the investigators until it's reproduced by other researchers. But in the meantime, it's on the front page of the newspaper. So there is this tendency for the least substantiated findings to be the ones coming out in the popular press, when in fact this is simply part of the scientific process, and a lot of suspected associations are not ready for the public to take action or even worry about."

In this interview, Dr. Willett very concisely describes the problem. Although some journalists do a very good job of communicating scientific research, the popular media is driven by very different motivations than are scientific journals. Does this mean that all articles related to scientific research that appear in newspapers, on websites, etc., should be disregarded? No, what it does mean is that those articles should not be viewed as conclusive or definitive. They should be viewed as a starting point. When faced with an article about a health topic of particular interest to you, do your own research of the primary source for that research.

HEALTH ON THE NET

Based upon the many studies that have assessed the accuracy of health information on the Internet, it should be quite apparent that there is a tremendous amount of inaccurate information in circulation. The issue is that the inaccurate/scientifically invalid information may look to be credible, particularly to someone without a technical background. The question then becomes, how does a student or consumer determine whether the information he or she finds is scientifically valid?

Health on the Net Foundation (HON) (www.hon.ch) is an organization that was founded in Geneva, Switzerland, in 1995. The creation of HON was in response to concerns regarding the proliferation on the Internet of health information with varying degrees of accuracy and scientific validity. The objective of HON is to provide guidelines for web publishers in order to ensure better consistency with respect to scientific accuracy among websites. HON's principles are the basis for the guidelines it recommends for health-related websites. The principles of HON are the following.[18,29]

Health on the Net Principles

Principle 1	Authority: Websites should provide qualifications of author(s)
Principle 2	Complementary: Information should be designed to support, not replace medical care from healthcare providers
Principle 3	Confidentiality: The privacy of site visitors must be respected and protected
Principle 4	Attribution: Websites must cite the sources and dates of valid medical information being provided
Principle 5	Justifiability: Health claims must be balanced and objective and based on referenced scientific information
Principle 6	Transparency: Website author(s) must be accessible by providing contact information, including email addresses, etc.
Principle 7	Financial Disclosure: Sources of funding for research and website hosting must be disclosed, together with potential conflicts of interest on the part of website author(s)
Principle 8	Advertising must be indicated and readily distinguished from website content.

Based upon the HON Principles, the HON *Code* represents a practical set of guidelines for publishers of health/medical websites to follow. Demonstration of compliance with the HON code allows websites to be HON Certified, meaning that they are allowed to display the HON logo.

As described by HON, "The HON code is a code of ethics that guides site managers in setting up a minimum set of mechanisms to provide quality, objective and transparent medical information tailored to the needs of the audience."[19,30]

THE IMPORTANCE OF PROPER CITATION

As any college student knows, professors who assign academic papers seem to place an inordinate amount of emphasis on the citation of one's sources. One of the reasons for style guides such as the APA and MLA is that they provide a set of rules by which a reader of a paper can easily determine whether the ideas and concepts presented belong to the author or some other source that the author of the paper relied upon.

FIGURE 4.3 Health On the Net Foundation Logo.

In the case of health information found on a website, citing statements of fact, research statistics, etc., are important for yet another reason. Without a proper citation, it is extremely difficult to find the exact research study that a website may be referring to. The reason it is important to be able to find the original study is that without it, there is no way to tell whether what the website says about the study is actually true or accurate.

Keep in mind, there is no expectation that you look up every citation found on every website that you view. However, in the case of a website that makes an extraordinary claim, the evidence to support that claim becomes even more important because even if the website claims that a study has produced findings that something has been proven or disproven, you don't really know for sure until you read that study.

Looking at it another way, when considering the potential validity of health information found on the Internet, it is particularly important to confirm that any statements of fact are accompanied by references to valid scientific sources. If a particular website cites a statistic or presents a matter-of-fact statement, there should be a detailed reference that provides you with sufficient information to find the scientific source of that information so you can read it for yourself. Once you read the primary source, you may reach one of three conclusions:

1. You agree with the research and the conclusion that was reached, reassuring you that the website is valid.
2. or you may find that although the research exists, the conclusions that were made are not reasonable, or the research itself may not have been properly conducted.
3. or you may decide that the findings of the study may be valid but are not being properly used in the website you are considering.

THE IMPORTANCE OF PROPER CITATION: A CASE STUDY

To help illustrate an example of possibility #3 above (how legitimate studies can be misquoted and taken out of context on the Internet), consider an actual online discussion that took place in August 2001 on the HealthFraud email list. The HealthFraud list is an online "Majordomo" discussion hosted by the National Council Against Health Fraud, in which several hundred physicians, nurses, dietitians, physical therapists, and other healthcare providers, and laypeople discuss a variety of issues related to the promotion of fraudulent healthcare products and services. In this particular discussion, a participant made a claim based upon what he described as research published in a major medical journal.

This particular discussion began with a post by Mike, a participant whose father-in-law was suffering from cancer, but had decided to forgo conventional cancer therapy (chemotherapy and radiation) in favor of alternative medicines and herbal supplements. It is important to know that his father-in-law's oncologist felt that because the cancer had been detected so early, he had an excellent chance of a full recovery if he immediately began radiation and chemotherapy. Mike's concern was that by delaying the start of chemotherapy and radiation, the cancer would continue to worsen, making a full recovery less likely. Given his concern, Mike posted a question to the group asking how he could help his father-in-law understand that stopping conventional treatment would probably shorten his life.

After Mike posted his question, a forum subscriber named Anthony posted a response. Anthony felt that conventional cancer treatments were probably not effective and that Mike's father-in-law was probably better off with the herbal remedies and other alternative treatments. In his response, Anthony discussed a study showing that cancer patients who did *not* undergo chemotherapy and radiation actually lived longer than those who did undergo conventional treatments.

Here is the exchange, starting with Anthony's original response to Mike.

Anthony's Response to Mike's Question

> *I heard, from a reputable source, that the mainstream peer-review journal, Annals of Oncology, published a study of 13 year survival rates for radiation and/or chemotherapy treated cancer patients (59% of the patients survived), compared to cancer patients who had no radiation/chemotherapy treatment (65% of the patients survived).*
>
> *Check out the study for yourself. Show it to your father and/or his Oncologist.*
>
> *I believe modern medicine and other medicine modalities should compare notes and work together. There is health fraud in both systems and much healing in both. I believe the adage "You are what you eat" pertains to many of the chemotherapy treatments; I do not believe the reason a person gets cancer, (starts cancering), is from a lack of toxic drugs in the diet. Remember to look both ways before choosing a path that will (hopefully) benefit you (your Dad).*
>
> *Anthony*

Note that in his response, Anthony based his opinion on a peer-reviewed study supposedly finding that cancer patients seem to live longer if they do *not* get chemotherapy and radiation treatments. If the study actually produced results that supported that conclusion, it would call the basis for most traditional cancer treatments into question. Since the study Anthony mentioned was the basis for his advice, understanding what it actually said was key to determining the best advice for Mike's father-in-law. A number of individuals responded to Anthony. For example, Jeff attempted to find and read the study for himself and then posted the following:

> **Response from Jeff to Anthony**
>
> *I went to the Annals of Oncology site and searched the 2000 abstracts and found only one article relating to your subject ...*
>
> *... It certainly does not support your conclusion. Nor did several other articles on similar topics. You have made a statement that should be documented. You will find their home site at:*
>
> *http://www.esmo.org/annals/annals.htm*
>
> *I have tried to find your article now it's your turn.*
>
> *Jeff*

Given that Jeff and others were unable to find the study that Anthony described, Anthony tried to be more helpful and provide some additional information to help Jeff find the article. In the following post, he provided some additional information about the study and the journal article written about it.

Response from Anthony to Jeff

Dear Jeff,

I wrote down, while making/eating lunch in my car and listening to the radio, "Annals Onc. V. 7 p. 245 13 Year Survival 59% No Therapy 65%." I tried obtaining Volume 7, Page 245 of the 'Annals of Oncology', after your reply and could not, because I do not belong to an "institution." I assume you do and did a search with the info of my last letter. Either the study is located in Volume 7 at Page 245 of the Annals of Oncology, or, I miswrote the info I heard, or, the radio personality lied.

Anthony

What is interesting is that in his post, Anthony now admits that he did not actually read the article. Instead, it appears that he heard about it from a radio personality while eating lunch in his car. This means that Anthony took someone else's word for what the study was about and for the conclusions that were reached.

Given that no one had been able to actually find the study at that point I decided to search for it myself. What I found was that the citation provided by Anthony was incorrect and led to an entirely unrelated study. However, by searching all articles published in the *Annals of Oncology* containing the specific combination of numbers (i.e., 59%, 65%, 13 weeks, etc.), I was able to eventually find the study. In my response to Anthony, I described its conclusions, along with my own interpretation of the findings:

Response to Anthony

Anthony

I did manage to find the following study abstract that seems to fit the numbers cited in your post. ... it appears though that rather than comparing a radiation/chemotherapy protocol to a control, Trial I was really the evaluation of the addition of prednisone [a steroid] to [chemotherapy] as a way to [help patients tolerate an] increased dosage [of the chemotherapy]. Someone with better background in oncology may want to comment on this but it certainly doesn't support your post ...

Elio

The study that Anthony had referred to did not contain the findings that he claimed. In fact, it did not even compare patients who had received chemo/radiation to patients who did not. It compared patients who received regular chemotherapy to patients who received chemotherapy *plus* a steroid. Since all of the patients enrolled in the study received chemotherapy, this in no way supported his conclusion that people who don't get chemotherapy or radiation live longer. In fact, the way the study was designed, it would have been impossible to even test that hypothesis. The study was really an attempt to see whether the steroid would help patients tolerate chemotherapy.

It is impossible to know what the radio personality's motivation was in distorting the results of the study, but it is very likely that he or she did not expect listeners to actually locate and read it for themselves (especially since the citation was given incorrectly). By reading the study, anyone with a basic understanding of research methods would have been able to determine that at best, the study was simply misinterpreted and that at worst, it was used fraudulently to lead listeners to the wrong conclusions.

Faced with this information, Anthony posted the following response:

Final Response from Anthony

I am not sure what some of the statistics mean. It seems that some people with a disease were treated with a medicine and others were treated with the same medicine AND another substance. The question was, does the additional substance help the first substance?

I was mistaken in my original assertion that the study showed survival rates are lower for those who are treated with chemotherapy, as compared to those who receive no such treatment.

I am sorry to not have researched my assertion before believing in it.

Anthony

EPILOGUE

Approximately three years later, on April 8, 2004, I received the following message from Mike, letting me know that his father-in-law passed away from cancer as a result of not having started treatment in the early stages while the cancer was still treatable:

My FIL died a week ago yesterday.

Some of you may remember my case. About four years ago he had early cancer in his neck and behind his nose. He had a 70% five year cure rate with just radiation, 90% combined with chemo.

A "friend" of his talked him out of it the day before he was to start radiation. He did the Lorraine Day program, Cantron, the Zapper, and a projector to shine colored lights on his head. During this course of period I kept researching all the stuff he was doing and showing that it had no chance of working and that it was a progressing disease and that he would soon reach the point of no return. I encountered a lot of hostility from my MIL, SIL, and others.
He suffered tremendously and his death was a blessing.

Medline Abstract of the Article That Anthony Referred to:

The following is the actual abstract of the study that Anthony claimed to support his position that chemotherapy and radiation reduce the life expenctancy of cancer patients. Pertinent sections of the article are underlined.

Author(s): Marini G; Murray S; Goldhirsch A; Gelber RD;Castiglione-Gertsch M; Price KN; Tattersall MH; Rudenstam CM; Collins J; Lindtner J; Cavalli F; Cortés-Funes H; Gudgeon A; Forbes JF; Galligioni E; Coates AS; Senn HJ Affiliation: International Breast Cancer Study Group, Ospedale Civico, Switzerland.

Title: The effect of adjuvant prednisone combined with CMF on patterns ofrelapse and occurrence of second malignancies in patients with breastcancer. International (Ludwig) Breast Cancer Study Group.

Source: *Ann Oncol* (Annals of oncology: official journal of the European Society for Medical Oncology / ESMO.) 1996 Mar; 7(3): 245–50 Journal Code: AYF **Additional Info**: NETHERLANDS

Standard No: ISSN: 0923-7534; NLM Unique Identifier: 9007735

Language: English

Abstract: BACKGROUND: The addition of low-dose prednisone (p) to the adjuvant regimen of cyclophosphamide, methotrexate, 5-fluorouracil (CMF) allowed patients to receive a larger dose of cytotoxics when compared with those on CMF alone. However, disease-free survival and overall survival were similar for the two groups. To test the hypothesis that low-dose prednisone might influence the efficacy of the cytotoxic regimen used, the toxicity profiles of the two treatment regimens and the patterns of treatment failure (relapse, second malignancy, or death) were examined. PATIENTS AND METHODS: 491 premenopausal and perimenopausal patients with one to three positive axillary lymph nodes included in International (Ludwig) Breast Cancer Study Group (IBCSG) trial I from 1978 to 1981 and randomized to receive CMF or CMFp were analyzed for differences in long-term outcome and toxic events. The 250 patients assigned to CMF and prednisone received on the average 12% more cytotoxic drugs than those who received CMF alone. RESULTS: The 13-year DFS for the CMFp group was 49% as compared to 52% for CMF alone, and the respective OS percents were 59% and 65%. Several toxic effects such as leukopenia, alopecia, mucositis and induced amenorrhea were reported at a similar incidence in the two treatment groups. Using cumulative incidence methodology for competing risks, we detected a statistically significant increase in first relapse in the skeleton for the CMFp group at 13 years follow-up with a relative risk (RR) of 2.06 [95% confidence interval (CI), 1.23 to 3.46; P = 0.004]. Patients with larger tumors in the CMFp regimen were especially subject to this increase with a RR for failure in the skeleton of 3.32 (95% CI, 1.57 to 7.02; P = 0.0005). CMFp-treated patients also had a larger proportion of second malignancies (not breast cancer), with RR of 3.34 (95% CI, 0.91 to 12.31; P = 0.09). CONCLUSIONS: Low-dose continuous prednisone added to adjuvant CMF chemotherapy enabled the use of higher doses of cytotoxics. This increased dose had no beneficial effect on treatment outcome, but was associated with an increased risk for bone relapses and a small, not statistically significant increased incidence of second malignancies. The effects of steroids, which are widely used as antiemetics (oral or pulse injection) together with cytotoxics, should be investigated to identify their influence upon treatment outcome. ERIC Identifier: ED447199 Publication Date: 2000-11-00 Authors: Brem, Sarah K. and Boyes, Andrea J. Source: ERIC Clearinghouse on Assessment and Evaluation College Park, MD

This exchange is a great example of how a legitimate article in a reputable journal can be taken *totally* out of context. In this particular case, the only thing Anthony got right were the thirteen-year "fatality rates" he quoted, although he was totally incorrect as to their significance.

Remember that Anthony did not read the study for himself. Instead he heard about it on a radio program and relied upon the radio host's interpretation and conclusions. The key here is that the radio host who originally quoted the statistics and stated the conclusion (that cancer patients who do not undergo chemotherapy live longer) relied on the fact that very few people, if any, would ever bother or know how to look up the article and read/understand it. In fact, from the radio host's perspective, giving out the citation information was a great ploy because it added credibility to his argument and it was unlikely anyone would actually read it. Although Anthony did not mention the specific radio program, it is quite possible that the real intent of the radio host was to sell a nutritional supplement or diet that would supposedly prevent cancer.

To take this example one step further, consider that this was not a situation in which Anthony simply made an erroneous comment to another person directly. In this case, Anthony posted his comment on an Internet discussion list with thousands of participants—each one of whom could forward the comment to countless others. Although Anthony ultimately realized his error and apologized for it, the damage had already been done as he had already publicized it on the Internet.

This points out the specific need to always locate *and read* articles when possible. Had Anthony made an attempt to find and read the actual article prior to relying upon it, he might have realized that the article did not support the premise that radiation and chemotherapy shorten the life expectancy of cancer patients. If he read it and found that he did not understand it, he could have asked someone with an appropriate background in biomedical research for an opinion.

In this case, although Anthony was not the cause of Mike's father-in-law making the wrong decision about his therapy, people like Anthony were responsible. When devastating health problems arise, the human tendency is to desire a simpler and easier solution to that problem. Unfortunately, the desire for the simpler and easier solution can often obscure the logic needed to ensure that health decisions are made based upon the best available empirical evidence rather than anecdotes and Internet folklore.

WIKIPEDIA AS AN INFORMATION SOURCE

In recent years, Wikipedia has become one of the most often used sources of information for students and non-students. The premise behind Wikipedia is that virtually anyone can create a topic and write about it on a Wikipedia page. Once a topic page has been created, any Wikipedia users can essentially make changes to that page if they believe something to be in error or not properly explained. Wikipedia relies on the community of users to police the quality of the information that is found there. Although many Wikipedia users add or edit content in a conscientious way, that it is not always the case. Some Wikipedia users may be well intentioned but lack the in-depth knowledge to fully understand the topic they are contributing to, resulting in an inaccurate explanation being used. In some cases, an individual may have a particular bias or opinion, which becomes the basis for his or her contribution.

Research regarding the quality of health and biomedical information found in Wikipedia suggests that there are issues relating to the accuracy of the content. In a 2014 study of Wikipedia articles relating to *complementary and alternative medicine*, it was determined that those Wikipedia articles were significantly shorter and had fewer citations to credible research when compared to conventional medical therapies.[20,31] Another study examining the quality of Wikipedia information related to the ten most costly medical conditions found that there was much disagreement between the various Wikipedia articles and that they contained many errors. The researchers recommended that caution be used when using Wikipedia for topics related to medical treatment.[21,32] Finally, another study examining the quality of Wikipedia information related to herbal supplements found that the articles were often incomplete with respect to safety information, and lacked consistency with information from reputable sources. The authors concluded that Wikipedia should not be a sole source of information with respect to treatment decisions.[22,33]

From the perspective of a student, Wikipedia has the appeal of generally containing content that is reasonably easy to read and that sounds authoritative. However, given the research cited above, it is clear that there are a number of issues related to the validity and reliability of the content. The conclusion reached by many researchers has been that information found on Wikipedia should be treated with caution. So what does that mean to the Wikipedia user? As a general rule, the best advice is likely to be that information stated on Wikipedia should not be treated as being necessarily correct. However, Wikipedia does serve a potentially valuable role in that information is relatively easy to find and, based upon Wikipedia's rules, it should contain citations. Rather than assuming that Wikipedia content is factually correct, a better approach is to use the article citations to locate primary sources and to read the source materials for oneself. It is important to keep in mind that in academic environments most professors will frown upon references to Wikipedia articles cited in academic papers. For this reason, Wikipedia can be a helpful resource to locate potential valid citations, read those sources, and then cite them directly rather than citing Wikipedia.

AN APPROACH FOR ASSESSING THE RELIABILITY OF HEALTH INFORMATION ON THE INTERNET

Having established some of the issues related to the validity of scientific data on the Internet, we can now examine some approaches to help assess the validity of health information found on websites. The approach discussed in this section assesses three aspects of a website, including the author of the website and his or her *credentials*, a critical look at the *content* of the website, and the *organization* that hosts or publishes the website.

CREDENTIALS

The reason for assessing the author's credentials is to get a sense of whether the information reported on the website is coming from an individual with the appropriate training and experience to interpret and report scientific data. Although one does not necessarily need to have a science background to simply report the results of a study, understanding research methods is essential to understanding the limitations of a particular research study and drawing appropriate conclusions.

If the website contains recommendations or conclusions related to research, the background of the website author is more likely to be pertinent. In particular, one of the key questions is whether the author of the website discloses who he or she is and what type of academic and/or professional background they have. If the individual responsible for the website is not willing to provide that information, it may be a tipoff that the information is suspect. For those who do provide information, it is helpful to note whether the individual has a research or clinical background and whether they have recognized degrees, certifications, and/or licenses.

This is often particularly important in the area of websites containing information about diet and nutrition, especially given how many of them who report very scientific-sounding statistics for purposes of selling an unproven nutritional supplement product. Although the authors of many websites will claim to be nutritionists or have some sort of nutrition certification, the best advice in this area typically comes from individuals holding the designation of *Registered Dietitian* (RD). The designation of RD requires that an individual complete the minimum of a bachelor's degree in an accredited program approved by the *Accreditation Council for Education in Nutrition and Dietetics*, a clinical internship program of six to twelve months, successful completion of a national board examination, and completion of continuing education courses in order to maintain RD status.

Another issue relates to individuals who claim to have lofty degrees, but whose degrees are not from recognized and accredited schools. The term *diploma mills* refers to organizations that essentially sell university diplomas requiring little or no real academic work. Often, the rationale is that the supposed school will award a degree based upon the student's life experiences rather than their academic work.

The State of Oregon has among the most stringent laws regulating the use of degrees from diploma mills on resumes and job applications; however, many other states are relatively lax in their regulation of diploma mills. As a result, a cursory look through the authors of a variety of health-related websites will often find a significant number of individuals who will claim to have legitimate bachelor's, master's, and doctoral degrees in a variety of scientific and clinical fields.

Although this problem is prevalent in the health and medical field, it can be found in many other areas. For example, in 2004 several federal employees at the National Nuclear Security Administration were found to have purchased master's and doctoral degrees while doing little or no academic work.[23,34] In another high-profile case, a senior director from the Department of Homeland Security was placed on administrative leave and ultimately resigned when it was discovered that she had been claiming a bachelor's, master's, and PhD from a diploma mill called Hamilton University.[24,35]

What all of this means to the individual who relies on the web for health information is that one should always check to see whether the author's background is being made available. If it is, that information should be reviewed to ensure the degrees and/or certifications have been awarded from recognized and accredited institutions.

CONTENTS

When critically reviewing the contents of a website, there are several areas that can help you determine the validity of a website. This involves focusing on what the website authors actually have to say and how they choose to communicate the message. Some of the key points to examine include the following:

Presence of citations This involves reviewing the website to determine whether statements of facts or statistics have been cited as to their sources. As described in the case study earlier in this chapter, references to valid scientific studies may be distorted or taken out of context. As a reader, the only way you can determine whether the references are being used properly is if you are provided with a full citation with sufficient information for you to find and read the primary source for yourself.

Citation validity If primary sources have been cited, it is usually worthwhile to at least spot check some citations to make sure that they are being used honestly. For example, a website may claim that that a study published in *The New England Journal of Medicine* found the approach recommended on the website to be effective. Without actually reading that study, it is impossible to know if that was actually the conclusion reached in the study. Checking the actual articles is particularly important if the claim being made is rather unusual or extraordinary.

Products for sale Websites that offer products for sale are not typically in the best position to provide unbiased information, given that the owner of the website selling a product will have a financial interest in positioning information in a way to increase the chances of making a sale. Unless the website belongs to a large and reputable organization, it is generally best to assume that information coming from a website that is selling something will most likely be biased.

Conspiracy theories Many of the least reputable websites often rely on the claim of some sort of conspiracy theory to explain why the information they are providing is inconsistent with what is considered to be scientifically valid. For example, a website might claim that they have the secret to curing cancer but that the large pharmaceutical companies have conspired to keep it a secret so that they can continue to sell cancer treatments.

Attention to detail Very often, the attention to detail with regards to spelling, grammar, and language can help you discern whether a website represents a professional effort based upon valid scientific evidence or simply an unsupported opinion.

ORGANIZATION

In this section we examine what organization, if any, hosts the website financially. The initial question to be answered is whether the website is the product of an individual person or that of a large and reputable organization. This is important to review since a website that is entirely an effort by one person will be much more closely tied to that person's background and experience, making the *Credentials* section an important factor.

If the website is the product of a larger and more reputable organization, it does not automatically mean the information contained on the website is correct, but it is much more likely that the organization has policies and procedures in place to help ensure that websites under their domain are consistent with the values of the organization. For example, many universities will have acceptable use policies in place that govern how technology resources, including websites, are to be used. Typical restrictions include bans on material deemed to be academically or scientifically dishonest, as well material used to advertise for-profit businesses on university webservers.

A WORKSHEET FOR ASSESSING WEBSITE QUALITY

There is no magical scoring formula that calculates the precise probability that a website is a good source of information. Instead, much like a jury in a legal trial, you must rely on a preponderance of the evidence to determine whether you believe the website to be a good choice for your purposes. Another important factor to keep in mind is that it is really not necessary to prove that a website is not valid. In many cases, you simply need to know that the validity of the information on a website is unclear. Even if you can't prove that it is concretely incorrect, the fact that there is a question about it is often enough evidence to discard that website and move on to another one that does offer better validity. For example, if a website provides information regarding the nutritional requirements of individuals with a particular medical condition and that website happens to sell nutritional supplements for that condition, that alone may be enough to determine that the information is potentially biased and that you should move on to another source.

The worksheet below is designed to provide a structured approach to reviewing and assessing a health or biomedical-related website from the standpoint of its potential scientific validity. It can be used by asking yourself the following questions as you review the material. The worksheet also includes space to record your observations as you work through the assessment. Once you have completed the worksheet, you should have a fairly clear indication of whether the health information on a particular website is likely to be scientifically valid. Also, keep in mind that in many cases you may not need to complete the worksheet in order to reach that conclusion since you may quickly find the one piece of information making it obvious that website is not credible.

SCREENING CRITERIA	**YOUR OBSERVATIONS**
CREDENTIALS	
What are the credentials of the individual who assembled the website or authored the information? Are they pertinent to the content? For example, if the individual is recommending dietary advice, is he or she a Registered Dietitian (RD)? Does the author claim to have a degree, license, or certification that relates to the topic? Note: *Nutrition "experts" can claim to be nutritionists without any license requirement or specialized training. A true nutrition expert is a Registered Dietitian (RD), which requires an accredited degree and passing an exam.*	

Do the credentials appear to be valid? If you don't recognize the school someone claims to have a degree from, see if you can find out anything about it. If it exists, does it appear to be a legitimate school with accreditation or is it a degree mill? Degree mills often offer degrees for "life experience" without having to actually attend classes. If the school the person attended is identified, try looking up the school's website to learn more about it. Some university websites have alumni databases where you can look up an individual. If so, try looking the author up.	
If the author claims to be a member of a trade association or industry group that you have not heard of, make sure that it exists by searching for it on the Internet.	
If the author claims to hold a license of some sort (MD, RD, RN, PT, etc.), see whether the state in which they are licensed has a website where you can look them up to verify the information. The Council on Licensure, Enforcement, and Regulation (CLEAR) provides a great clearinghouse where you can check the license status of almost any profession. Their website is at: http://www.clearhq.org/resources/license_verification.htm The American Board of Medical Specialties website has an excellent online resource that allows you to look up an MD to see what board certifications they hold. The address is http://www.certificationmatters.org/ You can also find out quite a bit about a physician by checking the AMA's Physician lookup website at https://apps.ama-assn.org/doctorfinder/recaptcha.jsp Keep in mind that people with PhDs, DScs, EdDs and other legitimate non-medical doctoral degrees will not be in the MD database since they are not physicians, although they can legally call themselves "Dr."	
Has the person been published in a peer-reviewed journal? Try searching Medline, LexisNexis, or other databases by author name to see if they can be found. This is particularly important if the author claims to have been published.	

CONTENTS	
What is the substance of the information on the website? Does it tend to be consistent with current scientific research?	
Does the author provide *scientific* research to back up health claims? (very important)	
Do the authors make difficult-to-believe claims or voice conspiracy theories as to why their opinion is not taken seriously? (For example, "Drug companies don't want you to know about our herbal cancer cure because they would lose money on chemotherapy sales.")	

Are all of the statistics cited? Look for references to studies every time a statistic is used. You should be given adequate information to locate the article that the statistic was cited from, find the statistic or fact that was cited, and then reach your own conclusion regarding the reliability and context of the information. Keep in mind that facts and statistics are often cited from respectable journal articles but are intentionally taken out of context to support a position.	
Can you actually find the references cited? Make sure they are actually published articles in peer-reviewed (refereed) publications.	
Are they trying to sell you anything? If so, they have a financial incentive for you to believe them. If products of any kind are sold, you should consider the information biased.	

ORGANIZATION	
Is there an organization at which the website is based or is it an individual effort?	
If there is an organization is it: A commercial entity? A hospital or medical center? A private research institute? A college or university? A government agency? A religious group?	
Try checking the URL to see what type of web server the site may be based at: COM—Commercial Web Server ORG—Non-Profit Organization GOV—U.S. Government Agency EDU—Educational Institution (probably a college or university) Keep in mind that a non-profit group is not necessarily a good thing, and a commercial organization is not necessarily a bad thing.	
Try to find information regarding the reputation of the organization. Search for the name of the organization using a search engine to see what types of results you get. Try to find commentary from others.	
Look for news stories about organizations in online access to newspapers. Look for both positive stories (awards, grants, etc.) and for negative ones (lawsuits, federal indictments, etc.).	

A STRATEGY FOR FINDING WHAT YOU NEED

One of the key issues related to finding any type of information on the Internet is that there is such a vast number of websites containing such a vast number of topics that all seem to get in the way of the one piece of information that is being sought. A common experience is that a person starts out with an idea of what he or she is looking for and enters a word or combination of words into a web search engine. The results that appear can easily number in the millions, making it effectively impossible to view all of the possibilities. And, it is almost a given that of those millions of results, skimming through the first few pages finds that most are only loosely related or completely unrelated to what was being searched. For example, a search for the term "diabetes" using Google results in approximately 67 million sites, with the first few pages containing links to pages discussing causes, symptoms, and risk factors, sites that sell diabetes supplies, and some that promote non-traditional treatments.

One consideration is that much of the difficulty encountered when looking for information often has to do less with *where* we look for information than it does with *how* we look for information. Having an organized approach and a very clear expectation and understanding for what you want in the results is critical to being able to conduct an efficient search. Taking a haphazard approach without first thinking through the strategy and without having a clear understanding of what you need almost always results in wasted time and effort, as well as a frustrating experience.

The first step in finding what you are looking for is to be able to first identify what it is that you are looking for. One of the most common problems when doing web searches is a lack of understanding as to precisely what it is that is needed. Very often an individual will begin a web search with a relatively vague idea of what he or she is actually trying to find. The very first step in conducting a search is to first have a very clear idea of what you specifically need to know. One of the best ways to do that is to formulate a research question. Research questions are commonly used by researchers constructing study methodologies. The basic rules for constructing a research question include the following:

1. It must be in the form of a question. In other words, there needs to be a question mark at the end and we should avoid the temptation of simply stating the topic the way it might go into a search engine. For example, "diabetes risk factors" is not in the form of a question.
2. The question must be very specific. In other words, rather than starting out with two or three words that are generally related to the overall topic, the research question should state in very specific terms what is needed and it should only focus on one specific aspect of the problem. Simply thinking through the process of creating a well-designed research question helps us to better understand what we are actually looking for. It should also be stated in such a way that it will be absolutely clear if the information found on a website answers the question or not. Although "What are the risk factors for diabetes?" is in the form of a question, it can be made much more specific. An example of a more specific research question is, "What are the controllable risk factors for Type II diabetes among adult males?" Making the question specific helps us to much better understand what it is we are actually looking for.
3. The research question must be written down and grammatically correct. Developing the question should be done with some attention to detail. That means that it can be referred to as the online research effort progresses. As results are found, it is often helpful to refer to the research question in order to help keep ourselves on track. Otherwise, we risk the common problem of becoming distracted and heading off in a different direction.

The use of a research question is a helpful exercise because it forces us to think through what we are looking for in very specific terms before we start the search. With a well-written and specific research question in hand, it is much easier to stay focused and on-task until the answer to that question is found. It is important to keep in mind that *a single research question will most likely not provide all of the information needed to solve the problem at hand*. Most likely, it will take several questions to do that. Although there may be a temptation to combine multiple questions into a single giant one, you should resist the temptation to do so. One of the reasons for creating research questions is that they help us to break down the information we are looking for into smaller bite-sized chunks.

As an example, a question such as "What are the controllable risk factors for Type II diabetes among adult males and what is the most effective intervention to prevent onset?" combines two very different questions into one. Trying to find both pieces of information in a single search will prove difficult and potentially frustrating. Consider that each question should be used as the focal point of a search, so the more focused and specific the question, the easier it will be to find an answer to that question. Using this approach means that you will need to write multiple questions and conduct a separate web search for each one. However, because each question is much more targeted, the results should generally be found much faster and with less overall work.

Below are some examples of well-written and poorly written research questions:

POORLY WRITTEN	**CRITIQUE**	**A BETTER QUESTION**
What are the effects of drug use among student athletes?	Problems: Too vague. Does "effects" refer to positive or negative effects? What type of drugs—prescription drugs that have been prescribed or recreational drugs and, if so, what kind? What type of students—high school? college?	What are the cognitive effects of long-term recreational drug use in high school student athletes?
What are ways to prevent drug use and how should drug users be treated?	Problems: There are two questions combined into one. Each portion should be its own question. It's also too vague—what type of drugs? What type of users?	What strategies have proven efficacy for preventing recreational drug use among high school student athletes?
How are schools addressing drug use?	Problems: Too vague and too simple. What type of schools? What does "addressing" mean?	What are the leading methods that have been implemented in U.S. high schools to prevent recreational drug use?
What is the cost of drug use?	Unclear and vague. Cost to whom? In the U.S.? What type of drugs?	What is the economic impact of drug abuse in the United States with respect to the cost of publically funded drug treatment programs?

EFFECTIVE USE OF SEARCH ENGINES

Once one or more questions have been written, it is time to use a web-search engine to begin searching for answers to those questions. To best use a search engine, it is helpful to have an understanding of how they do what they do. Web search engines such as Google, Yahoo, and Bing seem like rather magical programs that are able to sift through all of the content on the Internet in less time than it takes to click a mouse button. In reality, there are some limitations to how they work, and understanding those limitations can be helpful to using them effectively.

One of the first concepts that everyone should understand is that search engines do not actually search the Internet in real time. When a user enters a term into a search engine and presses the SEARCH button, no search engine is physically capable of checking every single website on the Internet to see whether it contains the word that was entered into the search box. Instead, all search engines work by constantly collecting information about websites and entering that information into indexed databases. Websites are found using *bots* (sometimes called *robots*, *webcrawlers*, or *spiders*), which are programs used by search engine providers to explore webservers on the Internet and to report back when a previously unknown website is found. After a new webpage is found, the contents of that webpage are copied into the search engine's database and the words are indexed, which means that they are sorted and related back to the websites containing those words. Using an indexed database, search engines can locate and return millions of website records that contain a particular word or combination of words in just a fraction of a second.

Given that when you conduct a web search you are actually searching a database and not the entire Internet, there are some limitations to the process that should be apparent. One limitation is that very new webpages that have not yet found their way into a search engine's database are less likely to be represented in your results. Conversely, a webpage that had previously been in existence but has subsequently been taken down may still be in a database, meaning that it will be returned as part of a search, yet clicking on it may return the familiar "Page Not Found" error message. The important consideration is that different search engines rely upon different databases and can return different results.

Another issue concerns the ranking of webpages in search engine results. All search engine providers have to deal with the dilemma of how to rank the thousands or millions of results that are returned by a search. All of them strive to have the most relevant results listed near the top of the list so that users will want to return to that search engine every time they need to conduct a search. For the developers of search engines, the exact logic involved in determining which of potentially millions of results should be near the top of the list and which ones should be near the bottom of the list is typically a very complex and a closely guarded secret. Each search engine has its own proprietary method for ranking results and each one typically advertises that their method is the best one. The factors involved in the ranking typically involve some of the following items:

- The number of times a search term (a word that the user is searching for) appears in a web page
- Whether a search term is in the actual title of the webpage
- Whether the search term appears in the HTML *keyword* meta tag of the webpages (meta tags are hidden from the view of users and they contain descriptive information about the webpage)
- Whether the search term appears as a hyperlink in other webpages. In other words, if the word *heart* is often a link to the website of the *American Heart Association*, the American Heart Association would likely be closer to the top of the list when someone searches for the word *heart*.

Also, most search engines will generally sell advertising space at the top of the results list. The first few results will typically be highlighted and labeled as either "sponsored links" or "ads" so that it is clear that they are not true results, but are really advertising.

Regardless of the exact logic that is used, the important consideration to remember is that every search engine (Yahoo, Google, Bing, etc.) has its own unique way of ranking the results, and every search engine has its own unique database of websites. Conducting the same search in several different search engines will return different apparent results because the results that most people see are usually the ones closest to the top of list. Although it is impossible to predict which search engine's ranking method will be best for any one search, the fact that they will return different results is an indication that one should not always rely on the same search engine over time. Unfortunately, many of us often become creatures of habit with respect to web search engines, but if the results returned by Google are not what you expected, try the same search using Yahoo, Bing, or another.

The following are some techniques that work with many of the popular search engines. Although every technique may not be appropriate for every search, some of them can be quite helpful in certain situations.

Searching for a phrase

This technique works best when you are searching for a literal phrase—a collection of words that should appear in a particular order. As an example, the term *first aid* has a particular meaning when the two words appear in that order. However, most search engines will generally just search for webpages containing the word *first* and the word *aid* without regard as to their order. As an example, a search using Google of the term *first aid* returns approximately 133 million results. However, it is possible to force a search engine to look for the literal phrase *first aid* by placing quotation marks around it. When quotation marks are placed around the term "first aid" in Google, the results drop down to about 89 million, as they now exclude all webpages that contained the two words in the incorrect order. This method works particularly well when searching for a first

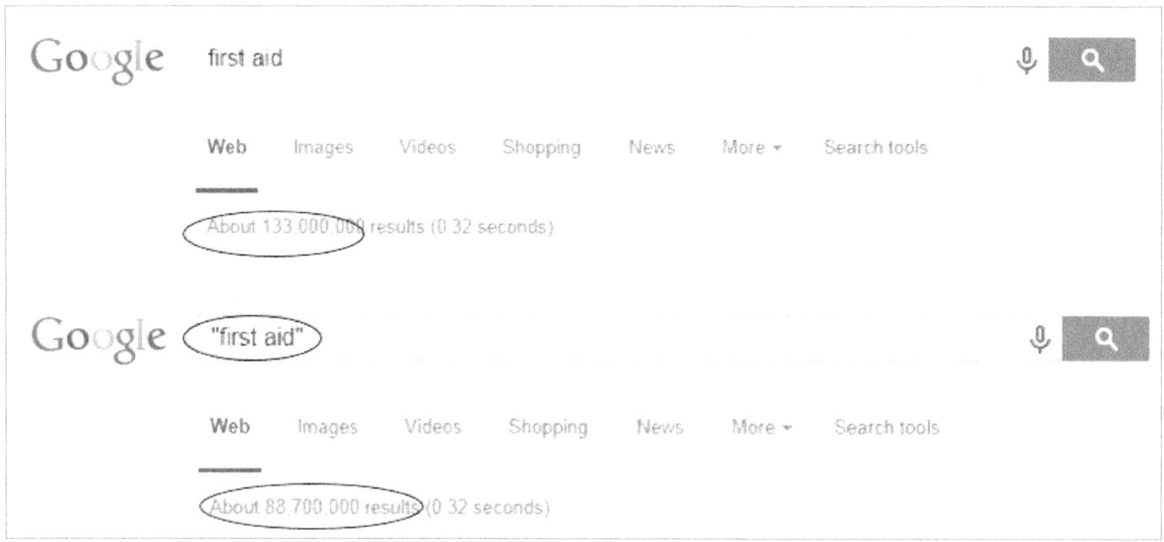

FIGURE 4.4 Example of a phrase search.

name and last name together. Keep in mind that using the quotation marks helps only in situations where you are looking for a specific combination of words in that exact order. Overuse or misuse of the quotation marks will likely return very few and limited results.

Site-Specific searches

Searches in most search engines can be limited to a particular domain or type of domain using the "site" keyword. For example, if you are searching for information about the incidence of heart attacks in the U.S., a common approach is to include the search terms *Incidence of Heart Attacks in the U.S.* However, if you are interested primarily in information published on websites of federal government agencies (those ending with .gov domains), you could limit your results to only those websites by adding *site:.gov* to the end of the search term (e.g., *Incidence of Heart Attacks in the U.S. site:.gov).* As in the example below, the results that are returned are all ones that appear on .gov websites. Conversely, you could change it to *site:.edu* if you wanted results only from university websites, etc. Or, you could enter a full URL, such as site:cdc.gov if you only wanted results from the *United States Centers for Disease Control and Prevention* website.

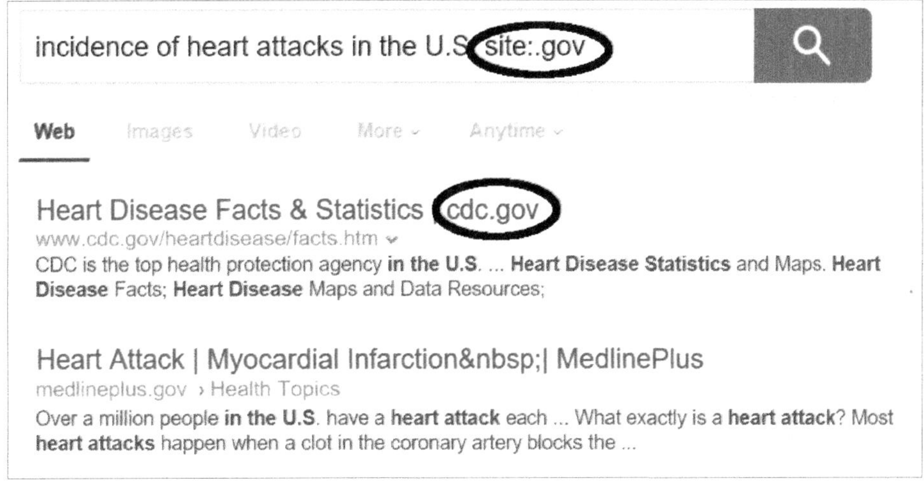

FIGURE 4.5 Example of a site-specific search.

Exclusion search

In certain cases, web searches may return results that technically meet the requirements of what you asked for but are not in the correct context. Consider the following example. Let's assume that you are searching for information about the use of steroids to treat asthma in high school athletes. Using the search terms *high school athletes with asthma using steroids* in Bing returns almost 3 million results, of which many relate to the use of anabolic steroids used by athletes to enhance athletic performance.

If some commonality can be found in the webpages that we don't want, those webpages can be excluded from the search, leaving only the webpages we care about. In this case, two words that are found in many of the unwanted sites are *anabolic* and *performance*. To conduct a search that returns results with the absence of a particular word, simply add the word to the end of the search, with a minus sign in front of it. In this case, we would add *-anabolic* and *-performance* to the end of our original search term. As shown below, adding the exclusions reduces the number of results from almost 3 million down to 35,300 much more relevant results.

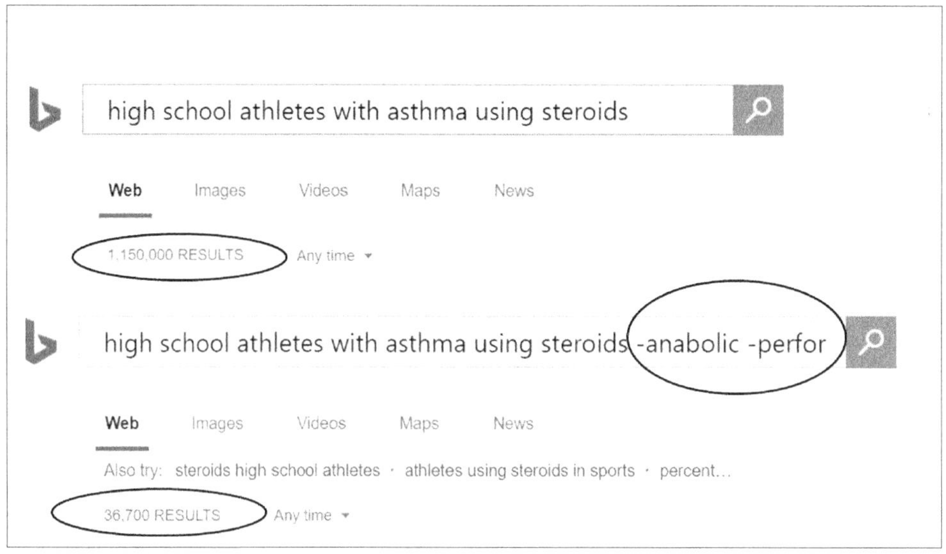

FIGURE 4.6 Example of a search with exclusion terms.

LITERATURE DATABASE RESEARCH

Literature databases can be defined as databases containing references to articles from a variety of publications. For our purposes, we will focus on scholarly literature databases that largely contain peer-reviewed journals areas such as biomedical sciences, public health, healthcare economics and healthcare administration.

The key distinction between a search of a literature database and a web search using an Internet search engine (such as Google or Yahoo) can be summarized as follows:

1. Web search engines search tend to be designed with the objective to search and return as many possible results as possible, with both closely related and loosely related connections to the search terms used. As such, they can be described as relatively sensitive tools, given that even a set of detailed search terms can produce millions of results. On the other hand, web search engines are typically not particularly precise, in that the results produced can vary substantially from being directly related to the search objective.
2. Literature databases are typically designed to produce results that are as precise as possible, although with fewer results. A search in which a web search engine returns millions of results, may only return a few dozen results in a literature database, although if the search is done properly, the results are much more likely to help answer the research question.

Although both literature databases and web search engines can return usable results, it is important to note that the two are very different from one another both in terms of their content and in terms of the approaches used to search them. Using the same approach that one might take with Google or Yahoo will generally return disappointing results in a literature database. However, using an appropriate search strategy with a literature database will often return superior results.

A SEARCH STRATEGY FOR LITERATURE DATABASES

When searching literature databases (or any other online information source) it is helpful to adopt a search strategy to be used. The concept of a search strategy is used to help generate the best possible results from the search effort, while minimizing the possibility of not returning a potentially useful result that would not have been found otherwise. A well-designed search strategy can also help optimize the search effort so that less time is spent on hit-and-miss searches and so that the most relevant results can be located with the least amount of time and effort.

There are number of procedural approaches that can be taken to develop a search strategy, although most that are suggested typically include many of the same or similar elements. One approach that has been found to work well was developed for use at Johns Hopkins Medical School[36]. The procedure incorporates seven steps that help provide a process for identifying the specific problem to be researched, locating the best set of results, and then documenting the process for future reference.

Step 1: Write a research question. The purpose of this step is twofold. First, it helps to clarify and articulate the specific piece of knowledge that is needed from the research effort. The second purpose of the research question is to provide a basis to evaluate the relative success of a search. At the point that sufficient information is found to answer the research question, the search can be deemed successful, and one can move on to the next question. To be effective, a research questions should be sufficiently detailed, written down (so one can refer back to it as necessary), grammatically correct, and in the form of an actual question. For a discussion and examples of research questions, please refer back to the earlier section in this chapter, *A Strategy for Finding What You Need*.

Step 2: Select a database to search. Different databases often tend to have specific areas of focus. The Medline database, for example, has traditionally been the one of the largest biomedical reference databases in existence, containing over 23 million articles. Depending on the focus of the research question, one should select the database most likely to contain the types of articles needed. For example, a specialized database such as PsycINFO, which largely contains articles from clinical and social psychology journals, would be a good choice for research questions related to psychology and behavioral sciences. Medline, on the other hand, would be a logical choice for research questions that would rely on articles related to clinical trials.

Step 3: Design a query statement. While the purpose of the *Research Question* is to establish the objective for the search, the *query statement* is what is actually entered into the computer. Query statements typically rely on the use of Boolean logic as a way of specifying the search criteria needed to locate the articles of interest. Boolean logic typically relies on a series of statements in which attributes of the articles are compared to specific constants that are desired. For example, the statement *TITLE contains DISEASE* compares the title of each article in a database to the constant, which in this case is the word *disease* in order to identify those articles whose titles contain the word *disease*.

Multiple comparisons can be connected to one another using the logical operators AND, OR, and NOT. For a detailed discussion of Boolean logic, please refer to Chapter 8.

Step 4: Perform the search. In Step 4, the query statement is entered into the database's user interface and the search is actually conducted. Different databases use different methods for entering a query statement, ranging from simplified to complex. Although most databases provide a form in which the key aspects of the query can be typed into a form and selections made from pre-defined drop-down menus, many also include text-based query syntax which can be typed into a search box in its entirety by the user. In the example below, a PubMed search for articles containing the words *disease* or *illness*, together with the word *respiratory* appear as follows:

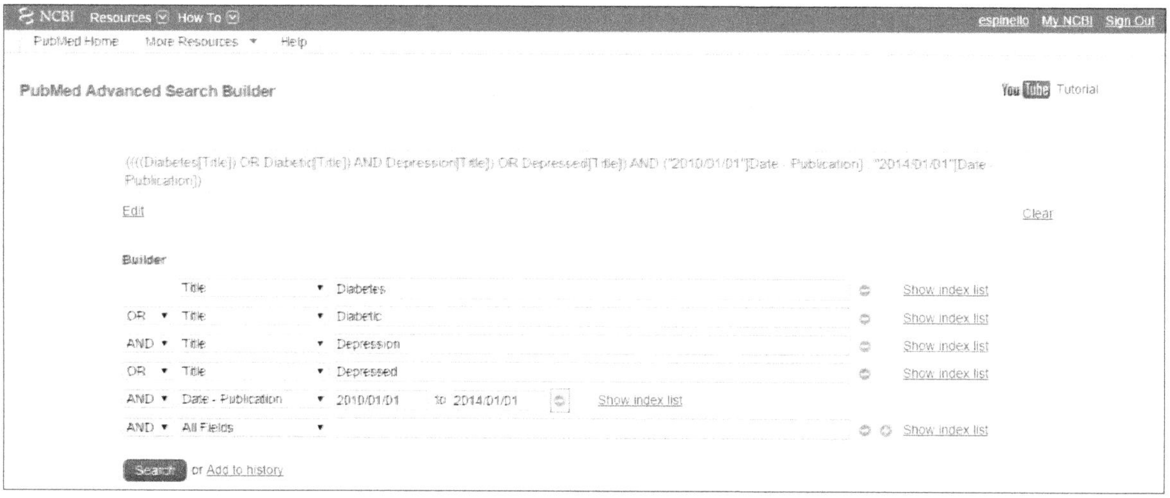

FIGURE 4.7 PubMed Search Screen showing both the search form and query syntax above the form.

The Medline syntax version of the search, however can also be used to conduct exactly the same search, and appears as follows:

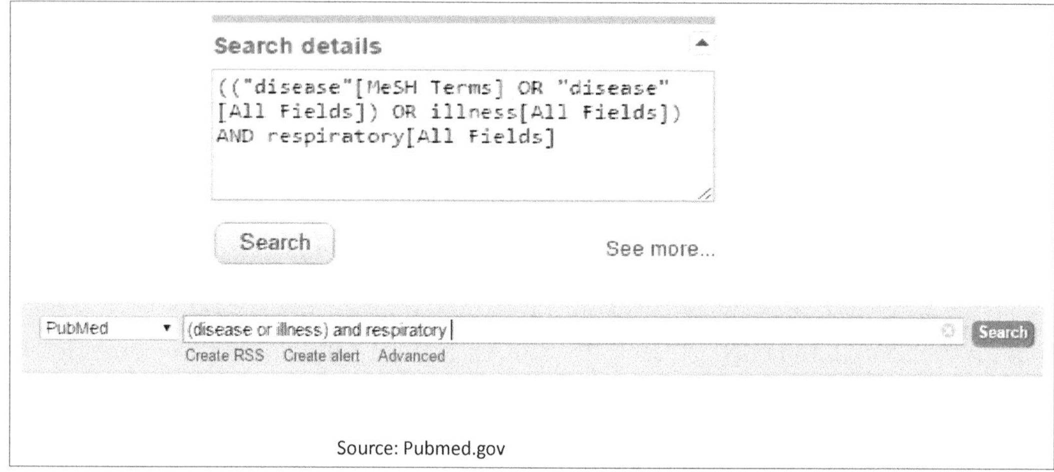

FIGURE 4.8 PubMed Query Syntax in Search Details box.

Most literature database, such as Pubmed and others typically offer a "Help" option that provides information about using the query syntax and other resources particular to the specific database.

Step 5: Evaluate the results. Once the search has been performed, the next step is to evaluate the results in order to determine whether or not sufficient information was found to answer the research question and, if not what were the reasons. The two measures to be considered when evaluating the results are those of *sensitivity* and *precision*. Sensitivity refers to the number of results that are returned by a search. A search is considered sensitive if a large number of articles are returned, regardless of their quality or relevance to the research question. Search precision, however, refers to the degree to which the results of the search are relevant to answering the research question. A search is considered to have high precision if a large proportion of the articles returned are relevant to the research question.

There is typically some tradeoff between search precision and sensitivity. Consider that a search with relatively vague criteria will typically return a large number of results, although many of those results are likely unrelated to the research question. As an example, consider the following research question: "What strategies have proven efficacy for preventing recreational drug use among high school student athletes?"

A Pubmed search using the single word "drugs" produces approximately 1.2 million results. This search can be described as highly sensitive. However, the vast majority of the articles returned have nothing to do with drug abuse prevention strategies in high schools, making the precision of the search quite low. Ideally, the sensitivity of the search should produce sufficient articles to provide evidence of scientific reliability, but not so many that cannot be quickly reviewed.

In this example, there is a need to improve the precision while reducing the sensitivity. One way to do so is to add additional search terms. By searching for the following terms "high school," "drug abuse," and "diversion" the result drop to just 57 articles, almost all of which being directly relevant to the research question. By improving the precision of the search, the sensitivity was reduced. Although increasing precision usually results in a decline in sensitivity, the opposite is not necessarily true. It is possible to increase the sensitivity of a search through the use of synonyms for search terms, while not reducing the search's precision.

Step 6: Make a decision. At this stage, the researcher decides where there is enough information to answer the research question and if not, what change should be made to the search in order to get closer to the best results. In the case of very low sensitivity, it is possible that there may not have been articles published addressing this issue. This is normally referred to as a "research gap." Another possibility is that an error was made in the search. For example, one of the search terms may have been misspelled, and possibly the AND or OR used incorrectly. Another possibility is that the database selected was not the correct one and that a different database will produce better results.

Based on the reason for the inadequate results, the decision is made at this step as to what change will be made to the search. This may include searching a different database, adding or removing search terms, correcting spelling errors, etc. Once the change is made, the search is run again and the new results are then evaluated.

At the point that the results contain adequate precision with a reasonable sensitivity, and there is enough information to answer the research question, the decision can be made to go forward to the final stage in Step 7.

Step 7: Document the search process. Once the search is complete and the needed articles have been found, the next step involves documenting the search so that it can be easily referred to again in the future if necessary. Documenting the search involve recording the research question being answered, along with the date and the database in which the search was conducted, the final query statement that was used, and the list of articles returned in the search. Although the process seems tedious, all of the information (with the exception of the research question) will be contained on the final screen of the search. This can be either printed or captured electronically by printing the screen to a PDF file by using the built-in Print-to-PDF capability of many web browsers, or with one of the many free PDF utilities available.

As another approach, the search can be recorded using a bibliographic management software, such as EndNote, Refworks, or ProCite. Additionally, there are free, open-source bibliographic managers such as Zotero and Mendeley, that provide much the same capabilities.

The advantage of bibliographic management software is that it provides the capability for a user to maintain their own personal literature database. As relevant articles are found online, they can be easily added to a personal database and referred to as needed. Additionally, most bibliographic management programs provide add-ins to popular word processors, such as Microsoft Word, allowing references to be quickly and easily cited when writing papers and articles requiring specific styles, such as JAMA, APA, etc.

WILDCARD AND TRUNCATION CHARACTERS

In addition to highly precise Boolean logic-based searches, most literature databases also offer the use of two types of "shortcut" characters, typically referred to as *wildcard* characters and *truncation* characters. While both wildcard and truncation characters allow a user to broaden the scope of a Boolean logic statement while keeping the query statement relatively short and elegant, they work in slightly different ways from one another.

Wildcard Characters

Wildcard characters allow the user to substitute a single letter in a word for any other character. Although different databases use different characters to denote the wildcard, a commonly used wildcard is the question mark, as is used in databases provided by EBSCOhost. As an example, consider the following query statement:

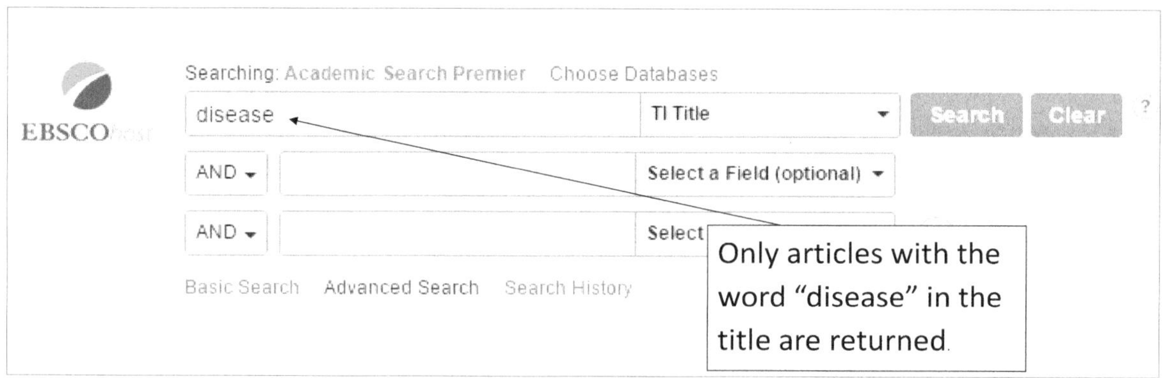

FIGURE 4.9 EBSCOHost Query using the OR connector to return variations of the word "disease."

In this example, the query statement will return articles containing the word "disease" in the title. However, given the precise nature of a literature database, related words such as "diseased" and "diseases" would be excluded since they are not spelled exactly the same way. One alternative would be to modify the query to the following:

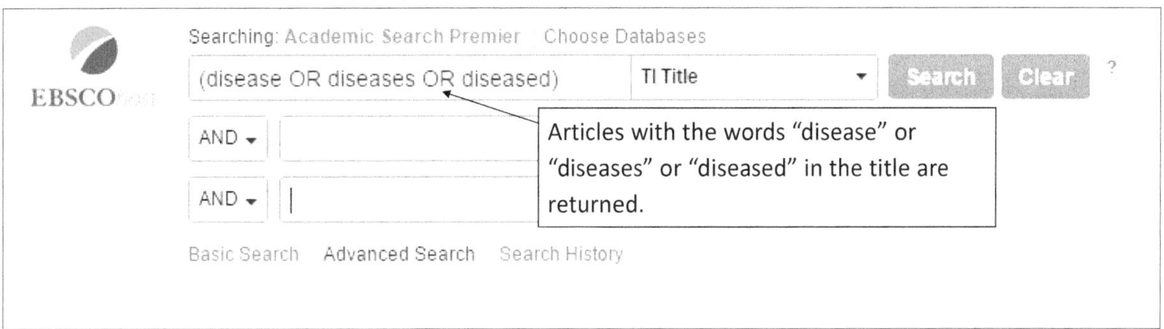

FIGURE 4.10 EBSCOHost Query.

By using the OR, the words diseased and diseases can be included in the query, although the length of the query becomes lengthy, increasing the possibility of a typo or other type of error. In this situation, another approach would be to use the wildcard character extend the logic of the query so that it will also include the additional words. Since a wildcard character replaces part of a word with any characters, adding it to the end of the word "disease" will extend the logic to look for the word disease followed by any one-character suffix.

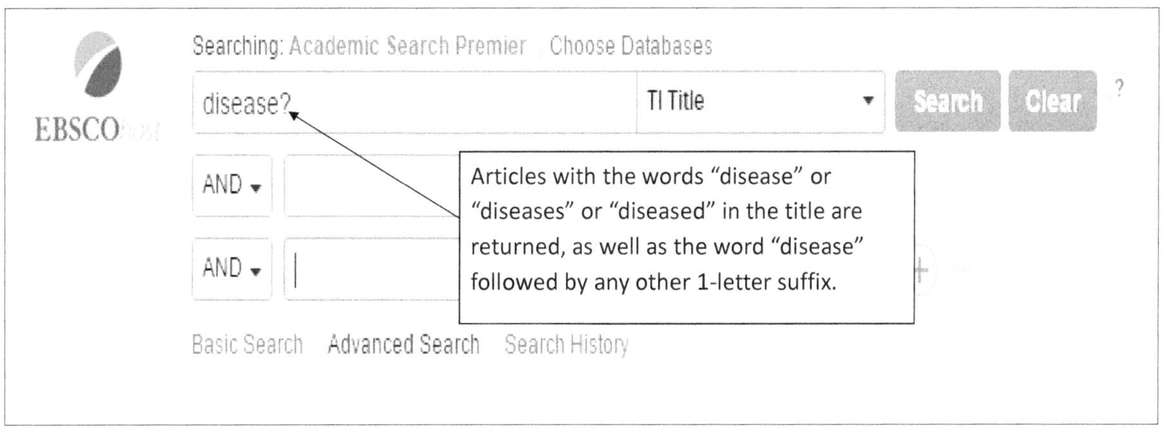

FIGURE 4.11 Wildcard character.

Truncation Characters

Truncation characters work in much the same way as wildcard characters, with one major exception. Truncation characters can replace part of a word with any number of multiple characters, rather than only the one character that is possible with wildcards.

Consider the following example where a search is performed in PubMed searching for articles containing the word "athlete" in the title. Since the wildcard character only replaces a single character, adding the wildcard at the end would not find articles endings longer than one letter to the word "athlete" (such as athletics).

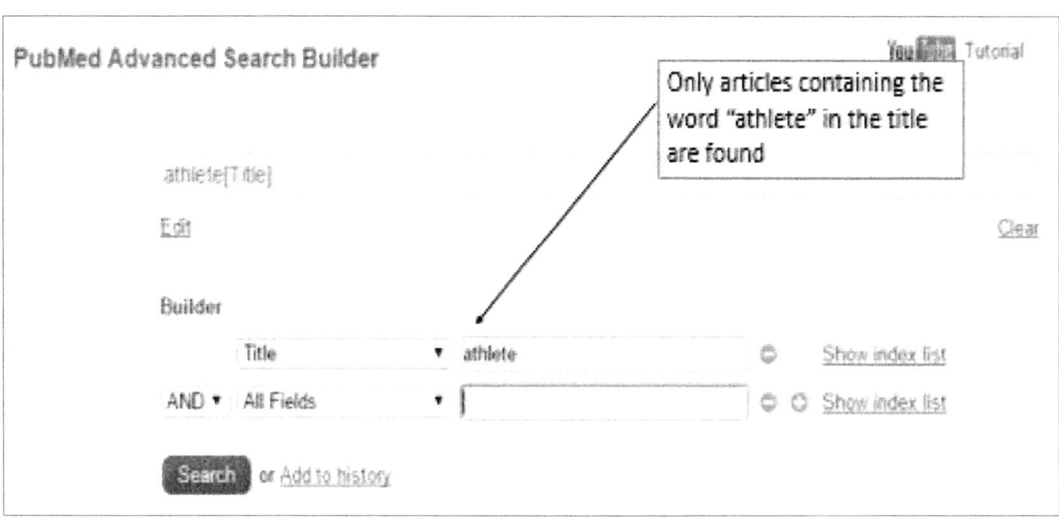

FIGURE 4.12 PubMed search for "athlete."

In order to also search for articles with other endings, such as athletes, athletic, athletics, etc., the truncation character can be used instead of the wildcard. In this case, the common root to the words is "athlet," therefore, if the truncation character is used at the end of that root, the possible results could include athlete, athletes, athletic, athletics, etc. The truncation character used in PubMed is that asterisk character, as shown in the following example.

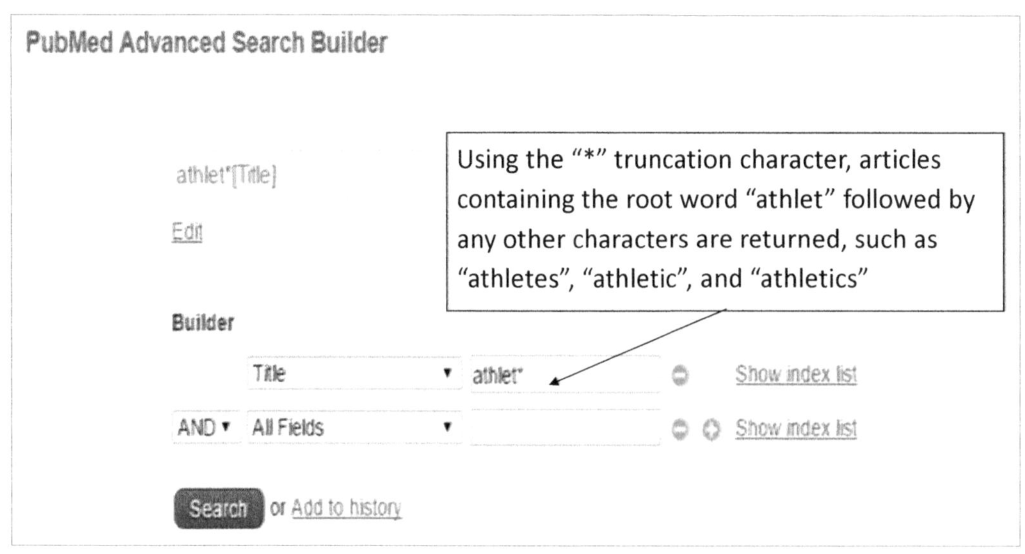

FIGURE 4.13 PubMed search using a wildcard.

SUMMARY

Searching for information using web search engines requires an organized approach that begins with having a clear idea of what specific information is needed. One way to organize the search is to begin by writing down specific research questions that clearly reflect what is needed. Each question should address one particular part of the overall problem being researched, breaking the problem down into smaller search efforts that are easier to deal with. Search engines return results not by searching the entire Internet but by searching through the databases of webpages they have compiled. Once the search is complete, different search engines have different methods for ranking and presenting the results. Given the differences between them, if a particular search using one search engine is not returning the desired results, it is often helpful to cycle through the various other popular search engines, as their results are likely to be different.

When evaluating online research, Information can be generally grouped into the categories of *empirical* and *anecdotal* information. Empirical data can be described as data that has been collected and analyzed with an adherence to the scientific method to ensure validity and reliability. Anecdotal data refers to information that does not necessarily have scientific validity. For purposes of decision-making in a healthcare environment, the highest standard is considered to be the practice of evidence-based medicine, by which medical intervention decisions are made based upon published empirical research, which reinforces the need to determine whether online research is empirical or anecdotal in nature. Some of the barriers to finding accurate information may include reliance on poor information, intentional or unintentional bias, fraud, and poor reporting/interpretation of published research.

Literature databases consist of collections of peer-reviewed journal articles in a searchable environment that is very different from a web search engine. The best results are obtained when a formal seach strategy is employed that begins with the writing of research questions, with each question used as the basis for its own search. Using a search strategy in combination with wildcard and truncation characters, it is possible to very precisely locate articles that specifically help answer the research question.

APPLY YOUR KNOWLEDGE

1. Assume that the issue you have been asked to work on involves the development of a public health program to reduce the spread of infectious respiratory diseases among elementary school students. Using the approach discussed in this chapter, write three research questions that would help guide your search to learn more about the problem so that you can recommend a solution. In keeping with the guidelines, your research questions should be in the form of a question, grammatically correct, and very specific.
2. Using just one of the research questions that you have written, develop a search using a search engine of your own choice. Utilize any of the techniques that are appropriate for the search and review the results to determine the effectiveness of your search.
3. If necessary, modify the search terms and try subsequent searches until you achieve results that directly address the research question.

4. Select one of the results from your search and complete the Website Quality Assessment Worksheet. Based upon you observations, what conclusions did you reach regarding the website? Does the website appear to be a scientifically valid source of information that you are willing to rely upon to make a decision?

IMAGE CREDITS

Fig. 4.1: Gust H. Bardy et al., "Home Use of Automated External Defibrillators for Sudden Cardiac Arrest"," New England Journal of Medicine, vol. 358, no. 17. Copyright © 2008 by Massachusetts Medical Society. Reprinted with permission.
Fig. 4.2: Copyright © by Yahoo! Inc..
Fig. 4.3: Copyright © by Health On the Net Foundation.
Fig. 4.4: Copyright © by Google.
Fig. 4.5: Copyright © by Yahoo! Inc..
Fig. 4.6: Copyright © by Microsoft.
Fig. 4.7: Copyright in the Public Domain.
Fig. 4.8: Copyright in the Public Domain.
Fig. 4.9: Copyright © EBSCOHost
Fig. 4.10: Copyright © EBSCOHost.
Fig. 4.12: Copyright in the Public Domain.
Fig. 4.13: Copyright in the Public Domain.

5

MICROSOFT EXCEL

Since the introduction of the first commercially available electronic spreadsheet, VisiCalc, in the early 1980s, programs such as Lotus 1-2-3, Quattro Pro, and Microsoft Excel have become the Swiss Army knives of personal computing for business. What is noteworthy about contemporary spreadsheets is that they allow users the capability to construct combinations of formulas varying from simple to complex, conditional logic, sophisticated functions, report formatting, data visualization, and advanced data analysis capabilities without the need for traditional computer programming expertise. Given their capabilities, electronic spreadsheets have become an indispensable tool for PC users, while expertise in the use of spreadsheets has become an indispensable skill, and an expectation of most employers hiring entry-level college graduates.

Traditionally, electronic spreadsheets were created to support the need for mathematical computer modeling. Computer models can be used to represent the mathematical relationships and logic inherent in a real-world situation. The following are examples of some of the many situations for which spreadsheets can be used:

- Modeling the financial dynamics of an organization. Through the use of a spreadsheet financial model, what-if scenarios can be tested so that the effects of varying economic conditions, pricing changes, capital investments, and hiring or layoffs can be observed under different conditions.
- Understanding the potential community impact of exposure to an infectious disease. Epidemiological models can be used to simulate the possible outcomes associated with the presence of an infectious disease in a community, as well as the likely effects of implementing various public health interventions.

Although electronic spreadsheets are characterized by incredible flexibility, they also have the distinction of having no real inherent structure other than what the user creates. Starting with a relatively blank slate, users must have the ability to envision not only the logical flow of a model but how it will be physically laid out on the spreadsheet itself. Given that the spreadsheet is not just the modeling platform but also the user interface for the model, effective model-building involves two distinctly different skills:

1. Programming the various formulas and logic to so that the model accurately represents the real-world phenomena it describes.

2. Effectively creating the user interface so that someone using it for the first time is able to intuitively understand how it should be used, what limitations are present, and how the results should be interpreted.

This chapter will provide an introduction to the use of Microsoft Excel, together with a discussion of best practices in the use of spreadsheet modelling.

THE SPREADSHEET ENVIRONMENT

Electronic spreadsheets are inherently made up of rows and columns. The number of rows and columns varies depending on the spreadsheet and software version but Microsoft Excel 2010 and 2013 have over one million rows and 16,384 columns.

Each row in a spreadsheet it named based upon its row number. For example, the first row in a spreadsheet is named Row "1," followed by "2," etc. In a similar fashion, columns are named using letters of the alphabet, with the first column named Column "A," followed by "B," etc. Given that there are many more columns in the spreadsheet than there are letters in the alphabet, following Column "Z," the naming continues with Column "AA," "AB," "AC," etc.

The intersection between rows and columns are referred to as "cells," which are the locations in which data, formulas, and labels can be stored. Every cell in the spreadsheet is assigned a name (commonly referred to as a "cell address") that identifies its location in the spreadsheet.

CELL ADDRESSES

Cell addresses are designated by combining each cell's column letter and row number, in that order. For example, the first cell in upper left-hand corner of the spreadsheet is designated as cell A1, since it is in Column "A," Row "1." In the example in Figure 5.1, Cell B2 carries this address because it is located in Column B and in Row 2.

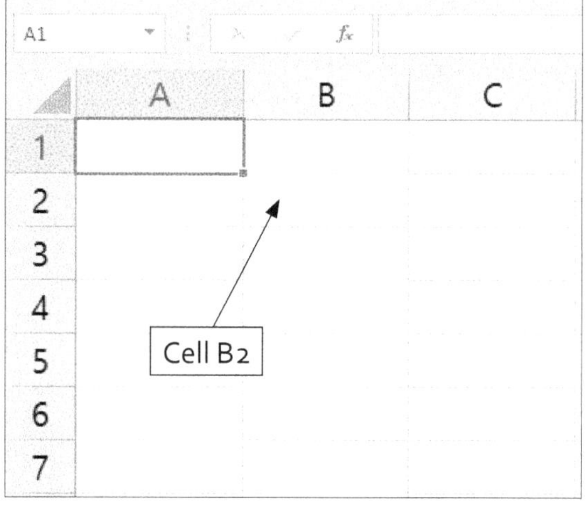

FIGURE 5.1 Example of a Cell Address.

CELL RANGES

When a contiguous group of cells is specified, it is referred to as a *range* of cells. When referring to a cell range in a spreadsheet, we simply identify the beginning and ending cell address in the range. Consider the example where the range of cells spans from cell B2 to cell B247. Ranges of cells are typically written using the convention of either a colon or a period separating the beginning from the end of the range. In our example, the range from B2 to B247 would be expressed as B2:B247 (or B2.B247), which means the same thing as "B2, B3, B4, ... etc.".

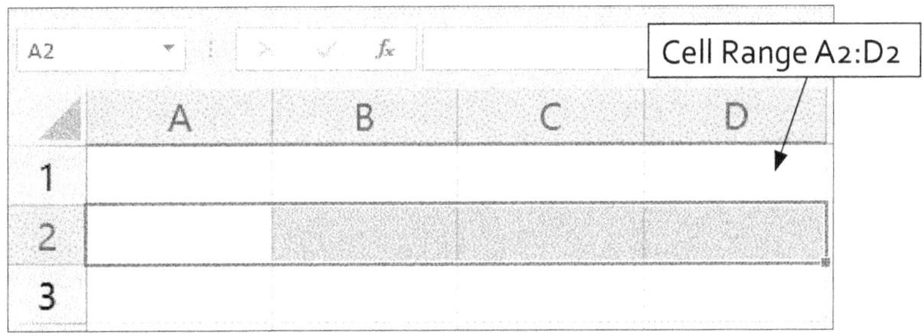

FIGURE 5.2 Example of a Spreadsheet Range.

CELL CONTENTS

There are essentially three types of items that can be placed in a spreadsheet cell:

1. Numbers, which can consist of any numeric value representing people, dollars, dates, or anything else that can be assigned a quantitative value.
2. Labels, which are essentially words or symbols that describe something on the spreadsheet.
3. Formulas, which may be either mathematical in nature, or may be used to manipulate text, evaluate logical conditions, or perform many other non-mathematical tasks.

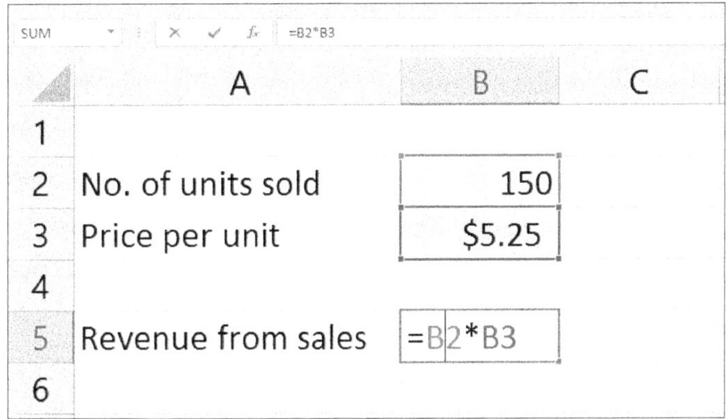

FIGURE 5.3 Examples of a Cell Contents.

Note the example in Figure 5.3 showing examples of cell contents. In Figure 5.3, Cells B2 and B3 contain *numbers* (150 and $5.25, respectively), cells A2 and A3 contain *labels*, and cell B5 contains a *formula*.

FORMULA CONSTRUCTION

The basic power of a spreadsheet is in its ability to quickly recalculate formulas using different input values. Consider the basic concept of a computer being an input/output device. Data is input into a computer, software provides instructions to the hardware about how to process the data, and the processed data is then output from the computer and returned to the user in some other fashion—with improvements made to it. Spreadsheets work in the same way. Data is input into the spreadsheet and formula logic created by the user instructs the hardware as to how to process that data so that processed results can be output back to the user.

TIP: After entering anything into a cell or making any changes to a formula, function, label, or input value, always end the process by pressing the ENTER key on the keyboard rather than clicking elsewhere on the spreadsheet.

In the example in Figure 5.3, the data values are being input into cells B2 and B3. Since those cells contain values manually typed into them by the user, they are referred to as *input cells*. The formulas are essentially the software, in that they provide the instructions needed regarding how to process the input data. Notice that in this example, the formulas are completely separate from the input data, in that they contain no numbers at all. In this example, the formula could have been written as **B2 * 5.25** (the asterisk is the multiplication operator in virtually all computer programs). Although the resulting answer would have been exactly the same, there is one important difference in usability. If the $5.25 is placed directly inside of the formula, there would be no way for a user of the spreadsheet to input a different price value in order to calculate the revenue if the price were $12.25 (or any other amount) without editing the actual formula. For this reason, including the actual value of $5.25 in the formula is *not* considered a best practice with respect to formula construction.

The basic concept of the spreadsheet is that the data values are separate from the formula logic. By entering the various inputs into cells and then having formulas reference the cell addresses instead of the actual numbers, the inputs can be treated as variables, allowing different input values to be plugged into cells so that the results can be immediately viewed without the need to modify formulas.

FUNCTIONS

Functions are common to spreadsheets, as well as to a variety of other types of software and programming languages. A *function* can be described as being similar to miniature computer programs that can perform very specific and specialized tasks within another program. Just like the spreadsheet, functions work on an input/output basis. Data is input or passed to the function, the function provides the instructions as to what to do to the data, and the processed results are returned for use elsewhere in the program or spreadsheet. For example, among the dozens of functions available in Excel, the SUM function performs the task of summing the numeric values contained in range of cells and returns the result. The inputs being provided to the SUM function consist of the cells or range of cells containing the values to be summed. The output consists of the sum value being returned by the function.

To better understand how functions work, it is helpful to first understand how they look and how we interact with them. In almost all programs, functions almost always have the same appearance, which is the name of the function followed by a set of parentheses. Note that there are no spaces between the name of the function and the parentheses. For example, the SUM function is more properly written as SUM() because the name of the function is "SUM" and it is immediately followed by the parentheses. Any time you see parentheses following a command, such as SUM(), AVERAGE(), etc., it is an indication that it is a reference to a function.

The parentheses following the name contain the *arguments* to the function, which are defined as the inputs and instructions needed for the function to do its job. Some functions may contain just one argument, while others may contain many arguments. The number of arguments needed depends on how a given function works. In the example of the SUM() function, only one argument is needed, which is the range of cells containing the values to be summed.

In Figure 5.4, an example of the use of the SUM() function is shown. In this example, the cells containing the values that we wish to sum are in cells B2, B3, and B4. Since the numbers of cells containing values could span hundreds of rows, it is generally much easier to refer to cells in ranges, in which the beginning and ending cell address in the range is used, with a period or colon separating the two. In the example, the formula entered into Cell B6 is =SUM(B2:B4). Once the ENTER key is pressed, the formula returns the result of "74" to the cell in place of the formula syntax shown in the illustration. Double-clicking on cell B6 places the cell back into Edit mode, allowing the formula to be viewed and edited.

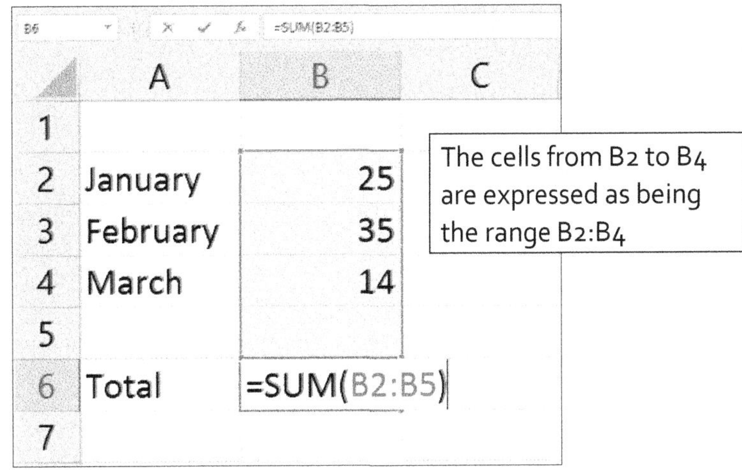

FIGURE 5.4 Example of the Sum () Function.

Finding the Right Function

In addition to the SUM() function, in Excel 2016 there are over 300 functions available, which perform a variety of specialized tasks related to statistics, financial calculations, engineering, calculus, trigonometry, logic testing, text manipulation, etc. As shown in Figure 5.5, the various functions can all be accessed by pressing the tiny arrow to the right of the AUTOSUM button on the HOME tab of the ribbon bar. The drop-down list presents a number of commonly used functions such as SUM() and AVERAGE(). To access the complete list of all functions by category, select the MORE FUNCTIONS option at the bottom.

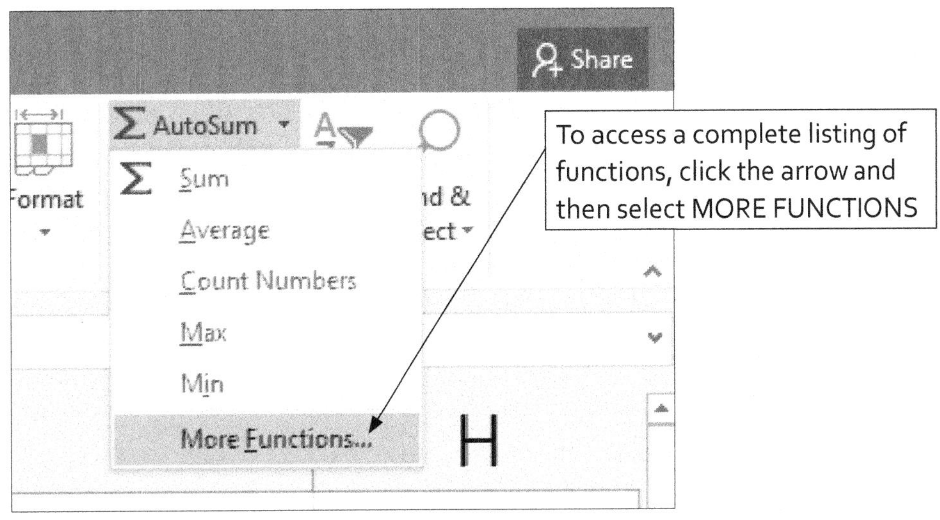

FIGURE 5.5 Location of Function.

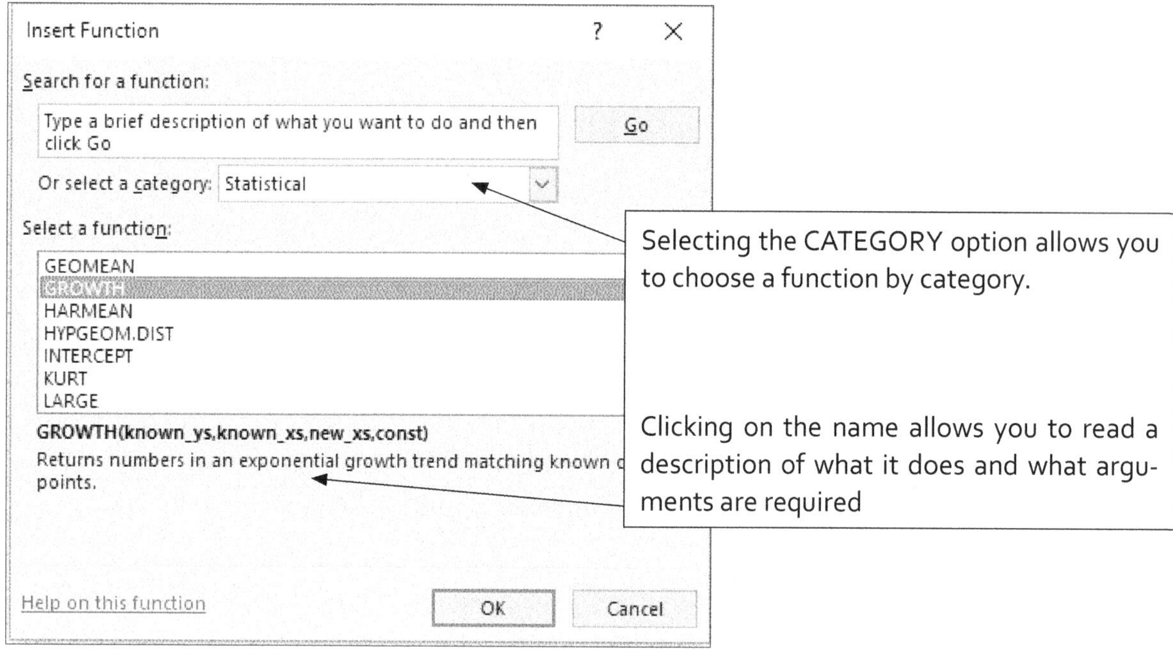

FIGURE 5.5 (continued)

RELATIVE VERSUS ABSOLUTE CELL REFERENCES

In the earlier section, cell references (or addresses) were described as consisting of the column and row designation for a given cell. For example, the cell in the upper left-hand corner of the spreadsheet is designated as cell A1 because it is in Column A, Row 1. When using a cell reference, it is important to consider that there are actually two distinct types of cell references, called *relative* and *absolute* cell references.

TIP: Absolute Cell References

1. All cell references are Relative unless you change them to Absolute
2. Cell references should only be changed to Absolute if the formula containing the reference will be copied to other locations on the spreadsheet
3. Cell references should only be changed to Absolute if the formula contains a reference to a single cell containing a value that only appears in one place on the spreadsheet

The two types of cell references are particularly important for use in formulas in which the formula will be copied to other locations in a spreadsheet.

To better understand the differences between relative and absolute cell references, consider the following example in Figure 5.6. In this example, the percent of patients by department is calculated by dividing the numbers of patients discharged for each department by the total discharged in cell B7.

Since creating the formula from scratch for each of the three departments is a rather tedious and error-prone process, it is much easier and more efficient to simply create the first formula for the Intensive Care Unit in cell B3 and then copy and paste that formula to the remaining cells in C4 and C5. As an experiment, create the spreadsheet used in this example, and then copy and paste (or Autofill) the formula in C3 to cells C4 and C5.

As shown in Figure 5.7, you will see that while the original formula works properly, the copied formulas in C4 and C5 produce an error. The error message produced is #DIV/0!, which indicates that the formula is attempting to divide by zero.

To troubleshoot the problem with the formula, double-click on the first error in Cell C4. Referring to the original formula created in cell C3, note that the formula was =B3/B7. However, the formula in cell C4 is different from the original. The cell reference B3 changed to cell B4, while the reference to B7 changed to B8. Those changes are the result of the formula using *Relative* cell references. In a nutshell, Relative cell references change every time they are copied to another location on the spreadsheet, such as in this example. Double-clicking on the formula in cell C5, you will see that the formula changes again, this time to =B5/B9. The value of a relative cell reference is that it allows you to reuse a formula in different areas of the spreadsheet without having to rewrite it each time. This is evident in the reference to the Intensive Care Unit (B3) changing to B4 for the Telemetry Unit, and so on.

SUM =B3/B7

	A	B	C
1			
2	**Department**	**Patients Discharged**	**Percent of Total**
3	Intensive Care Unit	125	=B3/B7
4	Telemetry Unit	350	
5	Obstetrics	75	
6			
7	Total patients discharged	550	

FIGURE 5.6 Relative Cell Reference.

If that cell reference were not relative, you would have to modify each formula individually for each department in order for it to work (otherwise each copied formula would simply calculate the percentage of patients for the ICU over and over again). **This example demonstrates that unless you specify otherwise, all cell references in the formulas you create are by default Relative cell references.**

	A	B	C
1			
2	**Department**	**Patients Discharged**	**Percent of Total**
3	Intensive Care Unit	125	0.22727273
4	Telemetry Unit	350	=B4/B8
5	Obstetrics	75	#DIV/0!
6			
7	Total patients discharged	550	
8			

FIGURE 5.7 Effects of Copying Relative Cell References.

In contrast to a Relative cell reference, an Absolute cell reference is one that never changes when it is copied to a new location. In the example above, if both cell references had been Absolute rather than Relative, the formulas in cells C4 and C5 would have both calculated B3 divided by B7. In our example, although the reference to B3 *should* be *Relative*, the reference to B7 should be *Absolute* because we always want to divide by the total discharges in cell B7.

CREATING AN ABSOLUTE CELL REFERENCE

Making a cell reference absolute is done by inserting a dollar sign ($) in front of the row or column reference you wish to hold absolute. Remember that there are two components to a cell reference: the row and the column designations. If the column alone is to be held absolute, a dollar sign should be inserted in front of the column letter in the cell reference. For example, placing a dollar sign in front of the "B" in B7 in the form of $B7, will hold the column designation of "B" absolute when copying and pasting reference, although it will *not* hold the row designation of "7" absolute. In our example, the issue is that the row designation of "7" is changing because we are copying the formula vertically down to lower cells (as opposed to horizontally to difference columns).

Therefore, in order for the row designation to be held absolute, a dollar sign must be placed in front of the "7," making the reference B$7. Since remembering whether the row or column should be held absolute on a given formula may add some confusion to the process of formula construction, it is sometimes easier to simply place dollar signs in front of *both* the column and the row designation, such as in the example of $B$7. Although the dollar sign in front of the "B" is not needed, having it there will not cause any problems in this example. Keep in mind, however, that there are occasionally situations in which only the row or column in a reference should be held absolute.

Returning to our example, the proper syntax for our formula in cell B3 should be =B3/$B$7, which when copied to the cells for the other departments will produce =B4/$B$7 and =B5/$B$7.

SUM | =B3/$B$7

	A	B	C
1			
2	**Department**	**Patients Discharged**	**Percent of Total**
3	Intensive Care Unit	125	=B3/$B$7
4	Telemetry Unit	350	
5	Obstetrics	75	
6			
7	Total patients discharged	550	

FIGURE 5.8 Formula Containing an Absolute Cell Reference.

Important: Note that you need to add dollar signs only to the very first formula that you created in cell B3. When that formula is copied and pasted elsewhere, the references to $B$7 never change.

Despite the ease with which electronic spreadsheets can be used to perform a vast variety of demanding tasks, they also have the capacity to cause a variety of administrative problems when not properly managed in organizations. The primary issue concerns the fact that although many spreadsheet users have the technical expertise to create the formulas and logic needed to solve an immediate problem, the spreadsheet itself is often created as a largely individual effort without regard to the broader organization.

Consider that organizations do not typically consist of individuals who work in independent vacuums. Instead, they consist of individuals who interact in a collaborative environment where workers must share work product and be prepared to support one another. The issue with an electronic spreadsheet is that it is entirely possible to create a spreadsheet that solves the immediate problem, but from a collaborative perspective, is virtually impossible for anyone else in the organization to understand or to be able to work with. Since an electronic spreadsheet begins as a blank slate in terms of the layout and logic that can be used to perform the task. Two different individuals can easily develop two entirely different spreadsheets that are equally effective, yet very much unlike one another. The problem is not that different individuals take different approaches; the issue is really more one of a lack of proper documentation and non-adherence to proper practices.

To be truly collaborative, a tool such as spreadsheet must be able to be shared with other colleagues and designed in such a way that others can understand how it works as well as its limitations. Otherwise, it is useful only to the individual who created it, and only for as long as he or she remembers how they did it. Another consideration is that over time it is entirely possible for someone to forget the logic behind their own design, resulting in them not understanding their own work.

In order to maximize the effectiveness of the electronic spreadsheet as a technological tool in a contemporary organization, best practices for their use should be considered and to the greatest extent possible, the best practices should be proceduralized as an organization-wide policy among all spreadsheet users. Organizations such as the *Spreadsheet Standards Review Board* (SSRB) have established recommended guidelines for the organizational use of spreadsheets and best practices for spreadsheet modeling. Although not all of the recommendations are necessarily appropriate in every situation, technology leaders should carefully consider those recommendations relative to their organization's needs and technology environment.[25,37]

The following are some of the practices to be considered when creating a spreadsheet model, particularly one that will be used by others.

Best Practice: Know the Purpose. The purpose of the workbook as well as each of the spreadsheets in that workbook should be well understood by its developer. Additionally, the purpose of the workbook and each of the worksheets should be communicated to the end-user. For example, one sheet might be used exclusively to collect user input assumptions, while another sheet may produce tabular results, while still another produces results in a graphical format, pivot table, or another method.

Best Practice: Font Colors. Through the use of font color, borders, and/or background fill colors, cells should be visibly identifiable as to whether it contains an input value or a formula. Consider that to someone who has not seen a particular spreadsheet model before, unless a visual clue is provided (or unless the user clicks on each cell one at a time), it is impossible to tell whether a particular cell contains a value that should be input by the user versus a formula that should not be overwritten. For that reason, the importance of proper and consistent formatting of a spreadsheet should not be regarded as simply for the sake of cosmetic appeal. Properly constructed, the use of color in formatting can add significantly to the usability of the spreadsheet. Additionally, color selections should be standardized so that the same color always means the same thing for different spreadsheets. The font colors suggested by the SSRB are as follows:[26,38]

- Blue: Used for constants/input cells
- Black: Used for formulas

Note that in the example below, the section on the left makes it difficult to tell which cells should have input values entered into them and which cells contain a formula. The example to the right utilizes the simple addition of a blue font color to indicate the cells that are input versus the black font to indicate a formula. Additionally, the formula cell was moved away by one row from the input cells to provide additional visual differentiation.

	A	B	C	D	E
1	**EXAMPLE 1 - No Formatting**			**Example 2 - Input Cells are Blue**	
2					
3	No. of patients	150		No. of patients	150
4	No. of nurses	30		No. of nurses	30
5	Patient/Nurse Ratio	5.0			
6				Patient/Nurse Ratio	5.0

FIGURE 5.9 Example of Standardized Formatting.

Best Practice: Assumptions should never be located together with outputs: Going back to the basic concept of a computer as being a data input/data output device, in a spreadsheet model, the input values (or assumptions) can be thought of as the user inputs the model uses to produce some sort of output. It is important that the input assumptions be physically located together and that they be physically separated from the outputs. A common approach is to organize all of the input values for a model on a single sheet within the workbook, while the outputs are located in one or more other sheets in the same workbook. In all cases, it should be clear to the user where the data inputs are to be entered in the spreadsheet and where the outputs are to be found.

Best Practice: Single assumptions should not be entered more than once within a spreadsheet. For example, if the spreadsheet model requires that the user enter a person's age, that entry should occur in only one cell. Providing more than one cell for the age input (where one entry is used for a particular formula and the other entry is used for a different formula) simply opens the door to the possibility that a user will forget to change one of the two or will misinterpret one of the two entries. Having only one cell for that input eliminates the possibility of that type of error occurring.

Best Practice: Data validation techniques should be used whenever possible. The use of data validation tools in Excel reduces the probability that a user will enter an incorrect entry or will misinterpret what is expected. Using a drop-down list of predefined values ensures that a user cannot input a non-expected entry. Data validation can provide rules to screen the user's entry, as well as a way to provide explanation and instructions to that user.

Best Practice: Complex formulas should be documented. Although the creator of a spreadsheet typically understands the logic behind the complex formula at the time it is created, it can be difficult for another individual (or even for the developer at a later point in time) to understand that logic. Use of the comment tool in Excel or an accompanying sheet should be considered to document that logic by describing it in plain English.

Best Practice: Use effective version control. In software development, a common practice is that of *version control*, which refers to the process by which a programmer keeps track of the different versions of his or her code that accumulate as repairs and modifications are made to a program. The process should be applied to spreadsheet models. A simple way to do this is to assign a version number to a spreadsheet; for example, *version 1.0*. As minor changes are made and errors are found and fixed, the next version can be incremented to *version 1.1*, and so on. Equally important is the need to include the last revision date on a workbook, so it is clear which version someone is using. Without tracking the versions of a spreadsheet model, it is entirely possible for two individuals to produce different results given the same inputs, without realizing that there are fundamental differences between the two workbooks.

TROUBLESHOOTING SPREADSHEET FORMULAS

Whenever a spreadsheet model or other type of computer program is constructed, it is almost inevitable that the initial effort will contain errors of some sort. The issue is that any model containing many inter-related formulas results will also contain a fair amount of complexity. That complexity makes it difficult to fully appreciate how each formula will work until all of the formulas are assembled and can be observed interacting with one another.

It is important to consider that the creation of a spreadsheet model is likely to produce one or more errors at some point during the development, particularly when formulas become more complex. Given that the presence of errors is pretty much expected, the ability to find and correct problems is an important skill for a spreadsheet user to develop. While much of the time the skill of effectively troubleshooting is acquired through experience, understanding the nature of the errors can go a long way toward making the troubleshooting process faster, more efficient, and less frustrating.

Generally, errors in any type of computer can usually be associated as being in one of two categories. They are usually classified as being either *syntax errors* or *logic errors*.

SYNTAX ERRORS

Syntax errors generally consist of mistakes in the writing or typing of formulas and commands when creating the spreadsheet. Since a syntax error results in the computer is being asked to do something that it cannot properly interpret, they will often result in an error message of some sort being produced. Mistakes that produce error messages are often relatively straight-forward to identify and correct, since error messages will draw your attention to the problem.

In Example 1, below, the Excel formula =SUM(A1:A3) will return the sum of numeric values located in the cells A1, A3, and A3. However, in Example 2, the formula was incorrectly entered using a semi-colon instead of a colon, which resulted in an error message being produced. In this example, Excel guessed at what was meant, and asks whether the user would like to accept the proposed correction to the error.

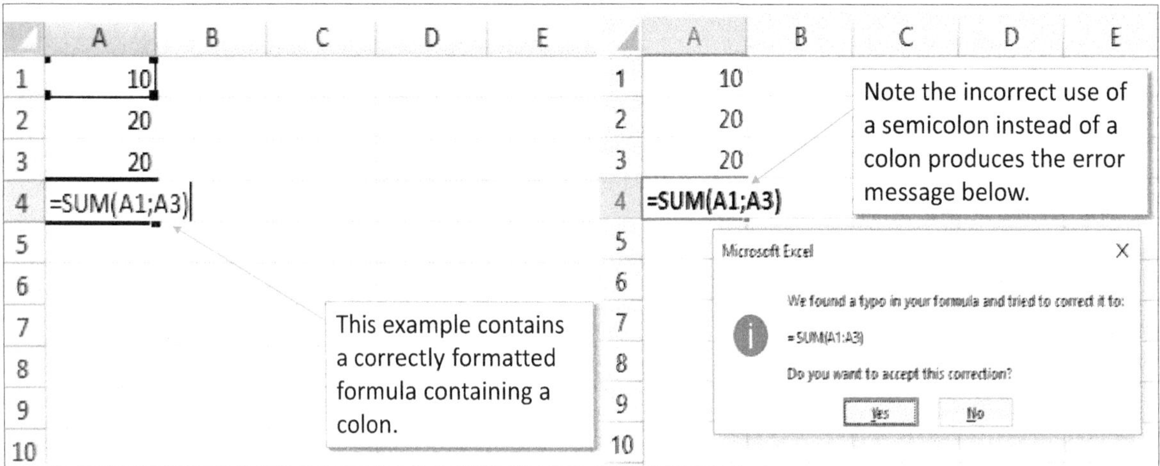

FIGURE 5.10 Syntax Errors Example 1 and 2.

Because syntax errors can usually be identified based upon the error message that is produced, finding the errors becomes less of an issue and the focus shifts toward correcting the errors. When error messages are produced in a cell, they are a valuable clue in finding and solving problems. Some of the more common error messages are referred to as error values and are will appear in a cell containing a problematic formula. Some of the more common error values in Excel include the following:

ERROR VALUE	MEANING
######### (the entire cell is filled with the "#" character	A cell containing all pound signs indicates that there is a number in the cell that is too large to be displayed given the column width. The solution is to simply widen the column large enough to display the value.
#DIV/o!	Divide by zero error. This error value indicates that the formula contained in the cell is attempting to divide by a value of zero, which is mathematically impossible. In most cases, the denominator in a formula is referencing a cell that is either empty or contains a value of zero. To resolve, simply trace all denominators in the formula to determine which one contains the zero value.
#VALUE!	Invalid value error. This error occurs when an invalid value is referenced within a formula. For example, trying to add a cell containing a value together with a cell containing a letter instead of a number will produce a #VALUE! Error.

ERROR VALUE	MEANING
#REF!	Invalid cell address or name error. This error occurs when a reference is made to a cell that no longer exists. If a formula is created with a reference to a particular cell, and the row or column in which that cell resides is then deleted, the formula that referenced the now-deleted cell will return a #REF! error.
#NAME?	Invalid cell address or name. This error occurs when a cell address is entered incorrectly into a formula. For example, a range that should be stated as A1:A5 is incorrectly entered as A1:5A.
#N/A	This message indicates that a result cannot be returned for the formula because there is no result. One example would be a Vlookup() formula in which the lookup value is not present in the lookup table. Since there is no result to display, Excel will return a #N/A to the cell.

LOGIC ERRORS

Logic errors consist of error that result in formulas that execute properly but do not produce the desired results. Like syntax errors, logic errors can be the result of a mistake while typing a formula. However, the mistake results in a technically valid formula that does not behave as intended.

Consider the example below in Figure 5.11. Note that in Example 3 the SUM() function contains a different syntax error, in which a comma was used instead of a colon. In this case, because a comma is a valid character in a SUM() function, the formula does not produce an error message. However, using the comma instead of a colon does change the formula's logic. Instead of summing the values in the *range of cells* from A1 to A3, the function only sums the values in cells A1 and A3, producing a result of 30, instead of 50.

This type of error can be considered a *logic* error because the syntax of the formula is valid, although the way in which it is constructed does not return the intended results. Logic errors are often much more difficult to identify because they typically do not produce error messages, although they can produce incorrect results.

The important thing to consider is that the absence of an error message is not a guarantee that the formulas in a spreadsheet are necessarily correct. For that reason, the results of a new spreadsheet model should never be blindly accepted until the formulas have been validated by checking their accuracy using test data and a calculator.

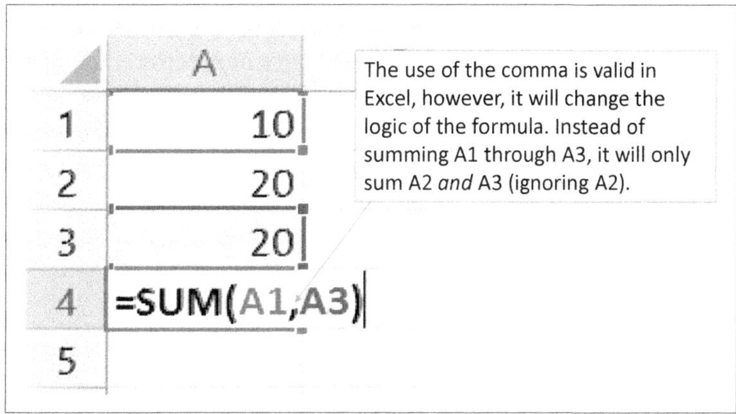

FIGURE 5.11 Syntax Errors Example 3.

Circular References

Circular reference errors occur when one of the following events occurs:

- A formula incorrectly references its own results
- Two (or more) formulas reference each other's results

Both of these conditions produce logic that is impossible to resolve. Consider the example below in which the SUM() is used to calculate the total population (those above poverty status and those below the poverty status added together). Rather than referencing the range from B1 to B2, the function incorrectly references the range from B1 to B4, which includes its own results. The resulting condition is one in which the result cannot be calculated until the result has already been calculated, which is an impossible condition to resolve.

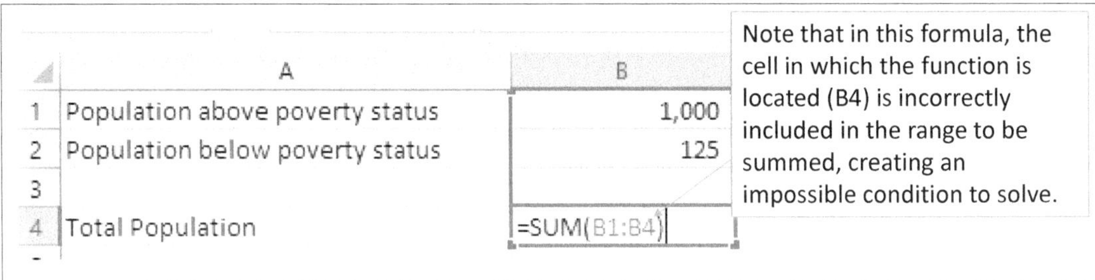

FIGURE 5.12 Circular Reference.

Excel will detect circular references and typically will produce an alert message when the formula is created. If the circular reference is not corrected, it will produce a message on the status bar at the bottom of the screen to indicate that a circular reference exists in the worksheet and where it can be found. In the example below, the message indicates that the formula in cell B4 contains the circular reference.

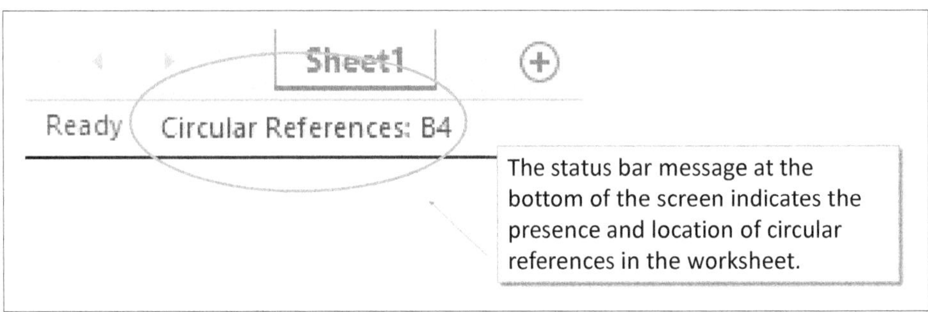

FIGURE 5.13 Circular Reference Notification.

Locating Logic Errors

Logic errors typically require that the formula's logic be followed step-by-step to see where the disconnect exists between your expectations and the results. The best way to start is by double-clicking the formula to view it and begin stepping through the logic with a calculator in hand. Note that once the cell that contains a formula is double-clicked, it will show the formula, with each cell reference color-coded, with matching-color cell borders surrounding the respective cells. This makes it somewhat easier to see what values are contained in those cells. In the example below, the denominator in the formula references cell B4, which does not contain a value, resulting in a divide-by-zero error.

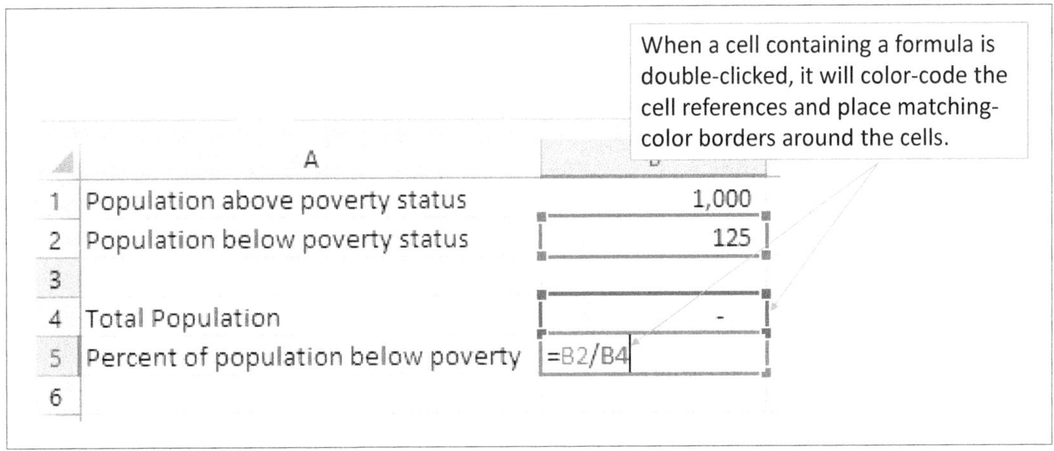

FIGURE 5.14 Viewing formula references.

Viewing All Formulas

In the event that there are multiple formulas that you would like to view simultaneously, you can toggle Excel's formula view mode by pressing CONTROL and ~ on your keyboard together (the Control key together with the tilde "~" key). This will then display all of the formulas instead of their results for the entire spreadsheet. To switch back to the normal view, simply press the CONTROL and ~ together again and the view will toggle back to the normal view.

	A	
1	Population above poverty status	1000
2	Population below poverty status	125
3		
4	Total Population	=SUM(B1:B4)
5	Percent of population below poverty	=B2/B4

Pressing the CONTROL key together with the tilde (~) will switch Excel into a formula view mode, so that all of the formulas can be viewed instead of their results. Press them again to switch back to the normal mode.

FIGURE 5.15 Viewing all formulas.

SUMMARY

Electronic spreadsheets, such as Microsoft Excel, represent a versatile tool that can be used for a variety of tasks such as assembling relatively simple formulas, maintaining simple databases, or modelling complex mathematical relationships. Formulas are constructed by referencing cell addresses, which contain the values to be used. Although cell references are by default relative, meaning that they change when they are copied to other cells, they can be made absolute through the use of the dollar sign. Excel contains over 400 functions, which can be used in formulas and act as small programs that perform very specific tasks.

Effective use of Excel in the workplace requires that attention be paid to avoiding potential errors in its use. By adhering to best practices, such as those proposed by the Spreadsheet Standards Review Board, work performed using Excel in the workplace can be constructed for maximum efficiency and accuracy throughout the organization.

APPLY YOUR KNOWLEDGE

MICROSOFT EXCEL HANDS-ON EXERCISES

Please refer to Active Learning Platform for exercises.

IMAGE CREDITS

6

VISUALIZING DATA

The term "data visualization" typically refers to a graphical or pictorial representation of data. Some of the most common approaches involve the use of tools such as pie charts, line graphs, and other similar techniques. When properly constructed, data visualization techniques help us to communicate relationships and trends found in data, ranging from simple to complex. By providing the ability to graphically visualize what a trend or pattern looks like, we can communicate concepts much more quickly and effectively, as well as to identify trends and patterns that might not be evident by simply looking at rows and columns of numbers.

THINKING ABOUT DATA

One way to approach the use of data visualization tools is to consider the mental process that occurs when an individual is presented with tabular quantitative data, such as a spreadsheet containing a table of numbers and/or other types of data. The typical response is that a person will first try to understand how the dataset is organized. Next, he or she will begin to try to make sense of what they are seeing by looking for patterns or trends that are similar to others he or she has experienced in the past. These could be trends representing growth or decline in values, changes in relative composition, or possible correlations between variables (for example, incidence of influenza consistently increasing during certain months of the year and decreasing during others).

Incidence and Mortality Counts and Age-Adjusted (2000 U.S. Population) Rates per 100,000 Males by Year and Race/Ethnicity, California, 1988-2011, Prostate Gland Cancer

	Incidence		Mortality	
	New Cases	Annual Rate	Deaths	Annual Rate
Year of Diagnosis or Death	Males	M	Male	M
ALL RACES				
1988	12,240	129.7	2,833	34.8
1989	13,084	135.7	2,894	34.5
1990	15,702	158.6	2,999	34.9
1991	20,275	197.1	3,275	37.4
1992	23,763	223.4	3,286	36.6
1993	22,120	202.0	3,360	36.7
1994	19,138	170.5	3,321	35.3
1995	17,997	157.0	3,191	32.8
1996	18,515	158.4	3,179	32.1
1997	19,342	161.2	3,117	30.6
1998	19,637	159.7	2,950	28.0
1999	20,947	166.2	3,085	28.7
2000	20,879	162.2	3,008	27.4
2001	21,529	163.4	2,936	26.0
2002	22,413	165.8	3,049	26.4
2003	21,045	151.3	3,013	25.3
2004	22,345	157.1	2,974	24.6
2005	20,632	141.6	3,059	24.6
2006	22,090	148.3	2,914	22.7
2007	23,882	155.1	3,043	23.1
2008	22,443	140.7	3,018	22.2
2009	22,280	134.2	3,093	22.2
2010	22,205	129.6	3,049	21.1
2011	22,124	124.6	3,067	20.5

FIGURE 6.1 Incidence and Mortality Counts and Age-Adjusted (2000 U.S. Population) Rates per 100,000 Males by Year and Race/Ethnicity, California, 1988-2011, Prostate Gland Cancer.

Consider the example above. Let's suppose that you are handed the report prepared by the California Department of Public Health regarding the incidence and mortality related to prostate cancer in California.[27,39]

After reading the title, the first thing that most individuals will do is to orient themselves as to what variables are being presented and how they relate to one another. In this report, each row represents a year, and then for each year, the columns represent the numbers of new prostate cancer cases, the incidence rate, the numbers of deaths, and the annual mortality rate for the given years. The report essentially allows us to compare trends in the numbers and rates of new prostate cancer cases to the numbers and rates of death for prostate cancer.

The next thing most will do is to try to identify what if anything is "interesting" about the data. In other words, we look for patterns, trends, and relationships between the variables. In this example, we can see that in 2011, which is the last year presented, the incidence rate of 124.6 is a little lower than the first year in the series, when the rate was 129.7. However, looking further it is clear that during that period, the rates increased and decreased over time. The challenge is the amount of time and mental effort involved in making the observations, reaching a conclusion, and then communicating that same observation to someone else.

The benefit of a properly constructed visualization is that it can allow us to observe and communicate the trend effectively and accurately, and in much less time. Consider the line graph below, in which the prostate cancer incidence rate is presented by year. The line graph allows us to quickly see some of the most interesting aspects of the trend.

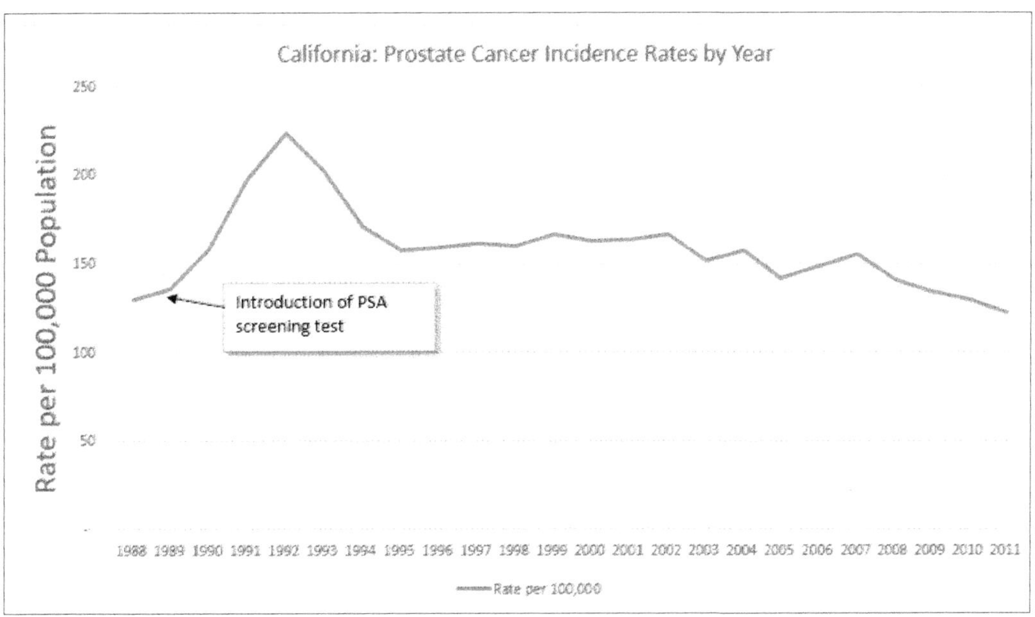

FIGURE 6.2 Data Visualization Example—Prostate Cancer Incidence Trend.

For example, the line graph above allows us to quickly see that although the 2011 rate is close to that of 1988, there was significant volatility, with the rates rising from 1989 to 1992, and then declining through 1996 before creeping up again slightly. Seeing the data in this format raises the obvious question of why there was an increase in the late 1980s and early 1990s. (One of the key reasons for the increase was that it coincided with the introduction of *prostate-specific antigen* (PSA) screening test, which uncovered previously undiagnosed cases, and resulted in some false-positive reporting.) A quick review of the annotated graph provides a summary of a key trend found in the tabular data, but it does so in much less time needed to analyze the table. Keep in mind that there is a limitation to this approach. The graph does not summarize every trend and relationship found in the table—it only summarizes one key finding, making it an incomplete description of the dataset.

The value of data visualization becomes apparent when complexity is added to the data. Although the first example allows us to view the trend of prostate cancer incidence, the graph in Figure 6.3 allows us to also examine the mortality rate trend, and to easily compare the two rates to one another. In the second example we can easily see that although there has been some volatility in the incidence of prostate cancer, the mortality rate related to prostate cancer has steadily declined over the same time period with significantly less volatility.

The advantage of the graph is that it allows us to appreciate the trends and the relationship between the two rates much more directly than simply looking at the table of numbers. Taking it one step further, the use of graphics also helps us to communicate the observations much more quickly. For example, imagine yourself giving a presentation in which you need to explain the trends to your audience in a limited amount of time, making it important that the concept be communicated quickly and concisely.

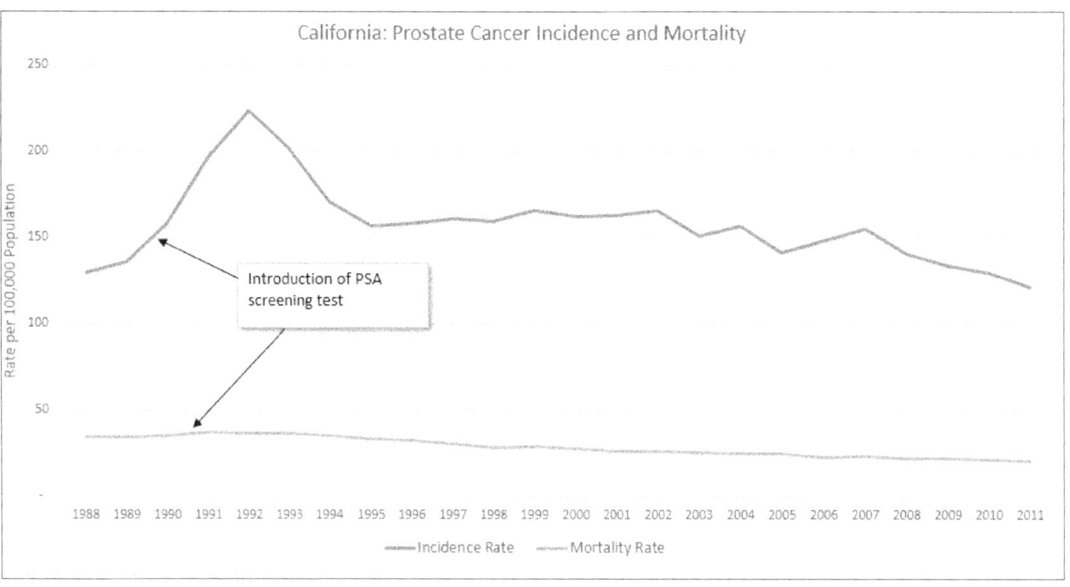

FIGURE 6.3 Data Visualization Example—Prostate Cancer Indicence and Mortality Trend.

COMMUNICATING THROUGH VISUALIZATION

If the objective is to communicate the quantitative relationship, using the graph is clearly a much more effective communication method in comparison to presenting the tabular data in the original report. One of the reasons for this is our limited ability to quickly absorb quantitative data in the form of numbers. Think back to the last time you sat through a presentation in which the presenter rattled off a series of percentages or other numbers. The mental effort required to absorb and construct meaning from those values can be considerable and the mental effort is tiring, resulting in many audience members "zoning out" during the presentation. However, doing away with the specific numbers in favor of focusing on the visualization of the relationships between them (such in the graph below) is much more efficient and interesting for the audience member. The difference is that the visualization is less work for the audience since the presenter has already done the "heavy lifting" with respect to mental processing.

What makes the use of data visualization a potentially effective analysis and communication tool? In a nutshell, it is the fact that data visualization to some extent allows the viewer of the visualization to bypass the need to mentally process the data, but instead allows them to view the results of someone else's interpretation. In other words, instead of analyzing the data and reaching a conclusion, the conclusion is essentially conveyed more directly, making the communication much faster and more efficient.

What should be apparent at this point is the fact that the person who creates the visualization holds the key to how it is interpreted by the viewer. If that visualization is accurately created, the viewer will have an accurate mental image of the quantitative relationship(s). However, if the visualization is created without consideration to best practices, and/or is created with an intent to mislead or deceive, the viewer can easily come away with an incorrect conclusion regarding the data.

Although a visualization has the potential to greatly enhance an individual's ability to convey a complex quantitative relationship quickly and effectively, there is also a potential downside to the use of visualization tools. That risk involves the potential for *miscommunicating* quantitative data whether intentionally or unintentionally. The problem stems from the fact that the person who creates a visualization is essentially doing some of the thinking on behalf of the person who will be viewing it. Since the person viewing the graphic will typically not spend quite as much time and thought analyzing the data for him- or herself (nor will they necessarily have the actual data available to them), the viewer is somewhat at the mercy of the person who creates it with respect to the graphic's veracity.

It is also important to note that a miscommunication through the use of a visualization is not necessarily intentional. It is entirely possible to create a chart or graph with the intent to communicate accurately, yet the viewer of the graphic may not end up with the correct interpretation. This may occur as a result of one of the following reasons:

1. An unconscious bias on the part of the person creating the visualization, resulting in the design of the visualization being created in such a way to subtly distort or misrepresent a quantitative relationship, trend, or pattern.
2. Designing the visualization in a way to take advantage of glitzy software features, which results in the accuracy of the visualization taking a back seat to an attractive appearance.
3. A conscious desire to deceive the viewer of the visualization resulting in a design that distorts or misrepresents a quantitative relationship, trend, or pattern, leading the viewer to a conclusion other than might have been reached if they had analyzed the raw data for themselves.
4. A poorly constructed visualization with insufficient attention to detail, resulting in the viewer having to make assumptions regarding its meaning and/or interpretation. Consider, for example, the first line graph above, in which the incidence rate is graphed by year. If the vertical axis had not been labeled "Rate per 100,000 Population," the viewer would have had to guess as to what the values represent—and could have guessed incorrectly.

BEST PRACTICES FOR GRAPHS AND OTHER VISUALIZATIONS

In general, there are several guidelines to be considered when using graphs and other visualizations in the communication of trends, relationships, and patterns in data.

AVOIDING THE OVERUSE OF GRAPHS

Generally, graphs can be an effective way to highlight specific patterns in data that you would like to communicate to others. Sometimes a picture can be worth a thousand words, especially when the picture summarizes something that would be difficult to express verbally. The downside is that "too much" is not better than "too little" when it comes to graphs. When too many graphs are used in a presentation or a document, the effectiveness of those graphs is greatly reduced.

As an example, in one of my first jobs after college, my manager was responsible for producing a quarterly management reports package that was reviewed by senior level managers. My manager had a particular problem when it came to working with tables of numbers, in that she did not like to deal with numbers. But she liked graphs—a lot. Consequently, she would produce the twenty- to thirty-page report using nothing but graphs to communicate the information. The problem for those reading the reports was that after the first few graphs, everything began to look the same. The graphs completely lost their effectiveness since there was no way to draw attention to really important trends and relationships.

The bottom line is that **graphs should be used only to communicate key concepts that you want to draw attention to**. Although there is often a temptation to use them gratuitously to add some color and pizzazz to a boring page, you should try to resist that temptation unless the graph says something important that you really want the reader to focus on.

AVOIDING THE USE OF GRAPHS WHEN DATA IS INCOMPLETE OR RELATIONSHIPS ARE UNCLEAR

In other words, if you have to guess at what some of the numbers might be in order to create the graph, there is not enough information there to be visualized. Certain types of graphs, such as line graphs, have the effect of smoothing some of the trends in data, meaning that skipping a data point will likely result in the illusion that there is no variance in the data, when there very well could be variation present. Using a graph to visualize data in which values are missing or relationships are unclear will not automatically add validity to the data, although it might *appear* valid to the reader. Unless the intent is to show a *lack* of a trend, association, or other relationship between data points, data for which a trend, association, or other relationship cannot be quantitatively determined should not be graphed.

ENSURING THAT THE VISUALIZATION DOES NOT MISREPRESENT THE DATA

When a reader looks at a table of numbers for the first time, a natural response is to look at the numbers analytically to determine what interesting patterns, relationships, or trends may exist. This process is similar to one called *pattern recognition* used by artificial intelligence programs. In the table below, you immediately can determine that the numbers all increase at a constant rate. Furthermore, you can tell that each number increases by an increment of 5. Your brain actually produces a mental image of that pattern that you can relate to.

5, 10, 15, 20, 25

When we graph numbers, however, the person viewing the graph bypasses that analytical process and focuses on the pattern that he or she is being told is contained in the numbers. Since the individual viewing the information is not analyzing the information but viewing what they are being told is the pattern in the information, the opportunity exists to distort the data.

In the example below, two sets of numbers are being graphed side by side. In this example, the graph on the left increases from a value of 500 to a value of 1,100 over twelve months. The combination of the y-axis starting at zero and ending at a value of 7,000 (way above the maximum value of 1,100 in the data) results in the curve appearing to be relatively flat and showing modest growth, visually.

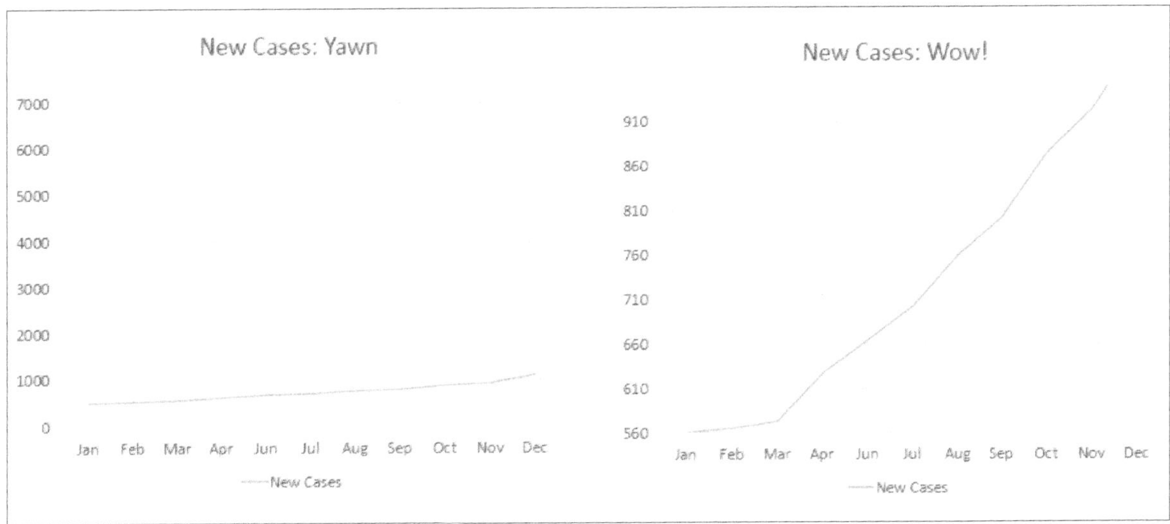

FIGURE 6.4 New Cases: Yawn vs. New Cases: Wow!

In the "Wow" graph on the right, the values increase from 560 to 950 over the same time period—an increase of only 390 versus an increase of 610 in the "Yawn" graph, which goes from 500 to 1,100. Although the "Yawn" graph appears to show very little increase, the values actually represent a larger increase than does the "Wow" graph. The reason is that the scale of the "Yawn" graph was set to a much higher maximum value than actually appeared in the data. As a result, the curve is artificially flattened. On the other hand, the "Wow" graph tends to exaggerate the curve because instead of starting at a value of zero, it starts a value of 560, which is the lowest value in the data, and it ends 910, which is slightly *less* than the highest value of 950. As a result, the "Wow" line appears to skyrocket, even though it represents less of an increase than the "Yawn" graph.

SCALES ON COMPARATIVE GRAPHS MUST ALWAYS BE THE SAME

As a best practice, whenever two graphs are being used to compare values side by side, the scales should always be set to the same starting and ending points in order to avoid potential misinterpretation as in the example above. Different scales will result in the comparison between graphs being of apples and oranges. To make the comparison valid, both graphs must have the same beginning and ending scale values.

PERCENTAGES SHOULD ALWAYS BE GRAPHED WITH A SCALE RANGING FROM 0 TO 100%

Line graphs and bar/column charts based upon percentages should always have scales that start at a minimum value of zero and end at a maximum value of 100. Consider the following as an example of why consistency in scales is important when graphing percentages. The following example is the result of a graph that was produced by CNN to communicate the results of a CNN/USA Today poll asking Americans whether or not they agreed with a Florida Supreme Court decision in 2005 that allowed Terri Schiavo, a woman in a persistent coma, to be taken off life support.

Notice that in the original graph on the left, the differences between Democrats, Republicans, and Independents seem rather extreme, with far more Democrats apparently supporting the decision in comparison to Republicans and Independents.

However, taking a closer look at the data, one can see that the actual difference between them is only 8 percentage points (the difference between 62% and 54%), which is just outside of the 7% margin of error. The issue with the graph is that its construction does not follow the best practice rule for graphing percentages, which is to make sure the scale ranges from 0 to 100%. In this case, the scale ranges from 53% to 63%, a range of only 10 percentage points, rather than 100 percentage points. The result is that the differences between the parties are effectively exaggerated by ten times.

To put it into perspective, compare the original graph to the corrected graph, which replaced it the following day. The revised graph on the right shows all of the bars drawn to the accurate scale. Notice that the differences between them are now much less dramatic, making it appear that there is relatively little difference in opinions.

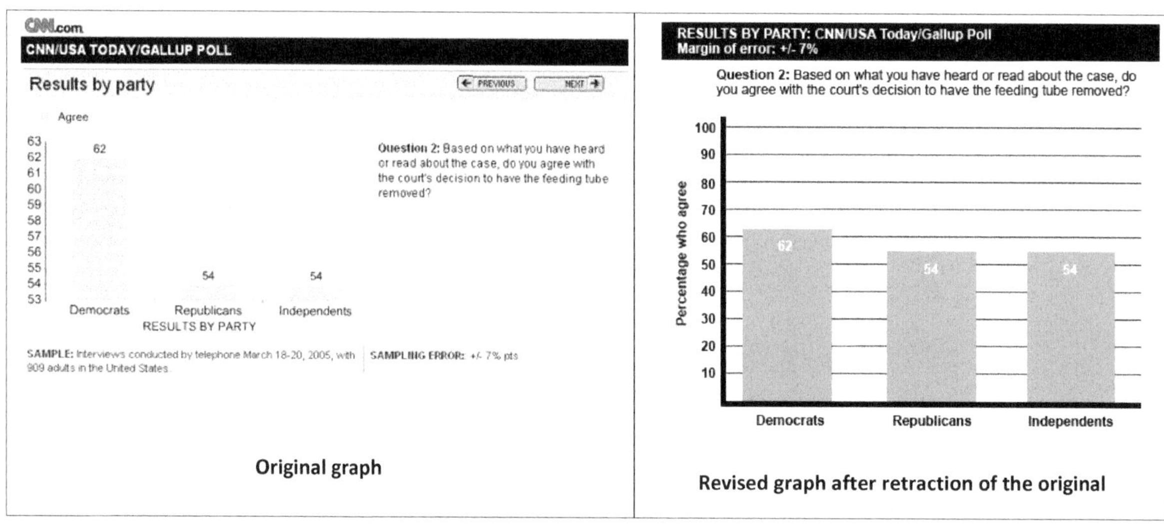

FIGURE 6.5 CNN.com Graphs for: Results by Party.

Axes Should Always Be Labeled As to What Units of Measure Are Being Used.

Unless an axis contains a title that specifically indicates the values, the reader may have to guess at what they mean. Consider the *Prostate Cancer Incidence and Mortality* graph in Figure 6.3. Had the y-axis not been labeled as Rate per 100,000 Population, it would be impossible to know whether the rate was per 100,000, per 10,000, or some other base.

APPROPRIATE USE OF 3-D GRAPHS

Microsoft Office programs provide a variety of attractive options for graphs, including three-dimensional versions of most graphs. Although the 3-D graph options provide an interesting visual appeal, they also have the potential to distort data. Keep in mind that the primary purpose of a graph is to communicate a quantitative relationship, not to be an artistic work. Although the use of color and perspective can result in an attractive and eye-catching graphic, the primary objective must always be the honest and accurate communication of quantitative data. If the artistic aspects of a graph result in misrepresentation of the data, they should be avoided.

One example of this is in the use of three-dimensional pie charts. A pie chart is inherently a relatively simple and effective way to communicate the proportions of something. Consider the example in Figure 6.6 in which the same values are shown using two side-by-side pie charts. The pie chart on the left was designed using a standard 2-D approach, while the one on the right was designed using a 3-D approach. The idea of a 2-D pie chart is very simple, in that a circle is cut up into slices, with the surface area of each slice representing the proportion of the data element the slice represents. In the example below, the "uninsured" slice represents 11% of total visits, and it also represents 11% of the total surface area of the circle (which can be readily calculated using basic geometry).

However, in the 3-D pie chart on the right, notice that the pie is no longer a geometric circle. In order to produce the 3-D perspective, it has been tilted back on an imaginary axis, so that it is now an egg-shaped ellipse. The result is that the pie slices are now physically distorted when compared to the 2-D version on the left. One of the most apparent distortions is the "uninsured" and "private insurance" slices, which appear larger and more prominent in the 3-D version. The reason is that the slices near the bottom not only show their surface areas but also their *thickness*, giving them a more prominent appearance. Conversely, the "Medicare" slice is shorter in the 3-D version and actually appears smaller than "uninsured," even though "Medicare" has a higher percentage of 17% versus 11% for "uninsured." Using the 3-D design, the surface areas and appearance of the slices are no longer directly proportional to the values that the slices are intended to represent.

The best approach when creating pie charts is to always stick to two-dimensional designs, since the improved accuracy of the visualization almost always outweighs a design with a more attractive appearance but inferior validity.

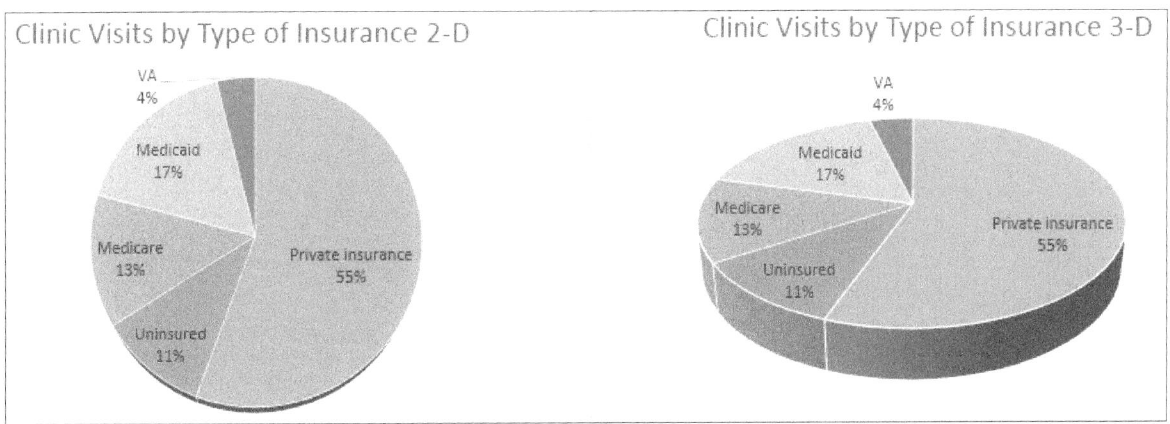

FIGURE 6.6 Comparison of 2-D and 3-D Pie Charts.

LINE GRAPHS

Line graphs are probably one of the most versatile graph types, and are often one of the best types to use to illustrate data in a time series. Time series data refer to data that relate directly to time. For example, the number of new patients discharged from a hospital in January, February, March, etc., is a time series. The reason line graphs are a good choice for time-series data is that culturally, when we mentally visualize time, we tend to think of it as progressing from left to right, which is how it is depicted in a line graph. Another advantage of a line graph is that no matter how many data points are in the graph, a line can generally depict them without clutter (as opposed, for example, to a bar chart, which requires one bar for each data point). Additionally, line graphs are simple to read and do not require much explanation as to their interpretation.

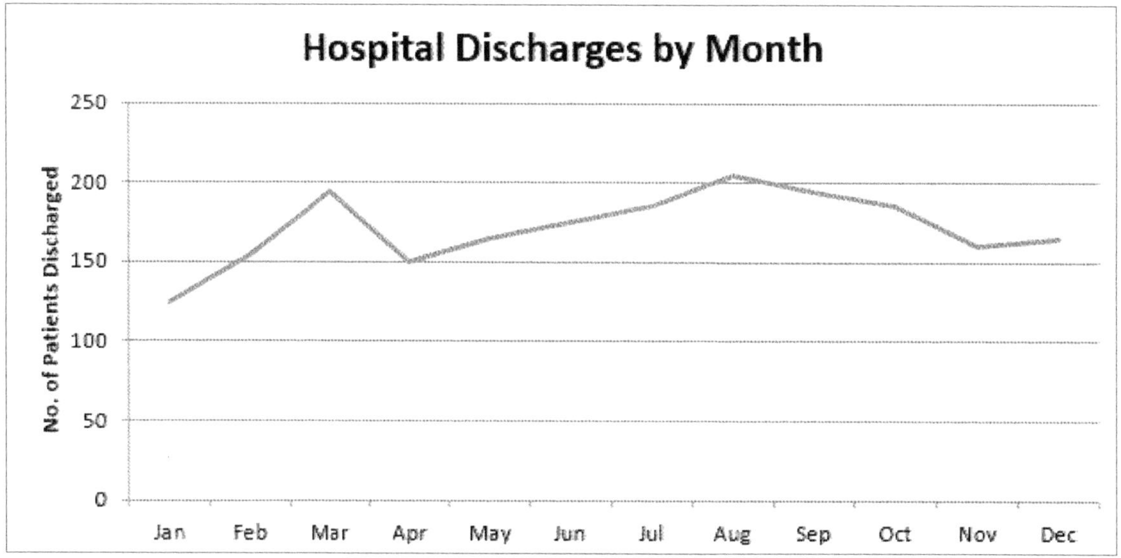

FIGURE 6.7 Line Graph Example.

COLUMN CHARTS

In Excel, *column charts* are what many of us typically call "bar charts." The bars are oriented vertically and can either be clustered by a grouping variable or they may be stacked. Keep in mind that Excel 2013 includes a graph type called a *bar chart*, but it is different than a *column chart* (Excel bar charts are essentially column charts that have been rotated 90 degrees).

Column charts can generally be used for time series data with one limitation. Datasets that extend over a large number of time periods and, therefore include a large number of data points, tend to produce too many bars to make an effective graph. For example, if the graph includes the number of new cases of tuberculosis each year from 1991 to 2000, a bar chart would be adequate since the chart would include 10 data points and, therefore, 10 bars. If, on the other hand, the chart is to include the number of discharges *by month* over the same period, there would now be 108 data points and, therefore, 108 bars. If that many data points were to be included, a line graph would be a better option.

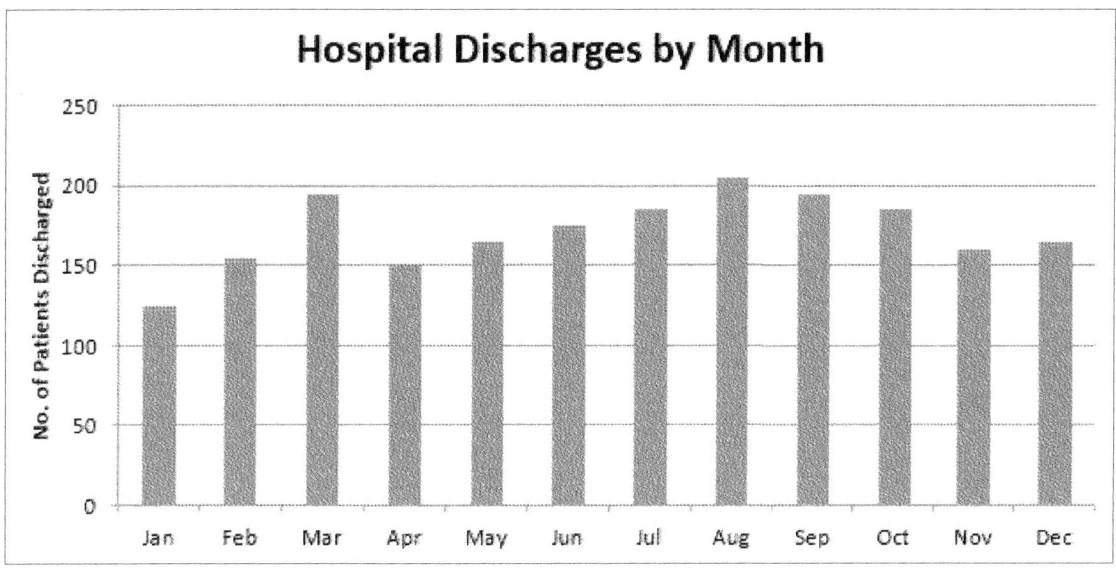

FIGURE 6.8 Example of a Column Chart.

CLUSTER COLUMN CHARTS

A cluster column chart is a variation of a column chart that includes more than one category. In the example below, the total hospital discharges by month are presented, along with the Medicare discharges for comparison. Note that when a cluster chart is created, a legend must generally be used so that the reader can distinguish the meaning of the two sets of columns.

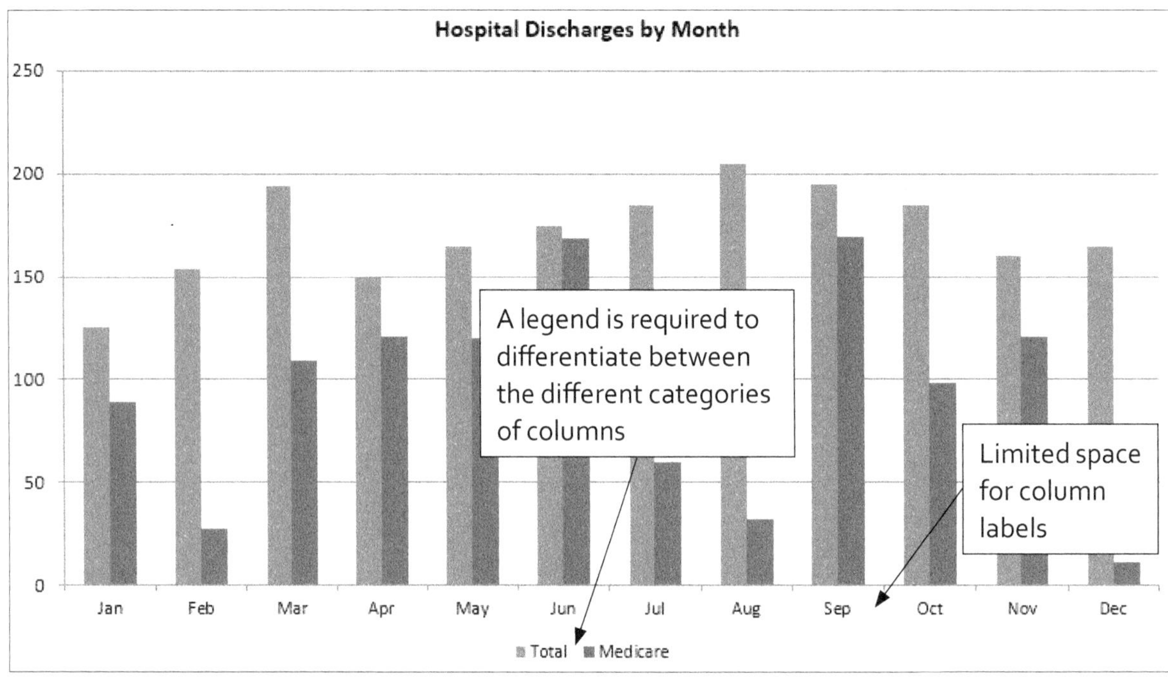

FIGURE 6.9 Example of a Cluster Column Chart.

BAR CHARTS

Bar charts are essentially column charts that have been rotated 90 degrees. Some of the important characteristics of bar charts:

1. Bar charts provide extra space for long descriptions of each bar. Since a column chart has only about as much horizontal label space as the width of a bar, the description needs to be fairly short. In a column chart, however, there is considerably more space to the left of the bar.
2. Bar charts tend to be inappropriate for time-series data. This is because we tend to be accustomed to looking at time from left to right rather than up to down or down to up.

In the example below, a bar chart is used to present data describing death rates in California in 2003. This example shows how the use of the bar chart format allows very long bar descriptions (the causes of death) to be used. In a column chart format, the descriptions would be too long to fit and be readable. Like column charts, bar charts can be used to display a single grouping, such as the one below, or multiple groupings in a cluster bar format.

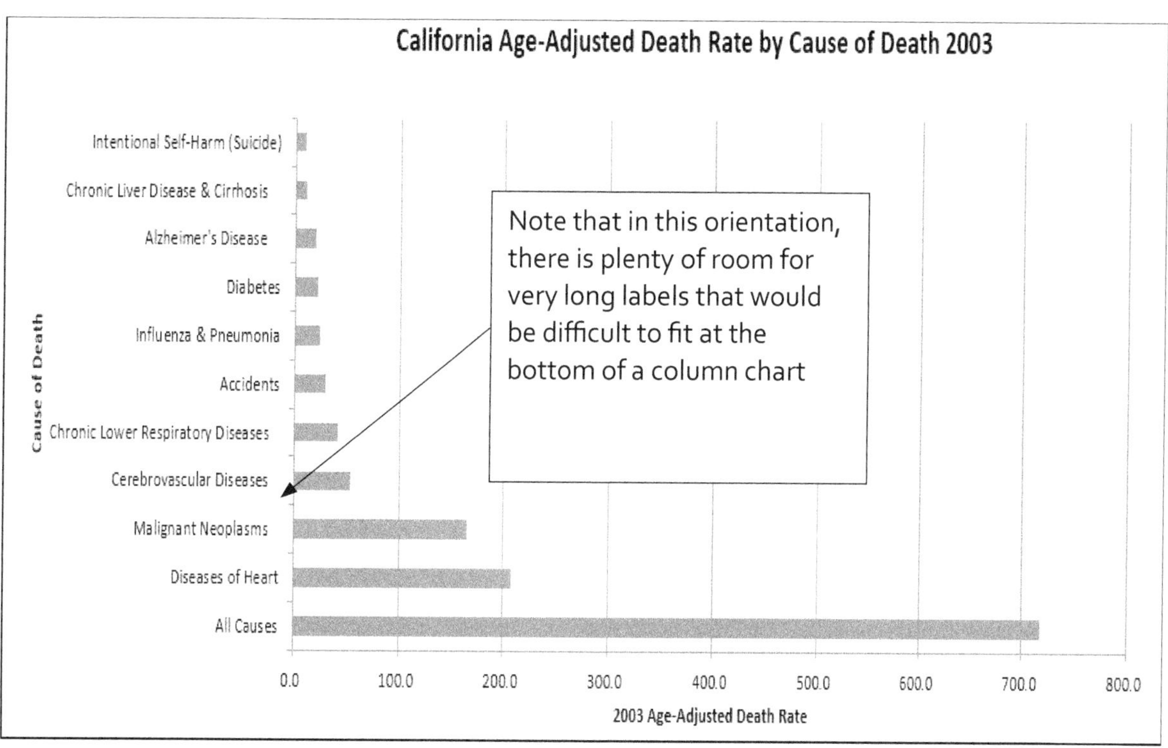

FIGURE 6.10 Bar Chart Example.

PIE CHARTS

Pie charts are often the best way to illustrate the relative proportions between the various components of something. The important thing to remember about pie charts is that the slices must add up to 100% of the whole.

Pie charts are typically unsuitable for time-series data since they do not portray trends very well. When time is a factor, comparative pie charts can sometimes be used to show how the proportions of the various components change over time.

Another consideration when using pie charts concerns the use of a legend versus labeling of the pie slices. Notice that in the example below, each slice is labeled separately so no legend is required. However, in cases such as the second example below, relying on a legend to differentiate the slices makes it much more difficult and time-consuming to use the chart. The use of the legend requires that the reader engage in much more "eye travel" to look back and forth between the legend and the pie in order to determine what each slice signifies. When relying on many different colors, an additional problem is introduced if a reader happens to be color-blind. Given that approximately 10% of the male population has some form of color-blindness,[28,40] it is possible that some readers will be unable to distinguish between some of the colors used for the legend. Finally, note that using the legend takes away from the amount of space available for the actual pie chart.

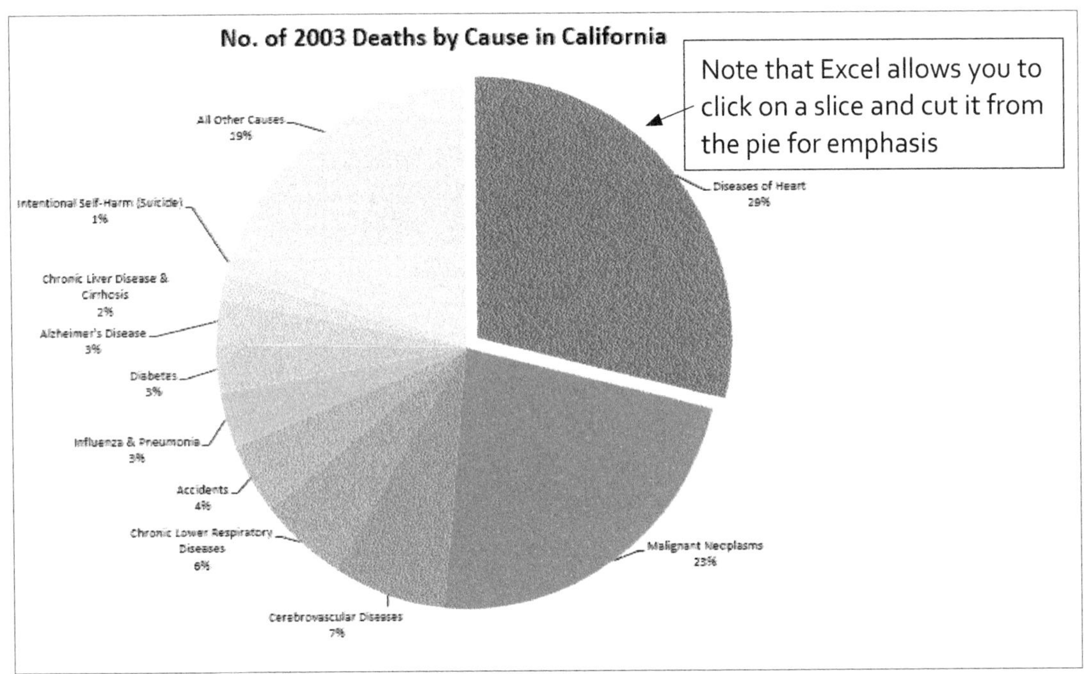

FIGURE 6.11 Example of a Pie Chart Without a Legend.

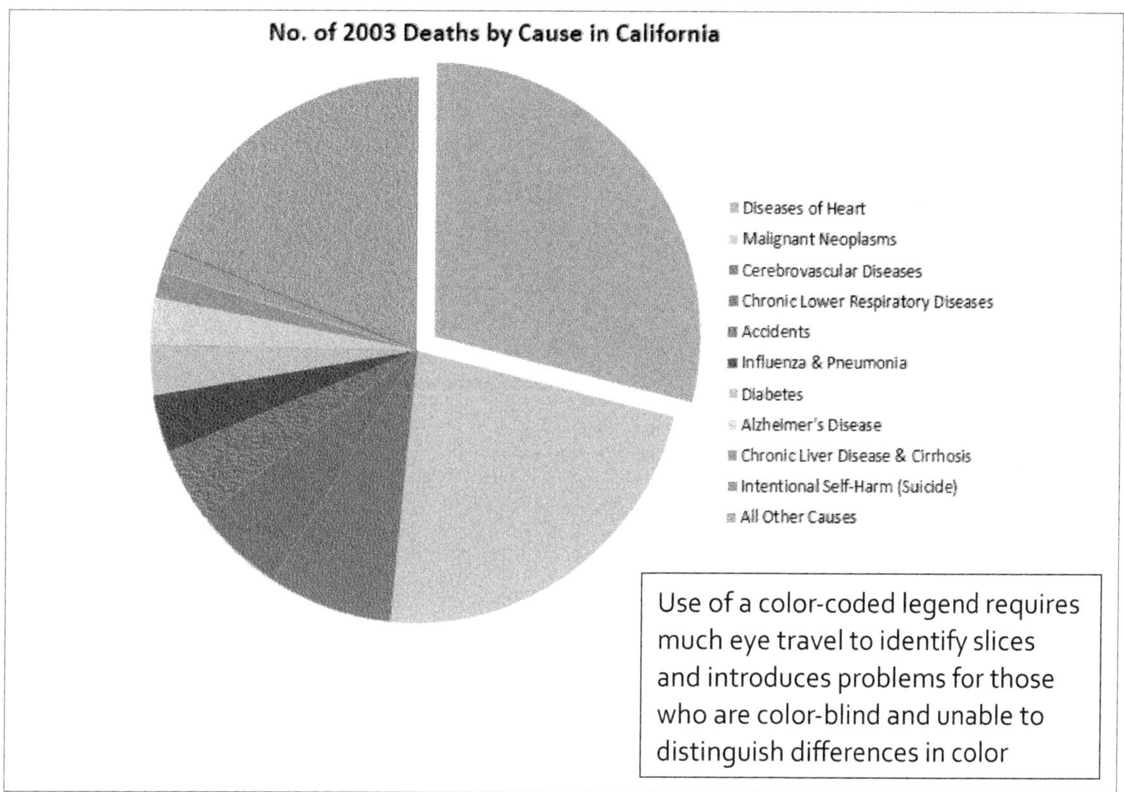

FIGURE 6.12 Example of a Pie Chart With a Legend.

STACKED BAR OR COLUMN CHARTS

If communicating the relative proportions of two variables over time is the objective, a stacked column chart is often a good option. Stacked column charts are essentially like a combination of a bar or column chart and a pie chart. Each column is broken down into segments that allow you to see the proportions of groups associated with each column, as well as the overall trend. In the example below, the total numbers of deaths can be seen for each cause of death, as well as what proportion of those deaths occurred in California.

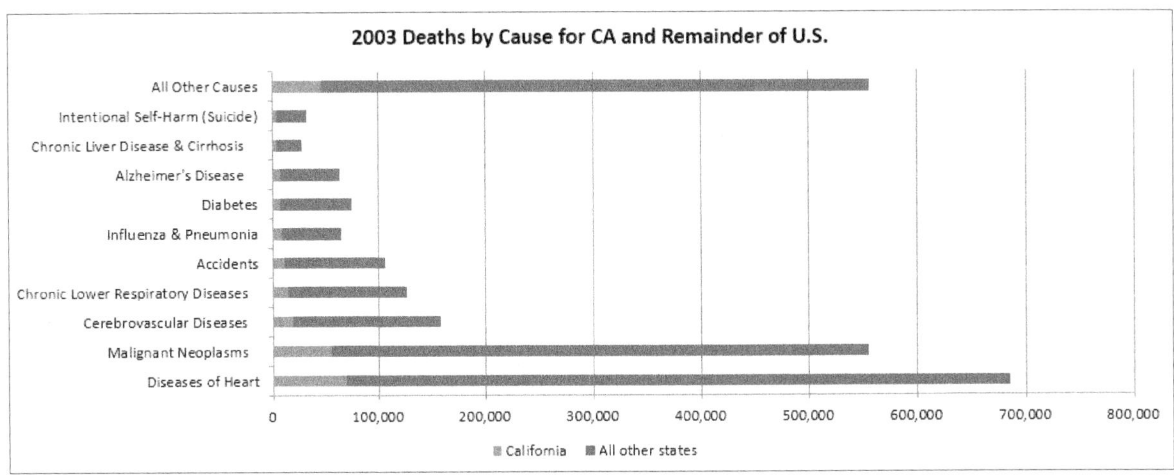

FIGURE 6.13 Example of Stacked Bar Chart.

In the following example of a stacked column chart, the numbers of cigarettes per day smoked in the United Kingdom are displayed by year, and broken down by the smokers' gender. Using this graph, it is possible to view the total trends in the consumption of cigarettes over time, while also viewing the relative proportion of those smokers who are male and female.

This graph allows us to see that although the overall numbers of cigarettes consumed has declined from the peak in 1979, the relative proportions have shifted. In 1949, most of the cigarettes were smoked by males with the number slowly shifting to women. In 2011, which is the last year shown, the portions of the bar for males and females is about equal, suggesting that about half of the cigarettes consumed were smoked by males and half by females.

The use of the stacked bar chart allows us to not only track the overall trend, but also the proportions of the components making up that trend—in this case males and females.

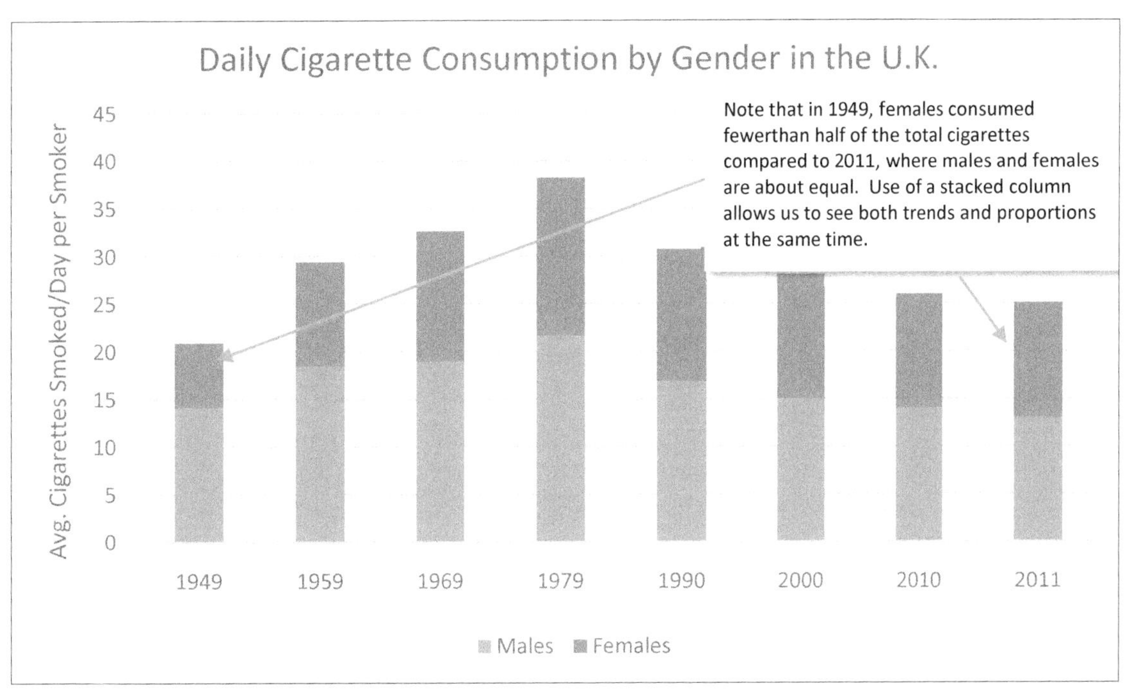

FIGURE 6.14 Example of a Stacked Column Chart.

SUMMARY

Data visualization techniques can be very useful in helping to communicate complex quantitative trends and relationships quickly and accurately. Although the use of charts and graphs can improve the communication of trends and relationships, when they are created incorrectly, they can miscommunicate and lead the reader to an incorrect conclusion. This makes it very important that the creator of a graph follow the best practices for graph creation. Selecting the appropriate graph type for a given situation is also an important way to help ensure that the reader reaches the correct conclusion through the proper interpretation of the graphic. Microsoft Excel and other similar spreadsheets, as well as programs like Microsoft Word and PowerPoint include the capability to produce a variety of graph types, as well as allowing for their annotation for effective inclusion in documents, presentations, and reports.

RESOURCES

There are a number of excellent resources that provide much more comprehensive discussion of the concepts related to data visualization. In particular, the work of Dr. Edward Tufte is noteworthy in his exploration of creative approaches that can be taken to communicate quantitative relationships in ways that help assure that the relationships are quickly and accurately understood by a reader or audience member.

Stacey, M., et al. (2013). *Visual Intelligence: Microsoft Tools and Techniques for Visualizing Data*, Wiley Publishing.

Tufte, E. R. (1990). *Envisioning Information*. Cheshire, CT. (P.O. Box 430, Cheshire 06410), Graphics Press.

Tufte, E. R. (2006). *Beautiful Evidence*. Cheshire, CT, Graphics Press.

Tufte, E. R. (2007). *The Visual Display of Quantitative Information*. Cheshire, CT, Graphics Press.

Tufte, E. R. (1997). *Visual Explanations: Images and Quantities, Evidence and Narrative*. Cheshire, CT, Graphics Press.

APPLY YOUR KNOWLEDGE

Please refer to Active Learning Platform for exercises.

IMAGE CREDITS

Fig. 6.1: Source: California Department of Public Health.
Fig. 6.5: Source: CNN/USA TODAY/GALLUP.

7

MICROSOFT ACCESS/ RELATIONAL DATABASE MANAGEMENT

Relational Database Management Systems (RDMS or RDBMS) are designed to manage datasets consisting of large numbers of standardized records. RDBMS systems are the basic technology that can be used to support everything from accounting systems to electronic medical records to personal Christmas card lists. Tools such Microsoft Access allow users to create customized databases that can contain custom-designed data entry screens, queries, reports, and user interface screens.

In order to better understand what an RDBMS does, it is first important to understand some of the basic theory of relational database management. This chapter explores some of the unique characteristics of RDBMS software, together with some basic relational database theories and concepts. Several of the key concepts can be applied in the *Apply Your Knowledge* section, which provides the steps for creating a database in Microsoft Access.

DATABASES VERSUS SPREADSHEETS

The database management system packaged in the Microsoft Office suite of programs is called Access. As we begin the discussion of databases, the description of Microsoft Access will initially sound similar in many ways to the description of a Microsoft Excel. At this point, it will be useful to take a look at the distinction between the two products and in general, the technologies of spreadsheets and databases.

One of the fundamental differences between spreadsheets and databases concerns the fact that spreadsheets tend to be something of a blank slate, where a user can begin entering data and creating formulas wherever they like. If the locations of the data or formulas turn out to be inconvenient, it is easy enough to move the contents of cells to new locations. In other words, one can create a spreadsheet by making up the structure as they go along.

On the other hand, RDBMS programs like Access require a very different approach. Rather than creating the structure as you go along, the structure must be created *before* any of the data is entered into the system. The logical structure of the database is essentially separated from the contents of the data. A very important distinction between databases and spreadsheets is that *databases require planning*.

DATABASES DEFINED

The basic definition of a database is that it is composed of a collection of one or more *tables*. Tables, in turn, are composed of *records* (sometimes called *rows*), which can be defined as information concerning places, things, events, or persons. Each piece of information within a record is referred to as a *field* or *column*.

To illustrate, let's consider a database you might use to maintain the information for your friends, relatives, and business contacts. At the most basic level, the information for a given person would be stored in an individual record. The fields associated with that record would contain items such as the person's first and last names, address, phone number, birthdate, an indicator as to whether the person is a friend, relative, or business contact, and maybe indicators as to whether you will send the person a Christmas card or birthday card.

Each of these fields is present for every record in your database, regardless of whether or not it will contain data. For example, you might have a field that contains a "Company Name." Although the field is present on every record it may not apply to every record. For records where there is no company name, the field is simply left blank. Database fields are essentially the building blocks of database management systems. To help visualize the structure of a database, it may be helpful to think about records as being like the rows in a spreadsheet, while the fields are similar to the columns in a spreadsheet. Think about the names of your contacts being contained in individual rows, while the information about them (names, addresses, etc.) is contained in the columns.

In the example below, the fields are represented as columns. Each field has a unique name associated with it (FirstName, LastName, Address, etc.).

FirstName	LastName	Address	City	State	Zip Company	Phone	Birthday	Type	Christmas Card	Birthday Card
Joe	Jones	123 Main St.	Jonensville	CA	90210	(818) 555-1234	7/1/1975	Relative	Yes	Yes
Sarah	Smith	4323 Oak Ln.	Smithville	CA	90210	(818) 555-1235	6/1/1985	Friend	Yes	Yes
Frank	Johnson	3434 Forest Bl.	Johnsonville	CA	90210 Acme Consolidated	(818) 555-1236	8/1/1980	Friend	Yes	Yes
Ed	Stone	3232 Walnut Ave.	Stoneville	CA	90210 St. Mary's Hospital	(818) 555-1237	9/1/1965	Co-worker	Yes	No
Susan	McDonald	4332 Cherry Ave.	McDonaldville	CA	90210	(818) 555-1238	10/1/1970	Relative	Yes	No

FIGURE 7.1 Example of a DBMS Table.

In a relational database management system such as Microsoft Access, before any data can be input into the table, the fields associated with the table must be created. Specifically, the following items must be defined for each field prior to inputting any data:

Name — Each field must be assigned a unique name, meaning that no two fields in a table can have the same name.

Size — Each field must be assigned a size. The size is typically stated in terms of how many characters a field will be able to hold. Unlike a spreadsheet, if the data being input into a particular field exceeds the size, the data will be truncated, meaning that it will be cut off. Conversely, a field that is assigned a particular size will reserve that amount of capacity of storage, whether or not any data is input into it.

Type — Fields must be designated as to the type of data that they will be able to hold. Once a field is designated as a particular type, it will be able to contain only data consistent with that type. For example, a field designated as "Numeric" can only hold numbers but not any alphanumeric characters.

DATABASE FIELD TYPES

Numeric Fields: Numeric fields are sometimes called *Number* or *Value* fields, depending on the DBMS software. A field that is designated as numeric can only hold numbers. There are different subtypes of numeric fields, such as integers, which can only hold whole numbers. For non-integer numeric fields, the number of decimal places can generally be specified.

Text Fields: A field designated as a Text field can hold pretty much any alphanumeric character (alphanumerics are combinations of letters, numbers, and symbols). Depending on the database software, text fields may also be referred to as *Character* fields or *String* fields. You can also enter numbers into a *Text* field, although you will not be able to conduct any mathematical operations on those values. Text fields are typically used to hold names, descriptions, and other text-based information composed of words and numbers that do not have mathematical significance (such as a street address number). In most database programs, text fields have a maximum size of about 255 characters.

Date Fields: Some database programs may refer to this type of field as a *DateTime* format. Fields designated as being *Date fields* can hold, predictably enough, only dates. One may wonder why there is a need for a field that can hold only a date, since you could just as easily input a date into a text field. The reason is that a date input into a date-type field, can be manipulated accordingly. For example, if a date is entered into a text-type field, and the table is then sorted by that field, the resulting record order will be in the numeric value of the dates—as opposed to the chronological order of the dates.

For example, consider two records in a database table *Text Field*, one containing the value of "02/18/2014" and the second containing the value of "11/01/2013." Although these values would have significance to a user as being two dates with the 11/01/2013 coming first in chronological order, a database program will simply see these values as meaningless characters, unless they are entered into a field formatted as having a *Date format*. Additionally, the use of a date field ensures that the dates will all be entered using exactly the same format for every record.

Logical Fields: Also known as *Boolean* or *Yes/No* fields, this type of field can contain only one of two possible values, a "True" or "False," or a "Yes" or "No" (*True* is the same as *Yes* and *False* is the same as *No*), or a 1 and 0 (a value of "1" is the same as a "yes," while a value of "0" is the same as a "no").

Logical fields are typically used for situations where the field can only be one of the two possibilities. In the example above, the ChristmasCard field could be defined as a Logical field since it can only contain a Yes or a No, depending on whether or not the person is on your Christmas card list. Since there is no other possible value than a yes or a no, a *Logical* field format is an appropriate choice.

Memo: A *memo* field is a field that can contain virtually anything, including complete documents, graphic objects, and links to documents.

The main advantages of memo fields are that they can store much larger field contents than text fields, and that they can often contain non-text data, such as images. In contrast to text fields, which can usually hold about 255 characters, memo fields can hold tens of thousands of characters.

RELATIONAL DATABASE STRUCTURE VERSUS FLAT FILE DATABASE STRUCTURE

A database can be designed using one of two basic structures: a *flat file* database structure, or a *relational* database structure. The basic distinction between a flat file and a relational database structure is fairly simple in terms of the definitions. A flat file database is simply a database that consists entirely of one table, while a relational database is one that consists of two or more interrelated tables. Flat file database structures often work best when a database has a rather simple, narrowly defined purpose, such as the address list example used above. In that example, each record can easily contain all of the information needed, making one table adequate for the entire database, making a flat file database structure a good choice.

Consider an example of a situation requiring a relational structure as opposed to a flat file structure. Let's consider a database containing information about patients who have visited a particular clinic.

FirstName	LastName	Address	Bdate	PatientID	VisitDate	Cost
Joe	Smith	123 Main Street	1/2/1985	5532243	1/8/2011	44.06
Joe	Smith	123 Main Street	1/2/1985	5532243	2/11/2010	112.71
Joe	Smith	123 Main Street	1/2/1985	5532243	2/11/2008	137.32
Larry	Jone	3445 Oak Ave.	2/6/1970	3343204	4/10/2003	93.33
Larry	Jone	3445 Oak Ave.	2/6/1970	3343204	4/17/2012	472.14
Larry	Jone	3445 Oak Ave.	2/6/1970	3343204	5/11/2011	257.14
Fred	Williams	5632 Walnut Blvd.	3/5/1969	7718271	10/13/2009	48.93
Fred	Williams	5632 Walnut Blvd.	3/5/1969	7718271	10/13/2008	299.90
Fred	Williams	5632 Walnut Blvd.	3/5/1969	7718271	10/15/2004	96.89
Fred	Williams	5632 Walnut Blvd.	3/5/1969	7718271	3/10/2009	358.10
Jim	Keating	2343 Cypress Dr.	6/1/1979	2483388	5/11/2009	469.78
Jim	Keating	2343 Cypress Dr.	6/1/1979	2483388	7/10/2012	369.63
Jim	Keating	2343 Cypress Dr.	6/1/1979	2483388	4/14/2013	161.56
Mary	Lou	4353 Redwood Ln.	8/3/1958	6881666	10/10/2012	19.00
Mary	Lou	4353 Redwood Ln.	8/3/1958	6881666	10/16/2011	483.74
Mary	Lou	4353 Redwood Ln.	8/3/1958	6881666	2/12/2011	479.42

FIGURE 7.2 Flat File Database Example.

In the example above, a flat file database has been used to track the information associated with office visits at a clinic. In this example, the visit date and cost associated with each visit is captured in the database, along with the name, address, and other information related to the patient. The issue with the structure of this table is that although a patient's name, address, and birthdate don't change, the information is repeated on every record for that patient.

The problem with this database design is that the entry of the same information requires considerable storage space to hold the repeated entries of the patients' names and addresses. Additionally, larger databases tend to have reduced performance when sorting, searching, reporting, etc., compared to smaller databases. Finally, it is important to consider the potential for error associated with re-inputting the same names and addresses for each record, as well as the problem associated with updating the records should an individual's address change. In other words, if Mary Lou's address needs to be entered three times, it increases the probability of data entry error compared to only entering it one time. If Mary Lou moves and changes her address, a total of three records will need to be updated for the database to be accurate.

The alternative to a flat file database is called a *relational* database structure. Since a relational structure consists of *multiple* tables, it is possible to have one table consisting of one record per individual (rather than one record per visit), containing the static information that does not change, such as the name and address, while the second table consists of one record *per visit*. The second table would be considered a transactional table, because the records in that table relate to transactions or events of some sort. Since the name, address, etc., are all present in the person-level table, there is no need to repeat those fields in the transactional table.

In fact, the only fields needed for the transactional table are the date, cost, and a key field containing a unique value that can be used to link the records together between the two tables. In this example, the PatientID is a patient account number that is unique to each patient, making it an ideal key field. This type of relational join is called a one-to-many join, because one record in the patient table is joined to many records in the visits table.

The figure below is one way of visualizing how the relational version of this database would be structured. Keep in mind that although the actual database structure in the illustration, below consists of two inter-related tables, working with the database in Access (or any other RDBMS) is very similar to working with a flat file database. In fact, the database can be viewed with all of the fields appearing on one screen, as if it were a flat file, even though it is really relational.

FirstName	LastName	Address	Bdate	PatientID
Joe	Smith	123 Main Street	1/2/1985	5532243
Larry	Jone	3445 Oak Ave.	2/6/1970	3343204
Fred	Williams	5632 Walnut Blvd.	3/5/1969	7718271
Jim	Keating	2343 Cypress Dr.	6/1/1979	2483388
Mary	Lou	4353 Redwood Ln.	8/3/1958	6881666

Table 7.1 contains only *one record per person*, along with fields that do not normally change each time a transaction occurs (e.g. names or addresses for an individual do not normally change from one visit to another).

PatientID	VisitDate	Cost
5532243	1/8/2011	154.29
5532243	2/11/2010	361.12
5532243	2/11/2008	372.78
3343204	4/10/2003	445.71
3343204	4/17/2012	243.11
3343204	5/11/2011	296.93
7718271	10/13/2009	456.85
7718271	10/13/2008	337.99
7718271	10/15/2004	359.41
7718271	3/10/2009	143.77
2483388	5/11/2009	267.12
2483388	7/10/2012	32.63
2483388	4/14/2013	183.24
6881666	10/10/2012	481.91
6881666	10/16/2011	194.85
6881666	2/12/2011	297.67

Table 7.2 contains *one record per transaction* (transactions are the same as "visits").

Figure 7.3 shows another view of the relational structure, this one as it appears in Microsoft Access. The tables are represented by the boxes on the screen, while the fields in each table are listed within the respective boxes. In Access, a relational database can be defined very easily by simply positioning the two (or more) tables on the screen, and then connecting the key fields by dragging and dropping a key field from one table to another. In the example below, the records contained in the Patients table have been related to the records in the Visits table by connecting the PatientID, which is common to both tables. *It is important to remember that tables in a relational structure must always have a key field common to both tables in order to relate the records in those tables.*

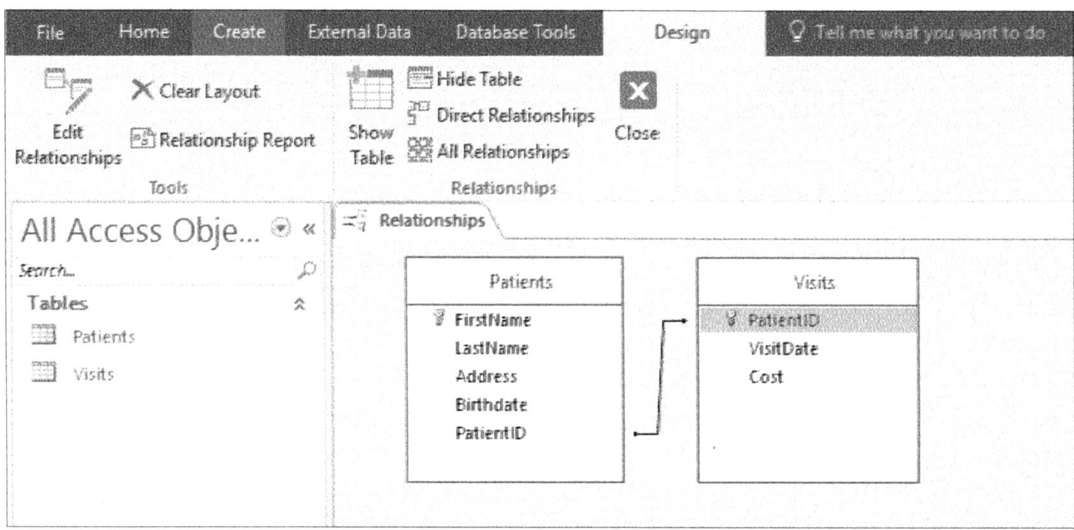

FIGURE 7.3 Relational Database Structure in Microsoft Access.

DATA HYGIENE

If you have ever received multiple pieces of mail from a single source but with each one addressed to you with your name misspelled or in a slightly different format, you are already familiar with the effects of poor data hygiene. Data hygiene refers to degree to which computer databases contain errors, such as typos, data entry mistakes, transposed numbers, outdated data elements, etc. In the modern world of relational databases and interconnected networks, a single data entry error that results in your name being misspelled in one database can quickly migrate to other databases, making the error widespread. While a misspelled name may be an annoyance, other types of errors can result in operational problems for an organization, as well as service quality problems for the consumer.

Consider the example of a patient medical record in a database maintained by a healthcare organization. Diagnoses are commonly identified using a numeric code based upon the *International Classification of Diseases 9th Edition* (ICD-9).* Under ICD-9, a diagnosis of *multiple sclerosis* is assigned

* As of year-end 2014, ICD-9 Codes have been replaced with International Classification of Diseases 10th Edition (ICD-10)

an ICD-9 code of *340*. However, if the code was transposed and incorrectly input into the computer database as *304*, the diagnosis would be incorrectly assigned as *drug dependence*, rather than *multiple sclerosis*. In addition to the obvious issues related to treatment modalities, consider the implications related to having a diagnosis of drug dependence on a medical record, which may then be sent to a health insurer as well as the *Medical Information Bureau*, where it could be eventually shared with other health insurance companies to which the patient later applies for coverage.

Although some errors are almost impossible to easily validate, other types of errors can be tested programmatically. As an example of an error that is difficult to detect, consider someone inputting an unusually spelled name that was handwritten on a hard-copy form. There are two factors that make this a difficult error to detect. The first factor is that a name with an unusual spelling may be one that the data input person has not seen before and would not intuitively recognize as an error if it was entered incorrectly. The second factor is that because the name is handwritten on a form, it may be difficult to interpret the handwriting as to how it was spelled. In this situation, it would be very difficult to establish a computer-based method to ensure data hygiene with respect to proper spelling of a name.

Although detecting a misspelled name that is also unusual may be difficult, other types of errors can be detected and sometimes corrected automatically. For example, let's assume that the same form contains the patient's birthdate, along with the date of a recent hospitalization. In that situation, we would know that for a given patient the birthdate logically has to come before the hospitalization date. Given that knowledge, we could use a database data validation method by creating a programmed rule specifying that the birthdate entered into the database must be chronologically earlier than the hospitalization date (and vice versa). As the dates are input into the database, the software can then test the two dates by comparing them to one another. If the hospitalization date is earlier than the birthdate, an error message will be produced to indicate that one of the two dates must be incorrect. Although the problem cannot necessarily be corrected automatically, the data input operator will be alerted to an error that otherwise might have been missed.

DATA VALIDATION TOOLS IN ACCESS

Microsoft Access, as well as most other relational database management systems, includes tools allowing database designers to create and implement data validation rules. Figure 7.4 provides an example of a data validation rule applied to the *DischargeDate* field in a hospital database. The rule is used to test whether the date a patient was discharged from a hospital falls after the patient's date of birth. If the discharge date input into the database is prior to the date of birth, one of the two entries would be presumably in error. In the example, the *validation text* indicates that in the event the rule is violated, an error message will appear, indicating "*Date of Birth must be an earlier date than the Discharge Date.*"

INPUT MASKS

Another type of data validation involves the use of an input mask, which allows the database designer to essentially force a user to input data using a specified format. Examples might include enforcing a rule that users enter a telephone number including a three-digit area code in parentheses, or a social security number that includes dashes, etc. The example in Figure 7.5 contains a definition for an input mask specifying that dates entered into the DischargeDate field must be in DD/MM/YYYY format.

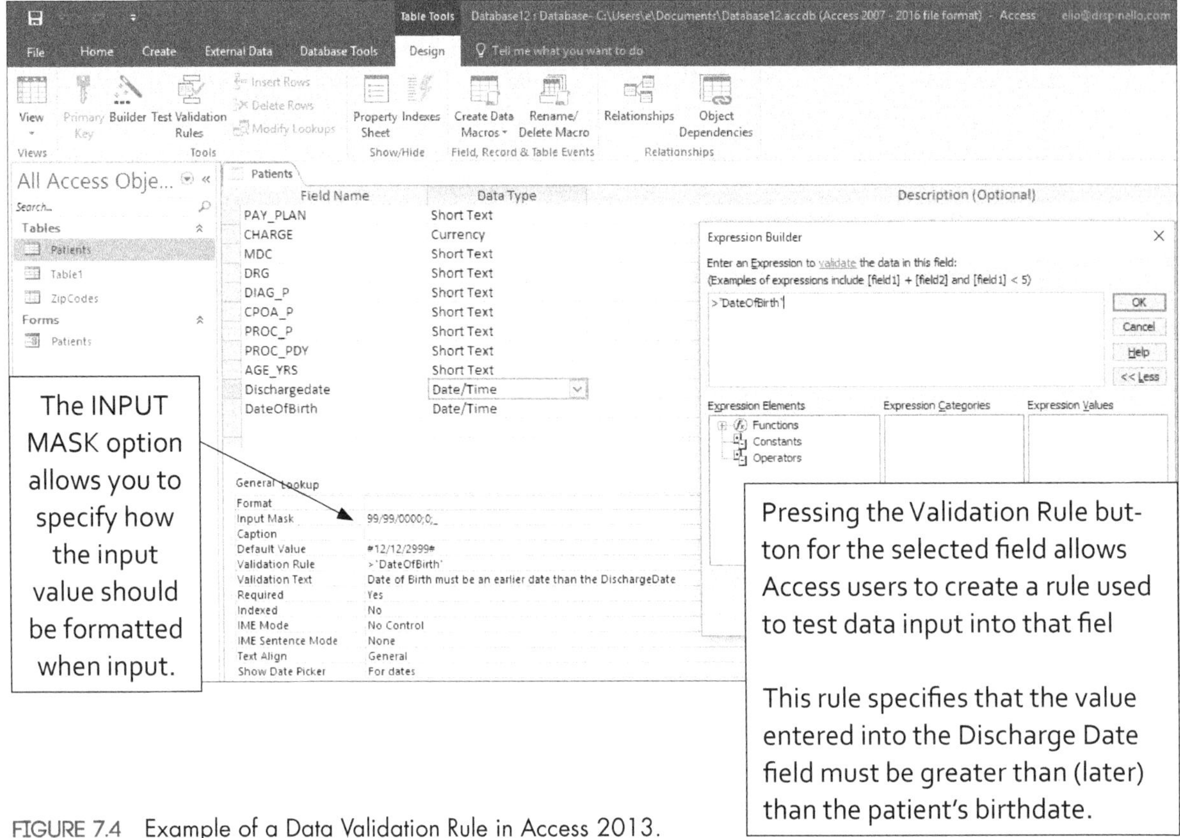

FIGURE 7.4 Example of a Data Validation Rule in Access 2013.

REQUIRED DATA ENTRY

A common problem in many databases is that of missing data elements. As a data entry operator is inputting values into to the system, they may skip over a particular field for a variety of reasons. One possibility is that it is inadvertently overlooked, while it is also possible that a hard-copy input form is illegible, or some other problem exists. Most DBMS systems allow fields to be specified as *required* for data entry, meaning that the data entry operator cannot skip over it and go to the next record unless it is filled. The example in Figure 7.5 shows the *Required* property for the DischargeDate field as being set to "*Yes*," meaning that the field must be populated with a value before the record can be saved.

Although this method ensures that a database will not contain a missing value, it produces a potential problem for a data entry operator who does not have access to the appropriate entry. If the value to be input is unavailable (or illegible), there must be a way for the data entry operator to deal with the situation. A common approach is to develop a set of predetermined values that can be used to indicate a missing or incorrect entry. For example, if the discharge date was not available, a default value of 12/31/2999 could be used. Although it would not be correct, it is different enough from a real value that it will not be mistaken for the real thing and more importantly, it could be easily identified in a query for later correction. *The key to this approach is in having predetermined values created and written into a formal data entry procedure that all data entry operators have access to and adhere to.*

General	Lookup
Format	
Input Mask	
Caption	
Default Value	#12/31/2999#
Validation Rule	
Validation Text	
Required	No
Indexed	No
IME Mode	No Control
IME Sentence Mode	None
Text Align	General
Show Date Picker	For dates

FIGURE 7.5 Example Default Value Used to Populate Missing Birthdates.

Note that Figure 7.5 provides an example of how the *Default Value* field option can be used to automatically provide a value of 12/12/2999 in the event that the actual birthdate is not input by the data entry operator.

SELECTION FROM PRESELECTED VALUES

Another strategy that can help reduce the numbers of errors in a database is that of minimizing the amount of typing that must be done by the data entry operator. Typing is an inherently inefficient process in that it is relatively slow and it is prone to error. Consider the number of times you review your own word processing documents, emails, etc., to find that you have made spelling or typing errors. When a user is required to input data into a particular field that has only a finite number of possibilities, it is faster and more accurate to allow them to select what they want to enter from a list of predefined options, and then have that value automatically inserted into the field. Examples are entering the name of a state, an individual's race or ethnicity, insurance status, or any other field containing options that are limited to a specific list of choices. This approach helps ensure that all entries are consistent with one another, avoiding situations such as having the field containing individual's race for one record entered as "African American" and other record entered as "Black." Using the predefined options approach, the user can only select a value from the options that are presented to them.

Another approach is to provide the data entry operator with access to input a zip code into a zip code field, and then have the names of the city and the state returned automatically for that zip code using relational lookup table containing a listing of all valid zip codes, along with the cities with which they are associated. An example of a zip code lookup table is provided in Figure 7.6.

Given the zipcode lookup table in the database, the field properties for the patzip (patient zip code) field in the Patients table can be set so that the data entry operator can simply select from a list of predefined zip codes rather than typing it.

Once the zipcode table is in the database, creating the selection list simply requires selecting the LOOKUP tab for the patzip field and then selecting COMBO BOX as the display control, followed by the table containing the lookup values in the ROW SOURCE option.

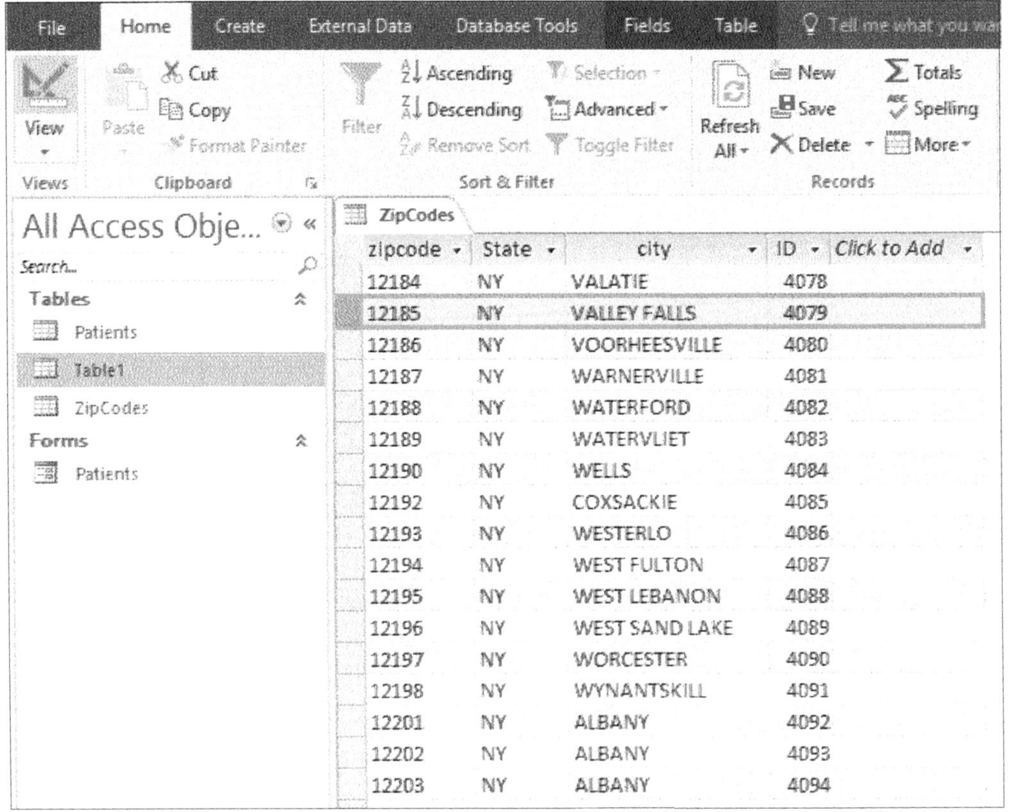

FIGURE 7.6 Example of Zip Code Lookup Table.

The BOUND COLUMN option is used to specify which column in the zipcode table will be used for lookup, while the COLUMN COUNT option is used to specify how many columns in the zipcode table will be visible in the drop-down list that is created for use on the data input form for the patzip field.

TAKING ADVANTAGE OF DATA ALREADY IN THE DATABASE

Consider that each time data are hand-input into a system, the potential exists for human error to be introduced. In the previous chapter the concept of *relational databases* was discussed. The idea behind a relational database is that certain types of transactional records may be repeated many times in a table for a certain individual.

For example, a consumer who has made multiple purchases of products or services could have several records in a database—one for each purchase. However, certain pieces of information for that consumer are always the same, such as the consumer's name, address and telephone number. Reentering those pieces of information for each purchase raises the likelihood of an error being made due to the increased data entry effort being expended (and raises the time and cost of maintaining that database). By utilizing a table containing each consumer's name, address, and other static information, the information in those fields can be linked relationally to each consumer transaction record, eliminating the need for it to be re-input each time there is a purchase.

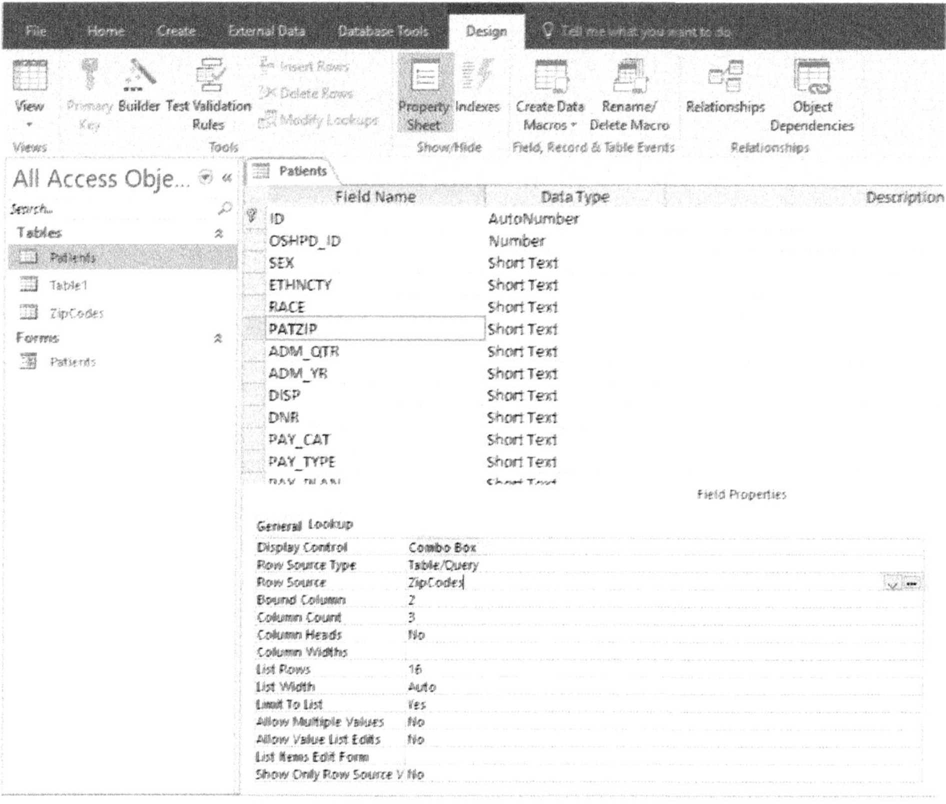

FIGURE 7.7 Creating a Selection List for Zip Codes.

In designing a database structure, a careful assessment should be made of which data elements are static and are best suited for use in a relational database in a look-up table, rather than requiring hand input. Keep in mind that in order to relate two tables relationally, both tables require a common that is unique to each individual. In the example of the consumer record, there should be a unique consumer number, account number, or some other reliable and unique identifier assigned to each consumer, and that identifier must be present in both tables that are to be related.

DATABASE SECURITY

The fields of healthcare and public health have unique issues due to the sensitivity of the data with which workers are entrusted. Medical records, along with the various forms of digital data such as medical imaging, scanned documents, and insurance documentation, contain vast amounts of information about the most personal aspects of a person's life. Ensuring that the data elements are correct is critical to providing a patient with the highest standard of care, while protecting the security of the data is critical to ensuring that a patient does not encounter a breach and/or misuse of their most private information. Those who require such data to provide healthcare products and services have both an ethical obligation to those who entrust their information to them as well as a legal obligation to protect that information. Chapter 1 provides an overview of the medical records privacy provisions of the Health Insurance Portability and Accountability Act (HIPAA), including the legal obligations of healthcare personnel who deal with medical records.

Although database management programs such as Microsoft Access provide an efficient and convenient platform to store, manage, and analyze medical data, it is important to consider that all computer-based platforms contain some vulnerabilities. It is the responsibility of those who design databases and the end-users of the systems to identify and understand what those vulnerabilities are, and take steps toward mitigating them.

Chapter 1 includes a discussion relating to a number of data security methods that can be used to help prevent unauthorized access to data. Among the methods mentioned are the following:

Anonymity: Removing all information from a dataset that refers to any patient information making them identifiable, such as names, addresses, and phone numbers.

Data Partitioning/Segmentation/User-Level Security: Based on the process of splitting up a database into multiple partitions in order to improve performance, or as a security precaution to individually secure the partitions and control database user access for each partition.

Encryption: A process by which digital information is converted into an unreadable state.

ANONYMITY

As described in Chapter 1, *anonymity* is a method by which personal identifiers (names, addresses, etc.) are removed from the database. Although anonymity is often used effectively to secure databases that are used for research purposes, it is important to note that as a data protection method, anonymity is virtually useless as a security method in an operational healthcare environment. The reason for its lack of usefulness operationally is that once names and other personal identifiers are removed from the database, with the exception of research and analysis, there is very little else the database can be used for.

In terms of employing anonymity as a security method in Microsoft Access, or any other RDBMS, the process can be as easy as simply deleting the columns in a database containing names, addresses, phone numbers, social security numbers, or other fields that can be used to identify the individual that the information is about. Although removal of personal identification fields will potentially make the database safe to share outside of the healthcare organization, it will be effectively useless for any operational purposes.

Under the *Health Insurance Portability and Accountability Act* (HIPAA), the "Safe Harbor Method" of de-identifying patient data describes the specific identification fields that must be detached from the medical record before that medical record can be released without patient authorization. The key to effective anonymity is ensuring that all of the fields containing personal identifiers are completely removed from the database prior to that database being distributed to anyone not authorized for access to the personal information. Figure 7.8 provides a listing of the personal identification elements defined under HIPAA, which must be removed in order for medical data to be "de-identified" using the *Save Harbor Method*.

<table>
<tr><td colspan="2">(2)(i) The following identifiers of the individual or of relatives, employers, or household members of the individual, are removed:</td></tr>
<tr><td colspan="2">(A) Names</td></tr>
<tr><td colspan="2">(B) All geographic subdivisions smaller than a state, including street address, city, county, precinct, ZIP code, and their equivalent geocodes, except for the initial three digits of the ZIP code if, according to the current publicly available data from the Bureau of the Census:
(1) The geographic unit formed by combining all ZIP codes with the same three initial digits contains more than 20,000 people; and
(2) The initial three digits of a ZIP code for all such geographic units containing 20,000 or fewer people is changed to 000</td></tr>
<tr><td colspan="2">(C) All elements of dates (except year) for dates that are directly related to an individual, including birth date, admission date, discharge date, death date, and all ages over 89 and all elements of dates (including year) indicative of such age, except that such ages and elements may be aggregated into a single category of age 90 or older</td></tr>
<tr><td>(D) Telephone numbers</td><td>(L) Vehicle identifiers and serial numbers, including license plate numbers</td></tr>
<tr><td>(E) Fax numbers</td><td>(M) Device identifiers and serial numbers</td></tr>
<tr><td>(F) Email addresses</td><td>(N) Web Universal Resource Locators (URLs)</td></tr>
<tr><td>(G) Social security numbers</td><td>(O) Internet Protocol (IP) addresses</td></tr>
<tr><td>(H) Medical record numbers</td><td>(P) Biometric identifiers, including finger and voice prints</td></tr>
<tr><td>(I) Health plan beneficiary numbers</td><td>(Q) Full-face photographs and any comparable images</td></tr>
<tr><td>(J) Account numbers</td><td rowspan="2">(R) Any other unique identifying number, characteristic, or code, except as permitted by paragraph (c) of this section [Paragraph (c) is presented below in the section "Re-identification"]; and</td></tr>
<tr><td>(K) Certificate/license numbers</td></tr>
<tr><td colspan="2">(ii) The covered entity does not have actual knowledge that the information could be used alone or in combination with other information to identify an individual who is a subject of the information.</td></tr>
</table>

FIGURE 7.8 Patient Data Elements Protected under HIPAA.

DATA ENCRYPTION

As described in Chapter 1, data encryption is the process of making a dataset unreadable to someone without appropriate authentication. Encryption of databases is based upon the science of cryptography, which essentially consists of converting recognizable writing into what is essentially like a secret code. Due to the speed with which contemporary computer systems can process and convert data, the cryptography methods currently in use can be extremely complex in their ability to secure data. The specific code used to secure a particular dataset is based upon a *cryptographic key*, which is assigned by the user. Since there are potentially thousands of different keys that can be assigned, every dataset can be secured using a different and unique cryptographic method, making it nearly impossible to convert the data into a readable format without authentication.

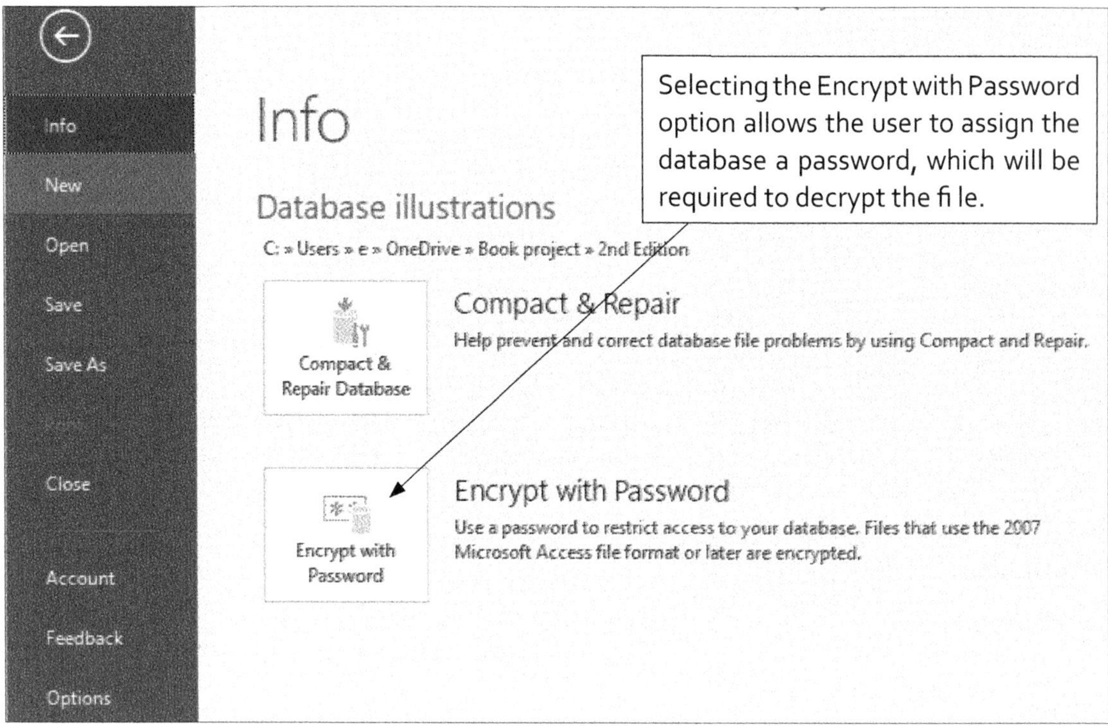

FIGURE 7.9 Microsoft Access 2016 Encryption.

As implemented in most consumer software, such as in Microsoft Office products, encryption authentication is based upon the assignment of a password (which also serves as the key) to an encrypted document, spreadsheet, or database.

In Microsoft Access 2016, encrypting a database can be accomplished rather easily, by selecting the FILE tab on the ribbon bar and then pressing the *Encrypt with Password* button.

Although the encryption algorithms often utilized are similar to military-grade security and extremely difficult to hack, the vulnerability of this method is that the authentication is based upon a single password. In essence, it is much easier to try to guess a password than it is to hack the encryption. In fact, computer programs have been created specifically to try to guess passwords in rapid-fire succession until they arrive at the correct one. Although password-based encryption can provide some measure of security, a user must keep in mind that it is only as secure as the password that he or she assigns to the database. The password should be as long as possible, contain a variety of character types (uppercase letters, lowercase letters, numbers, symbols, etc.), and should not contain recognizable or easy-to-guess words or names.

A generally much stronger method of data encryption can be found in a key-exchange cryptography. The key-exchange method employed by a number of encryption programs works on the premise that all users of the encryption program create a public key, which can be shared with other users, as well as a private key that they keep to themselves. The private key is generally a long string of random characters that can reside on a computer hard drive or on a mobile media device, such as a flash drive. Encryption of any file requires that the person encrypting the file use his or her own key, along with the public keys of the individual(s) who are allowed to decrypt the file. Using this approach, the encryption file will be encrypted by an algorithm that can be decrypted only by those holding the private keys. Consider this example:

Key-Exchange Encryption Example

Jonathon has an Access database containing sensitive data that he wishes to share via email with Susan and Chris. Utilizing a key-exchange encryption program, Jonathon must use his own *private* key, together with the *public* keys belonging to Susan and Chris, which they have provided to Jonathon. Additionally, Susan and Chris have assigned a *passphrase* for their private keys (similar to a password but potentially much longer and more complex). In order for someone to decrypt a file intended for Susan, that individual will require both Susan's private key and her passphrase. The encryption program utilizes the combination of those keys and passphrase to create a custom encryption algorithm that can be solved only using the private key of any of the individuals, and by providing the correct passphrase associated with their private key.

In order for Susan and/or Chris to decrypt the file, they must have access to their own *private* keys and know the correct *passphrase associated with their own keys*. Compared to the password-only method of encryption used by Access, the key-exchange method requires that both parties have access to each other's public keys, along with the correct passphrase, thus making it much more difficult to hack, assuming the private keys are kept secure.

Although key-exchange encryption is not built into Microsoft Access, it is available using third-party programs such as *Symantec/PGP programs* and the open-source program, *GPG Tools*.

CONTROLLING USER-LEVEL SECURITY

In a multi-user database environment, a common issue is that while many users can potentially have access to a database, not all of them necessarily need to have access to every field in the database in order to do their jobs. Consider that each person who has access to a piece of information becomes a potential point of vulnerability from a security standpoint. While the individual may not consciously or intentionally divulge that information, he or she might be hacked, or may inadvertently let down their guard by not taking appropriate security precautions to safeguard their password, or their computer could become infected with a virus or

User-Level Security in Microsoft Access

User-level security in Microsoft Access is available only when using older (pre-Office 2007) database formats. Although the more contemporary version of the Access database format (available in Microsoft Access 2007 and later) do not support user-level security, *database server* RDMS systems do provide user-level security support and are considered a preferred software platform for larger-scale multi-user systems.

Examples of database *server* software are *Microsoft SQL Server, Microsoft SQL Server Express, IBM DB2, MySQL,* and the open source options, *PostgreSQL* and *Firebird.* One of the key differences between desktop programs (such as *Access*) and database server programs (such as *SQL Server*) is that the database server programs are designed to support dozens to hundreds of simultaneous users of a database with both high performance and robust security.

other malware that compromises their security. Ideally, sensitive data should be made only available to the individuals on a need-to-know basis.

Contemporary relational database management programs typically support multi-user access across a computer network, and will often incorporate the capability to create *permission levels*, which are then assigned to users. Often referred to as *user-level security*, each permission level provides access to only a certain portion of the database, along with specifying whether individuals at that permission level are allowed to make changes to the database or to only view the contents. Each user of the database is assigned a permission level that corresponds with the information needs of his or her role within the organization with respect to their need for access to the database. Permission levels are generally associated with each individual's login, so that when an individual signs into the system, the permission level takes effect immediately.

As an example, in a medical environment a nurse, physician, or other healthcare provider would likely require access to a patient's medical history contained in their electronic medical record. However, someone working in an administrative capacity would more likely require access to insurance and billing information but would not necessarily need access to clinical history. The basic approach of data partitioning is to allow users access to only the fields or partitions that they require to do their jobs. Additionally, through the use of permission levels, access to certain database fields can be effectively controlled by allowing different users varying levels of privileges to access and/or modify the database based upon each individual's need to do their job. As an example, a user may be required to view a particular field on a patient's record, but would never be expected to make any changes to that record. That employee's permission level could be configured so that he or she would be allowed to view the required fields, but changes would not be permitted.

Note that newer versions of Microsoft Access (those after 2007) do not support user-level security. Databases requiring user-level security should be developed using database server software.

DATABASE ACCESSIBILITY

Maintaining data in an RDBMS system is useful only if the individuals who need it are able to get access to the database. There are a number of ways in which to configure a relational database system designed in Access or other RDBMS program, but the possibilities can generally be summarized by these three:

1. Single-user desktop
2. Multi-user access through a Local Area Network (LAN)
3. Multi-user access through a Wide Area Network (WAN)

SINGLE-USER DESKTOP

A single-user desktop configuration for a database is typically the easiest and simplest to deploy. One copy of the RDBMS software (such as Microsoft Access) exists on a single individual's computer, along with the database itself. The computer and the database can be accessed by only one person at a time, hence the term *single-user*. Only one installation of the DBMS software is required, and the software and the actual database are installed on the computer at which the end-user will be working. Under this scenario, anyone else who wishes to access the database must do so from the same computer.

MULTI-USER ACCESS THROUGH A LOCAL AREA NETWORK (LAN)

Local area networks require that all of the computers requiring access to the database either be connected using cable or through a wireless connection directly to the same router. The LAN is typically a closed system separate from Internet connectivity, so although the computers reside on the same local network, none of them necessarily need to be connected to the Internet.

It should be noted that it is possible to provide users access to a local area network via the Internet through use of a *Virtual Private Network* (VPN). VPN access must be specifically configured and made available by a system administrator. Accessing a LAN using a VPN requires that a program referred to as a VPN client be installed and configured on the user computer. The VPN client allows the user to essentially tunnel through the Internet and be authenticated on the LAN to which they are connecting.

Using this approach, the DBMS software and the actual database typically reside on a network fileserver that only selected users have access to. Each user is assigned user name and password that authenticates the users and allows them access to the parts of the database for which he or she has been assigned permission to view and/or modify.

Databases that are designed to function under a multi-user environment must be configured to deal with the possibility of conflicting modifications by more than one user. For example, consider the possibility that two users logged onto the same database attempt to modify the same record for a particular individual at the same time. Without one user knowing about the actions of the other user, the resulting changes to the record could result in a loss of data or some other error. Multi-user databases are generally designed to take such possibilities into account and to provide safeguards to ensure data integrity. In the example above, one approach might be for the database system to immediately lock a record as soon as the first user begins to make changes to it, resulting in the second user being unable to modify the record until it has been unlocked by the system when the first user has finished with it.

MULTI-USER ACCESS THROUGH A WIDE AREA NETWORK (WAN)

Database access through a WAN is very similar to that of a LAN, with the exception that the server holding the software and database is directly accessible through the Internet. As an Internet-based database, the user-interface for the system is typically accessed through a web browser such as Internet Explorer, Firefox, or Google Chrome.

One of the key differences between a LAN-based database and a WAN-based database often relates to the number of users who have access to that database. The very large number of users who can potentially perform simultaneous queries or "hits" on the database require that both the database software and the computer be sufficiently robust to support a large number of users while maintaining acceptable levels of performance.

Another issue related to databases in WAN environments concerns security vulnerabilities. On a local area network, individuals do not typically have exposure to the database server unless they are able to gain physical access to a computer on that network. However, on a wide-area network, one need only have Internet connectivity in order to try to connect to the database server. Although an individual must be authenticated in order to make that connection, the use of WAN database server brings a potential hacker one step closer to gaining access. For this reason, security measures applied to a database server with Internet exposure must be carefully planned and implemented to ensure that the database is accessible to those who need it, while simultaneously secured and protected from unauthorized access.

SUMMARY

Contemporary database management programs provide a wealth of tools that can be used to design and maintain complex databases. Database management programs range from desktop programs, such as Microsoft Access, to enterprise-level database server programs, such as SQL Server and MySQL. Given the capabilities of modern database programs and the sensitivity and legal requirements associated with the handling of medical records, healthcare professionals who deal with digital healthcare data must take the proactive steps of using data validation tools and data security procedures to ensure that the data security and data hygiene are protected.

The concept of a WAN adds an additional level of access to a database by making it accessible to a greater number of users through an Internet connection. Care must be taken to ensure that performance levels are adequate and the databases are protected from unauthorized access.

RESOURCES

A number of resources are available to users of Microsoft Access as well as other relational database management programs. The following websites may be particularly helpful:

Microsoft Online Training: A number of online training courses are available free of charge directly from Microsoft and can be found at: http://office.microsoft.com/en-us/training/

A Gentle Human Intro to Access 2013: Produced by Microsoft, this webinar video guides you through creating a database using a predefined template: http://blogs.office.com/2013/11/04/webinar-a-gentle-human-intro-to-access-2013/

APPLY YOUR KNOWLEDGE

Please refer to Active Learning Platform for exercises.

This exercise is designed with the objective of applying some of the key concepts discussed in this chapter. Using data simulating actual patient hospital discharge records, this exercise provides a step-by-step process of building a relational database using Microsoft Access.

IMAGE CREDITS

Fig. 7.3: Copyright © by Microsoft
Fig. 7.4: Copyright © by Microsoft
Fig. 7.5: Copyright © by Microsoft
Fig. 7.6: Copyright © by Microsoft
Fig. 7.7: Copyright © by Microsoft
Fig. 7.8: "Patient Data Elements Protected Under HIPAA Source," http://cancergenome.nih.gov/PublishedContent/Files/pdfs/6.3.1.1_HIPAA.De_ID_164.514_508.pdf. Copyright in the Public Domain.
Fig. 7.9: Copyright © by Microsoft

8

AN INTRODUCTION TO BOOLEAN LOGIC

The problem with having the ability to store massive amounts of data on a computer is that there needs to be a way to identify certain specific pieces of information within that vast sea of data. Although computer technology provides the ability to process and search though massive amounts of data extremely quickly, users must have a standardized approach to articulate the logic of which database records they are searching for. The selection logic must then be communicated to the computer so that the search can be conducted in a manner that will return the desired results.

That method is called Boolean Logic. Named after the nineteenth-century mathematician *George Boole*, Boolean logic represents the basis for modern database theory as well as the basis for most computer programming technology in use today. Boolean logic is based on the concept of *binary* logic, which reduces a complicated proposition to a series of simple yes/no questions. For example, consider the following proposition:

> *If the current temperature in my house is above 80 degrees, then I will turn on the air conditioning.*

This proposition is actually a conditional test in which a condition is being evaluated (whether or not the temperature is above 80 degrees), and a decision is made based upon the outcome of the condition (whether or not to turn on the air conditioning). The condition can be considered to have a binary outcome, meaning there are only two possible outcomes—either the temperature is above 80 degrees or it is not. In computer programming terms, if the temperature is above 80 degrees, the condition's outcome is considered to be *true*, whereas if the temperature is <u>not</u> above 80 degrees, its outcome is considered *false*.

Using a flowchart, the decision can be expressed graphically. Flowcharts traditionally use a diamond symbol to represent a conditional test or decision, and a rectangle to represent a process or action of some sort.

Another way to look at this logic is that a comparison is being made. In this case a variable (the temperature) is being compared to a constant value (80 degrees) in order to determine whether or not the constant is higher. We consider the temperature to be a variable because it is something that is expected to fluctuate. Conditional tests can generally be thought of as being a series of comparisons, where variables are compared to constant or target values.

In our example above, the test is really quite simple. If the thermometer indicates the current temperature is above 80 degrees, the decision will be made to turn on the air conditioning. However, many real-world decisions require much more complexity than one simple *yes* or *no* result. One of the powerful aspects of Boolean logic is that many simple binary tests can be combined to form the basis for a very complex decision.

As a way of seeing how more than one binary test can be used to create a more complex decision, consider the following example. Let's assume that you choose to turn on the air conditioning based upon the current temperature, but additionally you decide that the air conditioning should also be turned on if the weather forecast for later that day is for the temperature to be above 90 degrees, regardless of the current temperature at the moment. Using Boolean logic, we can express this decision using a combination of binary tests:

If the current temperature is above 80 degrees
OR
if the forecast temperature is above 90 degrees,
then I will turn on the air conditioning.

Notice that in this example, there are two distinctly different conditional tests. Each test can return a possible value of "yes" or "no." In order for the proposed action to occur (turning on the air conditioning), *either* of the conditions must return a result of "yes." The reason is that the two conditions were joined using the word "or," meaning that if one condition returns a result of "yes" and the other condition returns a value of "no," the air conditioning will still be turned on.

When using Boolean logic, there are two ways in which one condition can be related to another. The first way, as illustrated above is through use of the connecting word "OR," while the second way is through the use of the connecting word "AND." Because the two binary tests were connected using the word "OR," having just one of the two conditions being true will be sufficient for the air

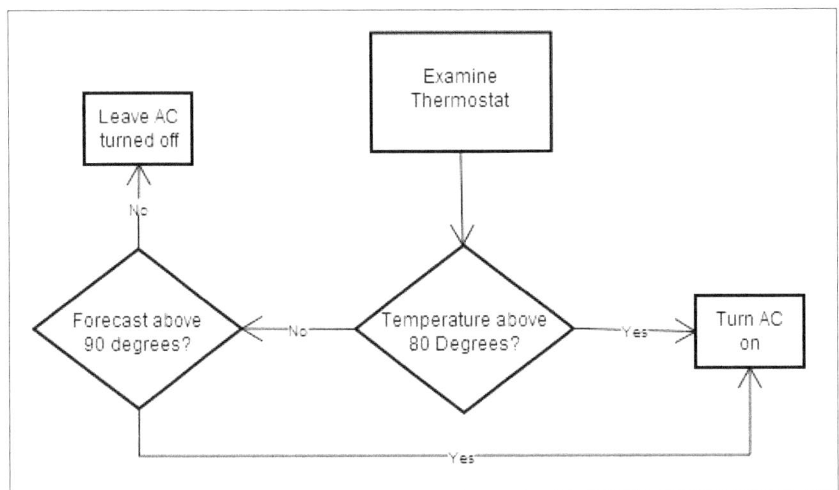

FIGURE 8.1 Flowchat of Decision Using "OR."

conditioning to be turned on. Graphically, this decision can be expressed in the form of the flowchart, below.

To illustrate the use of the connector word "AND," consider the following test in comparison to the one above:

IF the current temperature is above 80 degrees
AND
IF the forecast temperature is above 90 degrees,
THEN I will turn on the air conditioning.

Although the second decision looks similar to the first one, there is a very important difference. In the second example, the word "AND" tells us that in order for the air conditioning to be turned on, *both* binary conditions must be met: the current temperature must be above 80 degrees *and* the forecast temperature must be above 90 degrees. Unless both conditions return a result of "yes," the air conditioning will not be turned on.

Graphically, the decision logic can be expressed in the following flowchart. Note that in this flow chart the outcome of the first condition (is the temperature above 80 degrees) leads to another condition (is the forecast above 90 degrees). Outcomes of "yes" for both conditions then leads to the action of turning on the air conditioning. Also, notice it does not matter in which order the two conditions are tested. Regardless of whether the current temperature is tested first or the forecast is tested first, evaluating the conditions in either order will always return the same result.

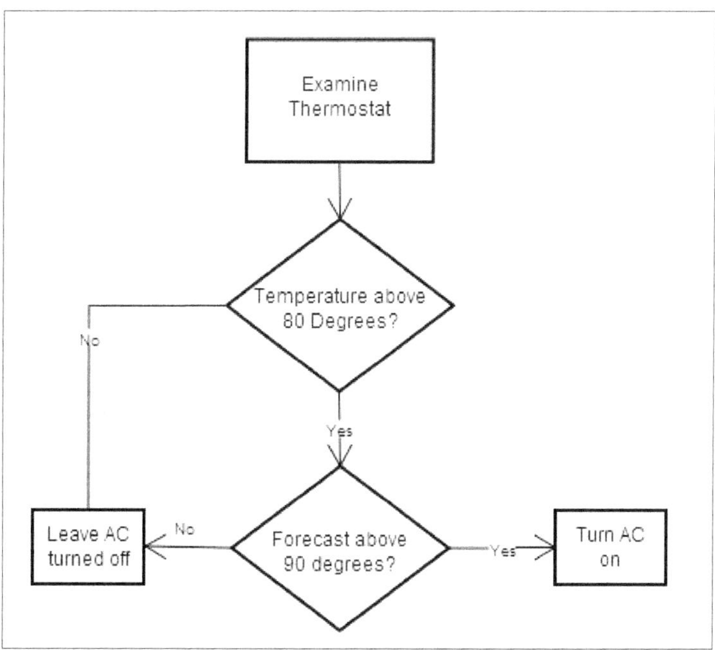

FIGURE 8.2 Flowchat of Decision Using "And."

WHAT ELSE?

Notice that in all of the above examples, the logic is stated so that if a condition(s) is/are satisfied, *then* an action will take place. However, if the condition is not satisfied, no action takes place.

It could also be written so that if the condition is *not* satisfied, an alternate action will take place. For example, if the condition is not satisfied to turn on the air conditioning, an alternate action might be substituted, such as opening a window. This would be written in the following way:

If the current temperature is above 80 degrees
OR
if the forecast temperatures is above 90 degrees
THEN I will turn on the air conditioning
ELSE I will open a window

As written, this example constitutes what is typically called an IF-THEN-ELSE statement. A condition is evaluated to determine whether or not it has been satisfied. **If** it is satisfied **then** a specified action is taken, **else** an alternate action occurs. In practice, the *else* portion of a conditional test is not used unless there are two specifically different actions that can be taken, one action if the condition is satisfied, and a different action if the condition is not satisfied. In the case of a decision in which an action is either taken or not taken, the *else* is typically implied, but does not need to be stated.

BOOLEAN LOGIC AND COMPUTER SCIENCE

In order to better understand how Boolean logic fits into computer technology, we can take a look at its use in a database management environment. For this example, consider the following simple database composed of six rows, which are typically referred to as *records* in database terminology. Notice that the patient rows also have column headers (referred to as *fields*), which provide multiple

TABLE 8.1 SAMPLE PATIENT DATABASE

PATIENT ID	INSURANCE	CHARGES	MONTH LAST SEEN
Patient 1	Med Protect	$1,500	June
Patient 2	Med Protect	$1,100	May
Patient 3	Yellow X	$237	September
Patient 4	Yellow X	$750	September
Patient 5	Yellow X	$1,250	April
Patient 6	Med Protect	$5,720	January
Patient 7	Medicare	$1,200	May
Patient 8	Yellow X	$250	November
Patient 9	Yellow X	$350	November
Patient 10	Yellow X	$100	November

pieces of information about the patients. For example, the "Amount Billed" field contains the amount of the bill charged to each patient, while the "Month Last Seen" field contains the month in which the patient was last seen.

In the case of a database, Boolean logic is typically used to identify the record or records in a database that are to be selected. For example, let's assume you are employed by a medical clinic and have been asked to send a letter to all patients who were seen in May. In order to identify those patients in the database, you would need to create a database *query*, which is a fancy way of saying a conditional test using Boolean logic. Visually, it is very easy to identify those patients in our small example by simply looking at each record to identify which ones were last seen in May. However, in a database of hundreds or thousands of records, that approach would not be feasible and you would need to rely on the ability of a database program to execute a conditional test.

In this example, we will concentrate on the logic involved in constructing the query, rather than the specific procedure involved in using the database management software. Further discussion describing how a query is used in Microsoft Access can be found in Chapter 7. In our example, the query logic would consist of a single conditional test:

If MONTH LAST SEEN = May
THEN Select the record for inclusion in the results

In order to help illustrate this logic, imagine that you have two buckets. As you evaluate the *month last seen* in each of the records, you place each record from the database into either one bucket or the other, depending on whether the record contains the month of May. This process is essentially how a computer database program processes a query. Although the selected records are not physically removed from the database, they are flagged as having satisfied the conditions of the query, after which they can be displayed, used to create a report, exported to another program, or used in some other way.

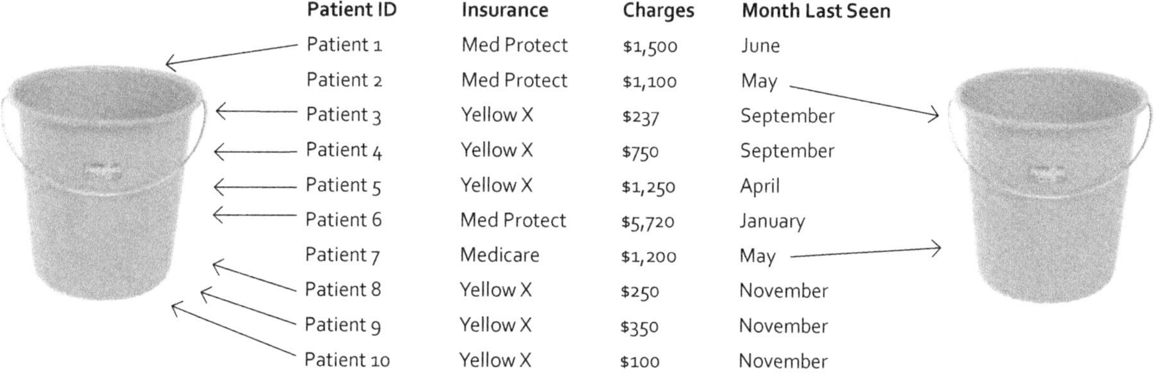

Patient ID	Insurance	Charges	Month Last Seen
Patient 1	Med Protect	$1,500	June
Patient 2	Med Protect	$1,100	May
Patient 3	Yellow X	$237	September
Patient 4	Yellow X	$750	September
Patient 5	Yellow X	$1,250	April
Patient 6	Med Protect	$5,720	January
Patient 7	Medicare	$1,200	May
Patient 8	Yellow X	$250	November
Patient 9	Yellow X	$350	November
Patient 10	Yellow X	$100	November

FIGURE 8.3 Patients Not Seen in May (left); Patients Seen in May (right).

AND VERSUS OR

In the example above, the query was designed to simply evaluate the month in which each patient was last seen. As with the air conditioning example, we can add complexity to this query by adding another criterion in the form of a new binary test. Let's assume that we would like to further refine our query by identifying patients last seen in May, and whose charges exceeded $1,000. Using Boolean logic, the query would be stated in the following way:

If MONTH LAST SEEN = May
AND
Charges > $1,000
THEN Select the record for inclusion in the results

In our query statement and for purposes of this example, we will arbitrarily label the "Month Last Seen" test as *Test 1* and the "Charges" test as *Test 2*. In the table below, the records that satisfy the condition of Test 1 and Test 2 are notated with a "Yes," while those that do not are left black (implying a value of "No"). Note that the Test 1 and Test 2 columns do not represent actual fields in the database; they are simply markers in our table to help us to visualize the outcome of the query.

TABLE 8.2 RESULTS OF QUERY USING "AND" VERSUS "OR"

PATIENT ID	INSURANCE	AMOUNT BILLED	MONTH LAST SEEN	TEST 1	TEST 2	SATISFIES "AND" QUERY	SATISFIES "OR" QUERY
Patient 1	Med Protect	$1,500	June		Yes		Yes
Patient 2	Med Protect	$1,100	May	Yes	Yes	Yes	Yes
Patient 3	Yellow X	$237	September				
Patient 4	Yellow X	$750	September				
Patient 5	Yellow X	$1,250	April		Yes		Yes
Patient 6	Med Protect	$5,720	January		Yes		Yes
Patient 7	Medicare	$1,200	May	Yes	Yes	Yes	Yes
Patient 8	Yellow X	$250	November				
Patient 9	Yellow X	$350	May	Yes			Yes
Patient 10	Yellow X	$100	November				

In our example, the word AND (typically referred to as a *logical operator*) was used to relate the "Month Last Seen" test to the "Amount Billed." Although patients 2, 7, and 9 satisfied the conditions of the first test, only patients 2 and 7 satisfied the conditions of both the first test and the second test.

Boolean logic generally relies on three possible logical keywords:

AND – *All* of the conditional tests separated by AND must be true

OR – *Any* one of the conditional tests separated by OR must be true

NOT – The logical test following NOT must be false

Evaluations of conditions are generally made using one of the following logical operators:

LOGICAL OPERATOR	MEANING
=	Equal to
>	Greater than
<	Less than
>=	Greater than or equal to
<=	Less than or equal to
<>	Not equal to*

**"Not equal to" can also be described using the NOT keyword. For example, "NOT Charges=1000" would return records that did not have charges equal to 1000. "Charges<>1000" would return the same result.*

Now, let's consider how the query would work if the logical operator OR is used in place of the word AND. Using the word OR, the query logic would be described as follows:

If MONTH LAST SEEN = May

OR

CHARGES > 1000

THEN Select the record for inclusion in the results

The results of this query can be found in the right most column of Table 8.4, which shows that while only two records satisfied the AND version of the query, six records will satisfy the OR version of the query. Using the OR version, a record qualifies as being selected if *either* of the two tests is satisfied, rather than requiring both tests to be satisfied as in the AND version. Conversely, the AND version of the statement below requires that both tests be satisfied for the condition to be satisfied.

If MONTH LAST SEEN = May

AND

CHARGES > 1000

THEN Select the record for inclusion in the results

Another way in which the logic can be illustrated is through the use of Venn diagrams, which are often used as a way to visualize relationships in set theory. The diagram in Figure 39 illustrates the use of the query utilizing the logical operator "AND." Although two sets of records are selected by each of the binary tests, the only records that satisfy the complete condition are those falling within the intersection of the two circles.

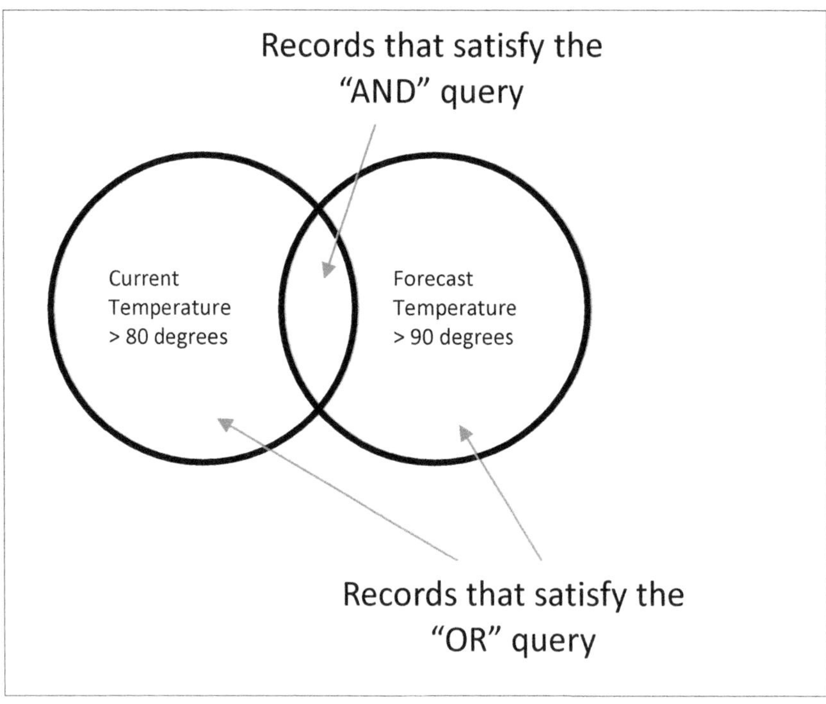

FIGURE 8.4 Venn Diagram Illustrating the Use of "AND" as a Logical Operator.

ADDING COMPLEXITY TO A QUERY

Up to this point, the basic concept of Boolean logic is relatively straightforward. In essence, a Boolean logic statement is constructed of one or more simple tests, each of with having only either a "yes" or a "no" outcome. The powerful aspect of Boolean logic is the potential to combine many simple tests into a potentially complex statement. Although any one given test can be quite simple, the potential exists to combine simple tests into an extremely complicated query. The complexity of a query statement is typically introduced when the tests are not all connected consistently with "AND" or "OR," but instead use combinations of "AND" and "OR."

Consider the following example in which the goal is to select records for patients who are insured by Med Protect and additionally were either last seen in May or were last seen in September. Using the approach we utilized for the earlier examples, the Boolean logic query could appear as follows:

If INSURANCE = Med Protect

AND

If MONTH LAST SEEN = May

OR

If MONTH LAST SEEN = September

THEN Select the record for inclusion in the results

FIGURE 8.5 Query Example 3.

A very interesting phenomenon occurs when AND and OR are mixed in the same query. In short, if you look carefully at the query statement and think through the logic, you may notice that there are two distinct ways in which the logic can be interpreted—with each resulting in a very different outcome from the other.

The first interpretation is the one which we intend: select only the patients insured by Med Protect who were either last seen in May or last seen in September. However, another interpretation is also possible. This statement could also be interpreted to mean that patients should be selected if they are insured by Med Protect and they were last seen in May *or* if they were last seen in September, regardless of their insurance provider. The difference between the two possible interpretations is best shown using brackets in the following illustration in *Table 8.3*. Using the logic in the second interpretation, it would be possible to select patients who were seen in September, but who are not insured by *Med Protect*.

TABLE 8.3 TWO WAYS TO INTEPRET THE USE OF "AND" & "OR"

INTERPRETATION 1	INTERPRETATION 2
If INSURANCE = Med Protect *AND* *If MONTH LAST SEEN = May* *OR* *If MONTH LAST SEEN = September* *THEN Select the record for inclusion in the results*	*If INSURANCE = Med Protect* *AND* *If MONTH LAST SEEN = May* *OR* *If MONTH LAST SEEN = September* *THEN Select the record for inclusion in the results*

The potential problems introduced by combining AND and OR in a query statement are similar to the potential problems encountered when expressing a mathematical equation that combines addition and multiplication. In the example below, if one did not know the rules for order of operation, there would be no clear way to determine the correct way to solve the equation.

$$5 + 2 \times 3$$

If you add 5+2 before multiplying, you will produce a result of 21. However, if you multiply 2 times 3 before you add, you will produce a result of 30. The order in which you process the calculations changes the results. However, note that if the equation includes only addition or multiplication (but not both combined), the order that you add or multiply will not make a difference. The same is true in Boolean logic. If the query statement contains only the connecting word "AND" (but not "OR"), no matter in what order you evaluate the conditions, you will always produce the same results. Similarly, if the query contains only "OR" connector words (with no "AND"), the order in which you evaluate the tests will not make a difference. However, when you mix an AND with OR in the same statement, the order of operation can produce two different outcomes depending which one is evaluated first.

The question you may be wondering is how the computer will interpret a Boolean logic statement that combines the use of AND together with OR, without the order being specified. The answer lies in the same approach used in math when multiplication, division, addition, and/or subtraction are combined in the same equation. There is a basic rule of operation in math, which says that unless the order is specified by using parentheses, multiplication is always assumed to occur first, followed by division, addition, and subtraction.

Boolean logic also relies on a rule for the order of operation in the event that is not specified in a query. Unless specified, the order in which logical operators are evaluated is the following:

1. AND (evaluated first)
2. OR (evaluated second, after AND)
3. NOT (evaluated third after AND and OR)

Given the rule for the order of operation in Boolean logic the statement in Query Example 3 would in fact be misinterpreted by the computer. Since the AND operator is evaluated first, the query would return patients who were last seen in September, but who were not insured by Med Protect. The logic that would be used is that shown as *Interpretation 2* in Table 8.3.

The next logical question you might ask yourself is how you specify that the OR should be evaluated before the AND operator. The answer to that question is exactly the same as how it is done with a mathematical equation. **To change the order of operation, parentheses are placed around the conditional tests that are to be evaluated first.** In the case of Example 3, parentheses would be placed around "OR" clause, as shown in the example below:

Adding the parentheses forces the "OR" clause to be evaluated first,which will produce the desired results.

If INSURANCE = Med Protect
AND
→ *(If MONTH LAST SEEN = May*
OR
If MONTH LAST SEEN = September)

THEN Select the record for inclusion in the results

A HELPFUL TIP REGARDING AND/OR

As you can see in the examples above, combining AND and OR together in the same Boolean logic statement is often necessary, but it can produce incorrect results if not done properly. Additionally, as more binary tests are added to the condition (more AND and OR statements), the complexity of the complete statement becomes much more difficult to interpret. Consider that two or three tests separated by ORs combined with two or three tests separated by ANDs can become extremely difficult for a person to interpret visually.

There is a method that can be used to help reduce the complexity of the statements and help ensure the accuracy of the logic. Whenever AND and OR are used in combination, consider *always* using parentheses, whether or not you think you need them. Use of the parentheses will accomplish three things:

1. They will help ensure that the order of operation is correct, so that the results are consistent with what was intended
2. They will help visually clarify the logic statement
3. They will force you to think through the logic of your syntax

Even if you are certain that the combination of AND/OR will work properly, as a logic statement becomes more complex, it also becomes more daunting to understand visually. The use of parentheses will make it much easier to understand while helping ensure that the results are those that are intended.

THE USE OF BOOLEAN LOGIC IN LITERATURE SEARCHES

Another common application for Boolean logic relates to conducting a search using a literature database, such as PubMed. Literature databases are essentially databases in which the records represent journal articles and the attributes represent information about those articles. Those attributes could include items such as the articles' titles, dates of publication, journals in which they were published, and page numbers. If you consider that the records represent articles and that the fields represent pieces of information about the articles, the application of Boolean logic in a literature database is exactly the same as for any other type of database.

Consider, for example, the task of searching for articles that help answer the question, "Are patients with Type II diabetes at an elevated risk for depression?" In order to answer this question, we will need to locate articles that have specific references to both Type II diabetes and depression. For this example, we can also assume that we are looking for relatively recent articles published after January 1, 2012 but before January 1, 2014. If we are concerned with finding articles that are most directly related to our research question, we would likely look for some of the critical words in the TITLE field, while using the PUBLICATION DATE field to test for the publication date (note that different research databases will often assign different names to the various fields). Using this approach, the following is a Boolean logic query that could be used to help answer this question:

(Title CONTAINS "diabetes" OR Title CONTAINS "diabetic")

AND

(Title CONTAINS "Depressed" OR Title CONTAINS "Depression")

AND

Publication Date >= 01/01/2012 AND Publication Date <= 01/01/2014

Note that alternate wording was used in conjunction with the OR keyword, allowing us to identify articles with the word "diabetic" or the word "diabetes" in the title. In the same way, the second line uses the OR keyword to identify articles with either "depressed" or the word "depression" in the title.

Although the query above represents the logic that would be used to identify the articles of interest, most literature databases employ user-friendly forms that make it easier to construct the query without having to type all of the syntax. The example below represents the Advanced Search form employed by the PubMed database. The PubMed form, which is similar to those used by a large variety of other literature databases, allows the user to enter the comparison value, along with logical operators and the key words AND and OR.

It should also be noted that many literature databases have their own query language/syntax that can be used to create a query as a command instead of using the form. Referring to the PubMed example, you will notice that above the form, PubMed displays the query syntax that was created automatically using the form. Note that although this query combines the use of both AND and OR key words, PubMed recognizes them and automatically interprets the logical order correctly.

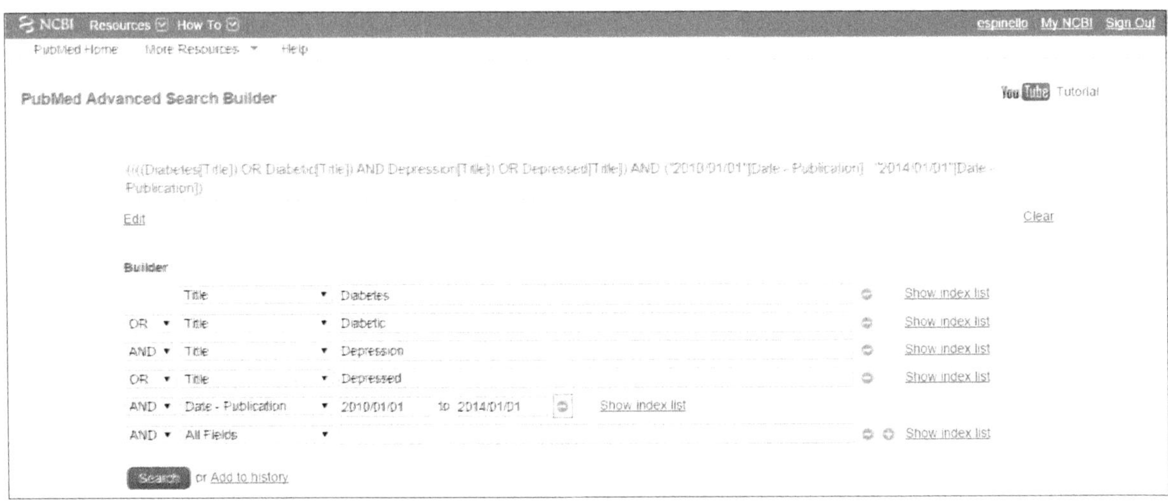

FIGURE 8.6 Screenshot from: PubMed Website.

((((Diabetes[Title]) OR Diabetic[Title]) AND Depression[Title]) OR Depressed[Title]) AND ("2010/01/01"[Date - Publication] : "2014/01/01"[Date - Publication])

SUMMARY

At its most basic level, Boolean logic is really very simple, as it works by taking very complex logic and reducing it to a series of simple yes/no questions or tests. Because binary conditions can return only one of two possible outcomes, they are very easy to grasp. However, since many decisions are more complicated than a simple yes or no outcome to a single condition, binary statements are combined using the connecting words AND, OR, and NOT in order to express more complex logic. Similar to the problem encountered in math when addition and multiplication are combined in an equation, the mixing of both AND and OR in a single query statement may produce unintended results, since the order in which the AND and OR are evaluated can produce different results. To address this issue, the use of parentheses is recommended in query statements that contain both an AND and an OR connector.

APPLY YOUR KNOWLEDGE

Please note that some of the software interfaces and example screenshots have changed since publication. Errata, revisions to instructions, and updated images can be found at http://drspinello.com/cohs.

The following example represents a database containing records related to the following questions:

PATIENT ID	INSURANCE	CHARGES	MONTH LAST SEEN
Patient 1	Med Protect	$1,500	June
Patient 2	Med Protect	$1,100	May
Patient 3	Yellow X	$237	September
Patient 4	Yellow X	$750	September
Patient 5	Yellow X	$1,250	April
Patient 6	Med Protect	$5,720	January
Patient 8	Yellow X	$250	November
Patient 9	Yellow X	$350	November
Patient 10	Yellow X	$100	November

FIGURE 8.7 Database Example

Using the Logical Keywords and Logical Operators discussed in this chapter, write a query that will select the following patients, and then list the patient IDs of those records that would be returned for each query:

1. Those patients with Med Protect insurance
2. Those patients with Med Protect Insurance with charges of at least $700 but less than or equal to $1,200
3. Those patients seen in either November or April who have Med Protect Insurance
4. Those patients seen in either November or April who have Yellow X Insurance and who had charges of at least $700 but less than or equal to $1,200

Referring to the table above, list the Patient IDs of the records that would be selected by each of the following query statements:

1. **Charges** >$100 AND **Month Last Seen** = November
2. **Insurance** = Med Protect AND **Charges** <=$1,250 AND **Month Last Seen** <> November
3. **Insurance** = Med Protect AND **Charges** <=$1,250 AND (**Month Last Seen** = November or **Month Last Seen** = April)
4. **Insurance** = Med Protect AND **Charges** <=$1,250 AND **Month Last Seen** = November or **Month Last Seen** = April

IMAGE CREDITS

Fig. 8.3: MarlonBSB, https://commons.wikimedia.org/wiki/File:Balde.PNG. Copyright in the Public Domain
Fig. 8.6: "PubMed Website," http://www.ncbi.nlm.nih.gov/pubmed. Copyright in the Public Domain.

9

SOFTWARE SELECTION

This chapter addresses the challenge of making a purchase decision for software for an organization. Contemporary computer programs have become rather complex products that often include a variety of features and ancillary services (such as cloud storage, consulting support, custom development). When selecting from a number of alternatives, making the best choice for an organization requires that the various alternative programs be compared in a way that considers all of the considerations most important to the organization.

For example, selecting the best accounting program for your organization requires that you compare a number of programs on the basis of cost, features and usability, technical support, documentation, etc. This chapter provides a structured approach that can be used to narrow down the field of possibilities.

NEEDS ASSESSMENT

Before any specific computer programs are considered, it is important to first fully understand the requirements of the organization that will use the program. For this reason, the first step in selection process is to conduct a thorough organizational needs assessment. The needs assessment is designed to help determine exactly what features the program **should** contain, what usability issues may need to be addressed, and what budgetary constraints may exist. Conducting the needs assessment consists of finding the answers to questions such as the following:

IDENTIFYING STAKEHOLDERS

Understanding the software objectives requires talking to those who will actually use the software, as well as individuals who may not directly use the software but who will directly or indirectly rely upon its capabilities. For purposes of this discussion, we will refer to anyone who will either use or rely upon the software as a *stakeholder*. The first step in the needs assessment should be to identify exactly who the stakeholders are (by organizational unit or by name, if possible) and what their relationships will be to the software (e.g., primary users, supervisors of users).

IDENTIFYING OBJECTIVES FOR THE SOFTWARE

Objectives involve the specific tasks will the organization need to accomplish with the software. Will the program need to be a "one-size-fits-all" type of solution that will be used by a large number of people, or will it be used by just one or two staff members? What are the specific types of reports, analyses, etc., that are required for the organization? It is very important to start off by being able to describe those objectives with as much detail as possible so that you have something to measure against when you begin looking at software alternatives.

To determine the objectives, it is typically necessary to question stakeholders who may not necessarily be using the program, but who will rely upon it. For example, a chief financial officer (CFO) will not be the individual who enters specific transactions into an accounting system, but he or she will rely upon the financial reports that the system will produce. In the case of the CFO, one would need to know the specific types of reports that will be required, as well as any unique requirements.

DETERMINING WHO WILL USE THE SOFTWARE

When assessing this aspect, it is important to determine not only who the actual users of the software will be, but also how technologically experienced they are. The issue at hand is that an individual who is more technologically experienced will be more likely to troubleshoot and solve minor issues on their own compared to someone who is less technically inclined.

Depending on the number of individuals who will be using the software, this part of the assessment may be done with individual interviews or, for a large group, using a survey.

Understanding the technical capabilities of the end-users is key in making a good decision. In the software development community, it is recognized that there is a tradeoff between how powerful a program is and how easy it is to use. In general, computer programs that are more powerful tend to be much more complex and difficult to learn—especially for someone with a less technical background. Programs that are relatively easier to learn and use tend to be somewhat less flexible and useful to the "power user" (power users are those users who fully understand the concepts and are often able to be more creative in making a program do exactly what they need it to). The goal in assessing the users is to determine whether the users are more likely to be non-technical novices, or whether they are power users who will demand the most sophisticated software, regardless of complexity.

DETERMINING WHERE IT WILL BE USED

This is an important question because different locations may present different issues. A noisy, open area through which many people pass is very different than a quiet office or cubicle with good lighting. If the work area is noisy, a program that relies heavily on audible prompts might not be the best choice. Other issues may be related to a particular screen size that is required to effectively use the program, etc. Other considerations may involve the need for other devices needed for the software, such as printers, scanners, digital cameras, lab equipment, and sensors. Ensuring that there is adequate space with an efficient physical layout is important to productive use of the system.

DETERMINING THE NUMBER OF USERS AND LICENSING REQUIREMENTS

There is a sizeable difference in terms of both cost and technology with respect to programs that just run on a single individual's computer versus programs that need to be available to an entire organization. Programs designed to be installed and run on a single computer are often referred to as *desktop* installations (regardless of whether they are installed on a desktop or laptop computer). Conversely, programs designed to be used by many individuals simultaneously are commonly referred to as *multi-user* or *server-based* systems. Multi-user programs are generally installed on a single computer, referred to as a *server*, to which many individual users have access.

Web-based software is another trend that has become much more common in recent years. Web-based programs are stored on a web server belonging to either the software vendor or to the organization that has licensed the software. The software is accessed using a web browser, such as Internet Explorer, Chrome, or Firefox. The data used by these programs may reside on the server or on users' local computers. A key advantage to web-based software residing on a vendor's server is that the latest version of the software can always be made available to users, without the need for an update, since the vendor manages the software and the computer where it is installed.

TABLE 9.1 SOFTWARE INSTALLATION METHODS

TYPE OF INSTALLATION	COMPUTER HARDWARE	ADVANTAGES	CONCERNS
Desktop	Resides on one or more individual computers	• Individual users have complete control over use and backup of the program and data. • Performance will not be affected by other users.	• If the program is installed on many computers, updates will require each computer to be individually updated. • May be more labor-intensive for IT staff to support many desktop installations of a single program. • Must be compatible with desktop computer's operating system (Windows, Mac, or Linux).
LAN Server Based	Software resides on a file server to which many users have access	• An Internet connection is not required, although secure local area network (LAN) access is needed. • The user of a server may reduce the need for high performance computers by end-users. • Management of licensing and software updates is facilitated. • Data security can be better controlled. • Access to the system and data can be controlled centrally.	• Hardware failure related to the server will affect potentially many users. • Many users accessing the program at one time may affect performance of the server. • An IT infrastructure and personnel are needed to manage the server and user access.

TYPE OF INSTALLATION	COMPUTER HARDWARE	ADVANTAGES	CONCERNS
Web Based	Software resides on a webserver and is executed by users through a web browser by visiting a website	• Performance is consistent for all users, since the performance of the webserver generally determines the performance of individual users, regardless of their computers. • Individual users do not require high-performance computers to run a demanding program. • Software updates are performed on a single computer by the software vendor or IT personnel. • Management of licensing is facilitated. • Access to the system and data can be controlled centrally. • Cross-platform operating system compatibility, meaning it will likely run on Windows, Mac, Linux, or other operating systems. A possible advantage when many different computers/operating systems are in use.	• Ability to use the program requires a reliable Internet connection. • Hardware failure related to the webserver will affect potentially many users. • Potential security concerns of having sensitive data accessible via the Internet. • Many users accessing the program at one time may affect performance of the server.

Another key question centers on whether users will need to have access to a single file or database simultaneously. An example is an accounting system, where everyone in the accounting department must be able to access the system at the same time and be able to make simultaneous changes. In that scenario, any change that an individual makes will potentially impact other users working with the same data. In contrast, a program may be configured so that multiple people are using different installations of the same program but where one person's changes will not impact someone else's use of the program or data. Understanding whether a program requires multi-user access is a critical step in assessing the needs of your organization.

Regardless of the type of installation, most software is typically licensed on a per-user basis. This means that the cost to license the program will vary depending on how many people will have access to the program. (Note that this does not apply to open-source software, since there is no cost for using open-source programs.) In most cases, the cost to license multiple software seats is based upon the numbers of users in ranges. For example, the cost for use of the program for one user may be $500, while the cost for two to five users may be $1,500.

COMPATIBILITY

In the complex world of interrelated systems, it is important to know whether there are other programs in use in the organization with which this program must be able to work. For example, will it be necessary to import and/or export data in the proper formats so that it can be exchanged between different programs? If that capability is needed, the specific requirements as well as the necessary file formats that will be needed should be identified.

Keep in mind that some types of software may also require that another system be in place. For example, programs that rely on the use of a Microsoft SQL Server (an enterprise-level Microsoft database management system) database will likely require that SQL Server be installed and available on the local area network.

Another key consideration concerns the operating system for which the program is designed. Although the operating system is less of an issue with respect to web-based software, programs installed on a desktop or LAN server basis will likely require a specific operating system (such as Windows, Mac, or Linux) to be in place.

MINIMUM HARDWARE REQUIREMENTS AND COMPATIBILITY

Different computer programs require varying degrees of computing power to run effectively. The hardware requirements for a computer program are generally described in terms of the minimum amount of RAM, available hard disk space, and CPU speed.

Make sure to look at the minimum hardware specifications to ensure that the computer(s) on which you will install the software will be adequate. As a rule of thumb, it is a good idea to make sure that the computers with which the software will be used do not have only the minimum requirements in terms of RAM, CPU, and hard disk space. In other words, the computers should have over and above the minimum requirements. The reason for this is that even though software will generally run on computers with the bare-minimum requirements, it may not have an acceptable level of performance. In general, it is a good idea to make sure that the computer hardware has a bit of "overkill" in terms of hardware requirement in order to ensure acceptable performance into the future. Generally, as datasets grow and software upgrades become more sophisticated, the demands on computer power increase, making it a good idea to have more computing power than is initially needed so that future hardware upgrades can be delayed. For this reason, the actual computers that the software will be installed on should be examined to determine whether new hardware will be needed to support a particular computer program.

MOBILE DEVICES

In recent years, an emerging concern is whether the program will need to be accessible by mobile devices and, if so, by what types. From the perspective of a software developer, the challenge for developing a program that works effectively on a mobile device is related primarily to the limited screen size and the reduced processing power compared to a desktop or laptop computer. Another challenge for developers concerns the need to create a program that is works equally well on the large variety of mobile devices ranging from cell phones to larger tablets, as well as the different operating systems in use.

In some cases the use of mobile devices may be a firm requirement. For example, some organizations employ analysts whose job it is to evaluate real estate in order to determine whether it should be acquired for use as a potential office location. Real estate analysts will often use mobile devices to collect and document observations, photographs, GPS coordinates, and other information that can be entered into a central database using a smartphone or tablet. A real-life example is that of a multi-state pest control company that uses a custom program for determining whether a property to be treated for pest control is close in proximity to endangered wildlife species that should not be exposed to the chemicals used to kill the pests. Pest control technicians are able to use their smartphones to enter the address of the property to be treated and are provided with information regarding any potential environmental issues. In these examples, the use of mobile devices is necessary to the goals of the organizations.

To effectively assess the organizational requirements, the following questions regarding mobile devices should be answered:

- Is compatibility with mobile devices necessary?
- Does the use of the software with mobile devices pose a security threat? (Consider that tablets and smartphones can be easily lost or stolen.)
- Are the mobile devices in use all of the same make/model and issued by the organization, or are they employees' personal devices?
- Are mobile devices standardized with respect to operating systems (Android, Apple IOS, etc.)?
- What type of Internet connectivity and data access are available?

COMPARISON OF PROGRAM FEATURES

Once the organizational needs assessment is completed, research can begin with respect to the various programs and their features. The following are some of the many issues to be considered when investigating the various alternatives.

DOCUMENTATION

A computer program's documentation is possibly more important than the program itself, given that it can provide the key to properly and efficiently completing a task with that program. Documentation that is well written and easily accessible can lead a user to a quick and easy solution, while documentation that is poorly written or nonexistent may lead to a frustrating and unproductive experience. Also consider the situation of having a supervisor ask for a seemingly simple piece of information while a user desperately tries to figure out how to make the program do what is needed to answer that question.

Many programs have now abandoned printed book-type manuals in favor of electronic manuals that are included on a CD, DVD, downloaded from a website, or installed on the computer along with the program. Some programs now offer electronic documentation that is available via the Internet. Online documentation has both advantages and disadvantages. While it can produce a problem if the Internet connection becomes unavailable, it is significantly cheaper for software companies to manage. Additionally, software vendors are able to change and update the documentation frequently, making those changes available in real time to users. Also, while paper manuals are sometimes more convenient, electronic manuals are easier to look up topics since users can typically search for key words. On the other hand, some individuals tend to feel most comfortable using a hardcopy manual, where they can make notes. In many cases, what used to be the software manual has now been integrated into programs' help systems.

Some vendors have also leveraged the interactions between users by providing online forums where users of the software are able to post questions regarding use of the software and where they can receive answers from technical support personnel and from other users. Those public forums are then accessible to other users who can search them to find others who have asked the same question or problem and then read the responses that were received.

When comparing the same type of program produced by different companies, it is important to understand what approach each program utilizes and how consistent that approach may be with respect to the end-users. Understanding the needs of the users and how those needs relate to the alternative programs is a key aspect of conducting an organizational needs assessment.

HELP SYSTEMS

The Help system is usually a key aspect of a program's documentation since it is often one of the first places users look to get answers to their questions. The typical approach for most software is that of a *context-sensitive* help system. In a context-sensitive help system, a single key (often the F1 key) and/or an on-screen button is used to trigger the help screen. Depending on the screen or the operation in process, the help system will present the appropriate topic related to what the user is doing at the time. For example, if the user has selected the option in an accounting system to create a new report, pressing the help button or key will result in the proper help topic being displayed.

When comparing the help systems, consider whether the help screens include screen captures and other graphics to help communicate complex procedures and concepts. Also, what may be a very intuitive help system to one person might not be intuitive to another. One should always confirm that the help system make sense to the person(s) who will use the program.

If the programs being considered for purchase offer evaluation versions, an interesting exercise is to try looking up the same topic in each program's help system as a comparison. A good way to determine the effectiveness of a manual or help screen is to look up answers to the same question in various programs' manuals. To do this, develop a fairly generic question that would apply to all of the programs being compared and then try to find the answer to the question in each program's manual or help screen. This will provide an indication as to how detailed, clearly written, and well organized each manual is.

USERS' RECOMMENDATIONS

A very good source of information regarding how effective a particular program may be is to ask for recommendations from colleagues. Networking with colleagues who work at other organizations or other departments/divisions of your organization can be effective to determine what types of experiences they have had. It is important to consider both good and bad experiences with respect to things like program bugs that were encountered, overall reliability, and positive and negative experiences dealing with a program's technical support staff.

What Selection Decisions Have Your Colleagues Made?

Find out what some of the specific programs are that have been chosen by others. Although it is entirely possible that another user might make a very different decision than yours, it can often be valuable to learn what specific aspects of a program other users do and do not like.

What Are the Specific Reasons for Colleagues' Selection Decisions?

This is an important issue because you want to make sure that people you take recommendations from had the same or similar objectives with respect to the software they selected. Try to find colleagues with similar objectives and working in similar organizations to yours.

RELIABILITY

A belief among IT professionals is that no company wants to be the first one to purchase a newly introduced large-scale computer program. In this section, we will explore why that is. When software is first developed, most vendors establish a rigorous process by which the program is tested first internally and then given to actual users in order to identify and fix program bugs. The process of testing a program internally (by software engineers and other staff employed by the software vendor) is referred to as *alpha testing*. The process of alpha testing is designed to locate and fix as many of the identifiable bugs as possible before the program is shown to actual users. The issue with alpha testing is that the individuals who conduct the testing generally test the program in the way they intend end-users to use it. However, in the real world, end-users will often use the program in less-than-predictable ways, which can trigger errors that were not previously identified.

Once the alpha testing has found as many bugs as is practical, the new program is given to actual users for what is commonly referred to as a *beta testing* process. During the beta test, end-users are given the program and allowed to use it for free, in exchange for them providing reports to the software vendor regarding any errors that were triggered. During this stage of the testing process, bugs that were not previously detected during the alpha phase are identified and fixed by programmers. Most large-scale software development efforts undergo several rounds of beta testing, whereby bugs are fixed and the repaired software is then redistributed to beta testers for further testing.

Once a program is perceived to be reasonably reliable in the beta test process, it can then go into general distribution where it is sold to the customer base. Once in general distribution, it is not at all unusual for end-users to find occasional bugs that were not found in the testing phases. Typically, when bugs are reported to software vendors, they will fix as many as is practical and then issue periodic updates that include bug fixes.

Over time, most programs are updated by having new features added, or modified to be made compatible with new operating systems or hardware. Whenever an update is made to a program, the alpha test and beta test processes must be started all over again to ensure that new bugs were not introduced into the software. In fact, whenever a bug is found and fixed, most software developers will employ a process called *regression testing*, by which all of the testing that had been done in the past is repeated to help ensure that new problems were not introduced.

At this point, it should be somewhat obvious that computer programs that have been in existence longer are generally going to have undergone the most scrutiny. The complexity of modern software makes it nearly impossible to identify and fix every bug present in a program. At some, point however, the vast majority of the most serious bugs are found and repaired. The longer a program has been in use, the less likely it is to have major bugs. A newly introduced program, however, may be technologically superior in some ways, but it is important to note that it will have undergone less real-world testing by actual users. For this reason the concept of software maturity is often considered with respect to computer programs. A mature program is one that has been in use for several years, has undergone updates and patches to repair bugs, and is considered to be reasonably reliable.

ONLINE USER DISCUSSION FORUMS

Many programs now have web-based forums that are created for users to ask and answer each other's questions and for technical support staff to interject, when necessary. Although these forums are generally designed to provide a communication medium for the user community, they are also an excellent way for prospective users to get an idea of what types of issues have been encountered, and how easily they can be dealt with. Reviewing the types of problems and questions that often surface can provide two important inputs into the purchase decision. First of all, you can begin to see patterns in terms of the types of problems that are encountered by seeing whether they appear to be related to software bugs, user error due to program complexity or poor documentation, or other issues. Secondly, you can see how responsive the technical support personnel and/or other users have been in resolving those problems. For example, if you see that many individuals complain about the same type of error message or problem arising in the program, it may indicate that there is a reliability issue present. While *all* computer programs have bugs present, a reputable software vendor will be very quick to respond by providing work-around procedures for a problem, as well as provide updates that fix the bug.

It is also important to keep in mind that those who frequent the forums are likely those who have encountered a question or a problem. If the user forums seem to contain an inordinately large number of frustrated users who are not getting their concerns addressed, this may be an indication that the program's support is less than adequate.

EVALUATION SOFTWARE

Many software publishers offer evaluation or trial versions of their programs that can be downloaded directly from their websites. These programs are often referred to as *trial*, *demo*, or *evaluation* versions, which are free to download and install for the purposes of determining whether the program will be a good choice. Keep in mind that an evaluation software version typically applies to programs that are sold under commercial licensing agreements, since those programs require that a license be purchased to use the program. Computer programs offered under open source licensing will usually not have evaluation versions because the actual program is free to use and there is no need try out an evaluation version.

Evaluation versions of software can be an effective way to help determine whether a program is right for a particular individual or organization since it can provide the opportunity to try the program in the actual environment where it will be used.

It is important to note that in most cases, evaluation versions of software are usually limited in some way. That means the program will do enough of its task to give you an idea of how it works but it will be limited, preventing it from being used in a production environment. For example, an evaluation version of a program may allow you to create new files but not to save them, or it may limit the size of the file that can be saved to something that is relatively small—making it unsuitable for day-to-day use, but adequate for you to determine how the program works. Sometimes, demo software is programmed to time out after a certain number of days, or it may prevent the user from being able to print so that you cannot continue to use the program without paying for it.

Although evaluation software is generally helpful, some types of software (like accounting programs) may require significant time investment to learn and use. That is because a large amount of data must be collected and input in order to run reports, for example. To solve this problem, many software vendors who offer evaluation versions of their programs will provide a sample dataset that you can use to explore the program's features.

USE UNDER REALISTIC CONDITIONS

Evaluation software can be useful in determining whether factors such as background noise, lighting, and workspace affect users' ability to use the program effectively. If a work environment is noisy and fast paced, ideally the evaluation software should be tested in that setting. Having environmental distractions for users means the program will need to be very simply designed so that you won't have to hunt for the options that will be most often used. For example, hospital emergency rooms or urgent care clinics can be very noisy and chaotic places, making it important to have a program's user interface be very simple and intuitive when it is difficult to concentrate. It is also important to use the evaluation program on the computer where it would reside to ensure that the screen size and other features are sufficient for users to be able to effectively see and read the content.

SOFTWARE SUPPORT

Technical support can be one of the most important aspects of a program. The ability to get quick answers to questions and resolutions to problems can be the difference between a successful outcome and a very negative outcome. Consider the common workplace situation where an individual is under time pressure to complete a task that requires the use of a computer program. In the ideal situation, the procedure to be used will be easily determined and the program will produce exactly the results that are desired. However, in the real world problems occasionally occur. For example, the necessary procedure may not be readily apparent, or the results may not be what were actually desired, or an error message is triggered, or any number of other things may go wrong, all while the clock is ticking away. Keep in mind that when problems arise, they may be due to a software bug, user error, or simply a limitation to the software. Regardless of the reason, in situations such as these, it is critical that users are able to access some type of support in order to solve the problem and become productive again.

TECHNICAL SUPPORT VERSUS APPLICATION SUPPORT

Technical support generally refers to getting assistance in resolving problems with the program. These are situations in which the program does not appear to function properly or produces errors. In these cases, the objective is to determine what is causing the problem and whether there is a solution and/or workaround. Application support, on the other hand, refers to getting assistance in answering how-to types of questions. Application support tends to be more of a consultative process in which a user may need to discuss how the software can be best used in a given situation.

Most software publishers offer at least some access to free technical and application support, sometimes for the first 30 to 90 days. After that, many software vendors will charge for support on an annual subscription basis that entitles users to a certain number of calls, or a certain number of minutes or hours, or sometimes unlimited support for that time. Although the thought of having to pay for technical support seems as though software vendors are nickel and diming their users, software vendors are often inundated with phone calls from users that sometimes monopolize the time of the technical support personnel by asking questions that can easily be found in the program's documentation. In doing so, they create longer wait times for all users of the software. By charging a fee for support, there is less likelihood of a user calling with a question that he or she could have easily found an answer to themselves.

CONSIDERATIONS WHEN EVALUATING SOFTWARE SUPPORT

Is there a toll-free number? Technical support calls can often take a very long time to resolve. If you are on the phone frequently for an hour or two, the long-distance tolls add up.

East coast vs. west coast time difference. Confirm that the vendor will continue answering the phones until the end of the business day in your time zone; otherwise you may find that at 2:00 P.M. in California the technical support people have gone home for the day since it is 5:00 P.M. on the east coast.

Other users' experience with tech support. Find out what other users of the software have experienced by asking colleagues and reading online reviews. Read some of the posts in online forums for users of the software to get an idea of how timely the responses have been.

Email support—Find out if the company offers support by email. Although you will not get a fast answer, email support is often free and can help solve a problem within a day or two.

Remote desktop software—For larger scale systems, companies often use remote desktop software, which allows them to take control of a user's computer remotely. This way, they can identify and resolve the problem as if they are sitting at the actual computer. Knowing whether a software company offers that option is valuable in the decision process.

Discussion forums—Many software companies have online discussion forums that allow users to ask and discuss problems, issues, and ideas with one another and with their vendor's software engineers. Check online forums and newsgroups to see what other users are saying or complaining about. These can give you tremendous insight into what that company's customers think of the company and its products.

A well-managed forum can be a huge asset to a software user because very often you can find someone else who has asked your exact question, along with the answer to that question. Having that resource can be a huge time saver because it will allow you to get to the answer to your question much faster than if you have to actually ask it and then wait for a reply. This requires that a discussion forum for users be available and that it is organized well enough for you to locate questions and answers, and that it is utilized by other customers.

MAKING THE DECISION WITH A DECISION MATRIX

Once the information has been collected regarding the various programs being considered, it is time to assemble the information so that it can be analyzed and a decision made based upon the programs' respective features and their costs. A decision matrix is an analytical approach that can be used to help make sense of the information that was collected in a way that is meaningful specifically to the decision maker.

A decision matrix is simply a way to organize the various characteristics of the programs being considered and to analyze them using a consistent methodology. A decision matrix is way of taking the aspects of the programs that are important to the decision maker and then scoring each program based on those aspects. Once each program has a calculated score, you can compare the programs on the basis of their respective costs relative to their scores. Programs with a high cost but low scores would probably drop out of the running as potential candidates, while programs with low or moderate costs and high scores would be considered more seriously.

CREATING THE MATRIX

Identify characteristics—The first step in your decision matrix is to identify what characteristics are important to the organization. For example, good technical support, ease of use, and ability to produce custom reports might be things that are desired in the computer program. Keep in mind that there is no universal list of program features that should be included. Although considerations such as free technical support and availability of application support are common to many types of software, different types of programs will have different types of features. For example, the features to be considered in an accounting system may be quite different than those to be considered in a patient scheduling system or a geographic information system.

In developing the list of characteristics, make sure to consider items such as support, compatibility with other operating systems, hardware and software, the ease with which frequently required tasks can be completed, availability of training for new users, overall ease of use, as well as how good the fit will be between the software and the organization's future goals for growth and expansion.

Assign points—After the characteristics have been identified, the next step is to assign a weighting to each of the characteristics. In essence the goal is to assign a maximum number of points based upon the importance of the characteristic. A characteristic with a weight of 50 points would be twice as important to you as characteristics to which you assign 25 points.

A good approach is to start with 100 points and then allocate some of those points to each characteristic until you have used up all of the points. For example, if *ease of use* is extremely important, you might allocate 50 points to it, but only 25 points to custom reporting, if that is less important. Make sure to use up all of your points and not to exceed what you have defined as the maximum.

Note that there is no mathematical reason for using 100 points as the total, other than it is easier to ensure the individual items will add up correctly and because the results are somewhat easier to communicate and understand. Using this approach, a program that receives 100 points gets a perfect score while one that receives 50 points is half as attractive using the logic of your decision matrix.

CREATING A DECISION MATRIX

Finally, you will need to grade each characteristic for each program based on the possible number of points for each characteristic.

In the example below, a total of 50 points was allocated to documentation, but 100 points was allocated toward technical support and 100 points allocated toward compatibility, suggesting that technical support and compatibility were more important considerations in the decision than was the documentation. Each possible program was then rated given the number of possible points that were allocated to each category. For example, since documentation was allocated 50 points, each program's documentation was rated on a scale from 1 to 50, with 50 being best. Each program's technical support was rated on a scale from 1 to 100, since 100 points were allocated toward technical support, and so on.

In some cases, the number of points you assign will be very subjective. For example, if you have reviewed each vendor's online forum and notice that one of the vendors seems to have many more complaints and unhappy users, you will likely rate them lower for that item, although it is up to you how much lower you rate them. To make the process as unbiased as possible, it is a good practice to establish guidelines for the rating system. In order words, one should try to quantify the point assignment to the best extent possible.

In the case of the evaluation of the online forum activities, one approach is to sample ten random questions that were asked by users and then determine what percentage of each questions for each vendor appeared to have been answered to the user's satisfaction. Keep in mind that you may find what you initially define as your rating method may change somewhat as you get a better idea of what the results are like. The important thing is to have a methodology with which you begin the process, and an understanding that it may be subject to change.

This also brings up another consideration, which is that this type of analysis is best done as a collaborative effort. Given that the different individuals will have different opinions regarding the value of the various characteristics and how they should be rated for the various programs, input from others can be key to making a decision that is not only methodologically sound, but will also be easier to achieve organizational buy-in.

TABLE 9.2 EXAMPLE OF A DECISION MATRIX

PROGRAM	DOCUMENTATION 50 PTS. POSSIBLE	PERFORMANCE 35 PTS. POSSIBLE	COMPATIBILITY 15 PTS. POSSIBLE	TOTAL POINTS (100 POSSIBLE)	COST
FastCalc	25	25	10	60	$750
SpeedyCalc	20	30	13	63	$1,450
RocketCalc	40	35	9	84	$1,100

In the very simple example above, three hypothetical spreadsheet programs are under consideration: FastCalc, SpeedyCalc, and RocketCalc. The three programs are compared on the basis of three factors, documentation, performance, and compatibility. A total of 100 points is distributed among the three factors based upon each factor's perceived relative importance. By allocating the point valued in this example, documentation is the most important factor and is assigned 50 (one half) of the 100 possible points, with 35 points assigned for performance, and 15 possible points for compatibility. By assigning 50 points for documentation, each program will be rated subjectively on a scale from one to fifty points. Likewise, the programs will be rated on a scale from one to thirty-five on the basis of their performance, and they will be rated on a scale one to fifteen relative to their compatibility with other software.

Next, each program is individually rated by assigning points for each of the three factors. In the example, when the points are summed for each program, FastCalc receives the fewest points (60) and has the lowest cost, while RocketCalc, which received the most points, has a cost that is somewhere in the middle, making it potentially the best choice, and assuming that cost is not an issue. SpeedyCalc received only 63 points and had the highest cost, making it the least desirable option.

SUMMARY

The process of selecting a computer program for purchase for use in an organization requires that the needs of the organization be first understood. The process of conducting a needs assessment is a way of collecting information about the specific goals of the organization with respect to the software, as well as information about the employees who will use it and the environment in which it will be used. Once the needs of the organization and end-users are determined, information about the alternative programs can be assembled and analyzed using a decision matrix in order to facilitate final selection of the best software for the organization.

APPLY YOUR KNOWLEDGE

Please refer to Active Learning Platform for exercises.

Using web searches identify three accounting software systems that are advertised as being appropriate for use in a small business environment (fewer than 25 employees). For each of the programs, identify the following:

1. Cost and availability of technical support
2. Cost and availability of application support
3. The minimum hardware requirements to run the program (consider available hard drive space, RAM, and CPU speed)
4. Operating system requirements needed for the program
5. Cost and availability of training
6. Compatibility with multi-user environments (can it be installed and used by multiple people simultaneously)
7. Cost of licensing for one user and for up to five users

10

GEOGRAPHIC INFORMATION SYSTEMS

The technological advancement of GIS (Geographic Information System) technology has provided the field of public health, and particularly epidemiology with an important tool making analysis possible that was once technologically out of reach for many. In the field of public health, GIS systems have provided a means to analyze data from a much more sophisticated perspective than is possible with just spreadsheets and statistical analysis programs. In addition to being able to assess information with a definition of "place," GIS systems have provided the means to analyze *spatial/temporal* relationships (spatial/temporal refers to patterns found with respect to both time and place) between sets of variables, allowed users to identify spatial patterns in data, and have provided the means to integrate databases on the basis of geography.

The rapid technological development of the Internet together with GIS has had a significant impact on the practice of healthcare and public health. Geographic Information Systems have provided solutions to healthcare and public health problems that had previously been approached in much less sophisticated fashion or had been largely ignored. This has been particularly true in the area of public health needs assessment—an area in which the application of GIS technology makes it possible to specifically locate and profile a target population to a degree never previously possible without the use of costly primary research. Although the need for primary research will always exist, GIS technology allows the researcher to apply it more specifically, saving both time and cost.

MAPPING AND THE BIRTH OF MODERN EPIDEMIOLOGY

The first documented use of geospatial analysis for epidemiological research can be traced back to Dr. John Snow and his work related to the 1854 cholera outbreak in London. At the time, the mode of transmission of cholera was disputed among medical professionals. Although many considered the mode of transmission likely to be a result of inhalation of the disease agent, Dr. Snow was convinced that cholera was a water-borne pathogen and that the means of infection was the drinking from a contaminated water source. Dr. Snow described his hypothesis in his 1849 pamphlet entitled, *The Mode of Communication of Cholera*. In 1854, an outbreak of cholera occurred in the

The term *spatial* refers to information related to where someone or something is physically present. The term geospatial further narrows that definition to a physical presence somewhere on the globe (versus in a microscopic environment, in outer space, or in some other environment not typically considered to be human geography.)

Soho district of London, giving Dr. Snow an opportunity to test his hypothesis.

One of the prominent beliefs of the time related to a prior epidemic that had occurred in London nearly 100 years earlier. During that earlier epidemic, hundreds of bodies of cholera victims had been buried in an area that later had houses built over it. Residents believed that infectious vapors were somehow given off from the bodies, leading residents in the newer housing to become infected with cholera. Snow, sought to dispute that theory by mapping the new cases of cholera to show that the numbers of new cases in the areas built over the cemetery were not any higher than elsewhere in the city. As expected, the map showed that the numbers of cases over the cemetery were not any higher than the rest of the city, suggesting that the presence of the previously buried bodies was not a risk factor in the 1854 epidemic.

However, Snow did notice from his map that there was an observable pattern to the number of cholera cases. At the time, the Thames river, which runs through London, was used as the primary water source for local residents. Access to the water was provided through pumping stations, situated throughout neighborhoods along the river.

FIGURE 10.1 Dr. John Snow.

FIGURE 10.2 A re-creation of Dr. Snow's Cholera Map.

His observation was that the largest cluster of cases seemed to be concentrated around one particular pumping stations on Broad Street. He hypothesized that the Thames River water supply was being contaminated with sewage in the area of the pump's water source, causing the epidemic. Snow's approach was to petition the local officials to remove the pump handle from the Broad Street pump so that residents would be forced to use an alternate water source. The pump handle was subsequently removed and the numbers of new cholera cases began to drop quickly afterward. In his request to have the pump handle removed, Snow mentioned that it was possible that the epidemic had already peaked, given that the numbers of cases had begun to plateau and then declined. Although epidemiologists today still disagree as to whether removing the pump handle actually had an effect on the epidemic, all agree that Dr. Snow provided an invaluable contribution to the field of epidemiology with the analytical process that he used and documented. In doing so, he also established the use of mapping and geospatial analysis as a key tool in the practice of epidemiology.

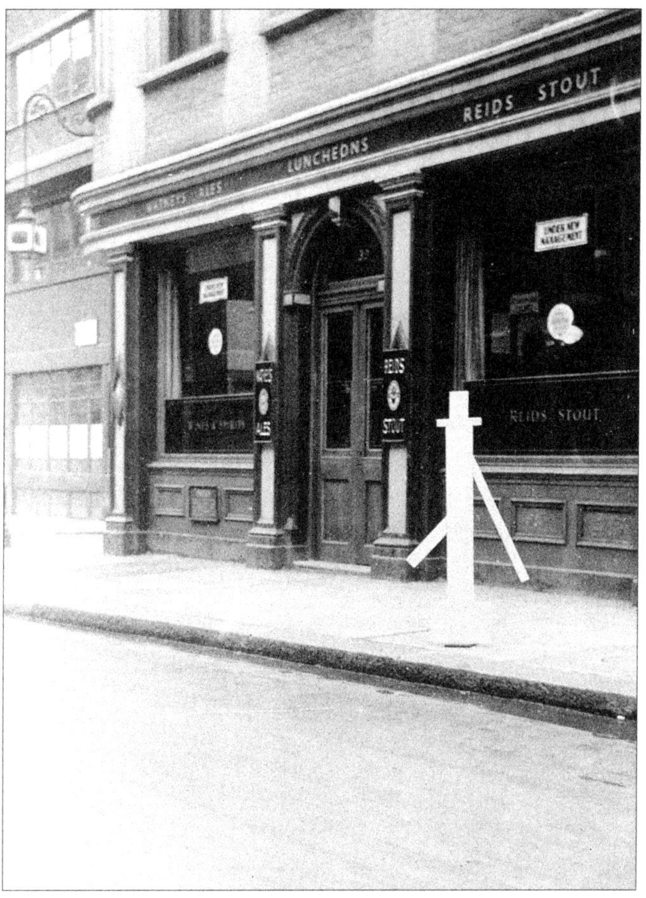

FIGURE 10.3 A wooden Replica of the Broad Street Pumb near it's original location.

Today, geospatial analysis conducted using modern geographic information systems software and datasets provides a sophisticated tool for the surveillance and analysis of disease patterns, environmental risks, and traumatic injuries in the practice of public health. Additionally, GIS software is an effective tool for tasks such as: assessing public health needs, analyzing consumers' access to healthcare services, and determining how healthcare provider networks can be modified or expanded to better serve consumers while optimizing costs, as well as many other types of analysis involving the locations of healthcare consumers and of the providers who serve them.

GIS SOFTWARE AND DATABASES

Although the concept of a geographic information system may seem foreign and unfamiliar to someone who has not worked with one before, GIS software is really based upon a much more familiar software technology, the relational database system. GIS programs at their most basic level are really relational database programs that happen to have some additional functionality. If you are unfamiliar with relational database management systems, you may find it helpful to first review Chapter 7.

The concept of a relational database refers to databases composed of tables whose records can be interrelated with one another. GIS systems are also capable of maintaining database tables with interrelated records, and the software provides the functionality to query those records, much in the same way as a program such as Microsoft Access does. The key difference is that GIS software also has the capability of managing records that carry information about location, in addition to the many other variables they may contain.

For example, it is possible to have a GIS database table in which each record represents a patient who visited a particular public health clinic and was diagnosed with an infectious disease that requires mandatory reporting to the CDC. The fields in the table would likely contain information about the demographic characteristics of each patient, their treatment regimen, and if they are likely to be infectious. Additionally, the table could contain the *geospatial* information related to the location of the patient with respect to work or home locations. Although in everyday life we tend to think of locations as being addresses, a GIS program relies on coordinate systems, such as those based on *latitudes* and *longitudes*. With the addition of geographic coordinates, a GIS program can be used to analyze the geospatial relationships between features, such as the following:

- Identifying associations between the incidence of a disease and the location of a common environmental risk factor.
- Visualizing geographic patterns on a map, making easier to understand and communicate economic, health, or sociological patterns and trends that are related to geographic location.
- Relating tables together not only on the basis of a key field (such as what is used in a database program like Access), but also based upon location. For example, a table of patients who have sought public health services can be geographically interrelated with a table of public health clinics, based upon the clinic that each patient resides closest to.

- Querying records based upon database attributes, but also upon geospatial relationships: where they are located. For example, a query could be constructed to select all patients over the age of 60 who have not yet had a flu shot, and are located within one mile of a particular clinic location. Note that this example contains elements of a database query (over age 60 and no flu shot), as well as a spatial query (within one mile of a clinic, which must be calculated based upon spatial coordinates).

GEOGRAPHIC LAYERS

One way to visualize how data tables are organized in a GIS system is to think of geospatial tables as being layers in a map. Each layer may contain information about a different type of geographic features, such as roads, rivers, city boundaries, and state boundaries. When the layers are stacked on top of one another the features in each layer combine to form the complete map.

One way to visualize the concept of GIS map layers is to think of them as being like an electronic version of elementary school science books that often contain transparent overlay pages with different components of human anatomy, such as the circulatory and skeletal systems. When the transparent sheets are layered on top of one another, they combine to form a complete view of human anatomy. Map layers work much the same way in that the various types of geographic features are digitally layered to form a complete map containing roads, rivers, highways, and other layers that make up the complete map.

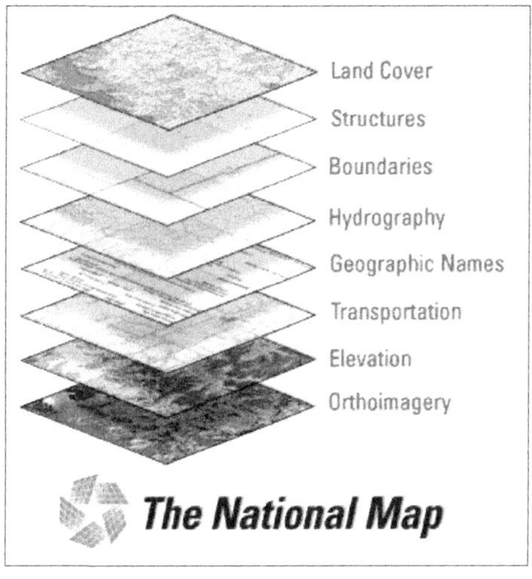

FIGURE 10.4 Geographic layers.

Attribute tables related to the geographic layers can contain attributes, which are fields or pieces of information about the geographic features. In the prior example, the boundaries layer could contain the boundaries of area cities, while the attributes for those boundaries could contain information about the population counts of each city, the number of homeowners, how many gas stations or liquor stores are located in each, and almost any other type of information that can be collected and stored in a database.

GIS TERMS AND THEIR MEANINGS

The following are some of the more commonly used terms related to the use of geographic information systems.

Attributes — The term *attributes* refers to information about geographic features. If for example, the geographic features in a map consist of zip codes in California, the attributes might include population counts, household income, and number of housing units in each of the various zip codes.

Centroid The coordinates representing the center of a region; generally there are two types of centroids. *Geographic Centroids* represent the geometric center of the region. In the case of a circle or a square, the centroid is always equidistant from the sides. *Population Centroids* represent the point inside of a region containing the greatest population density.

Clusters A larger-than-expected number of incidences of a disease (or other type of event, such as crimes) related by time and place.

Coordinates Most geographic coordinate systems are based on plane geometry, which relies on a combination of an X value and a Y value to identify a location on a plane. Geography is based on the same concept, with several different types of coordinate systems. One of the most common methods is the use of latitudes (representing Y-axis values) and longitudes (representing X-axis values).

Geocoding The process of determining the geographic coordinates of a specific location based on its street address or its existence within a known region. Coordinates, assigned as a pair of XY coordinates or a latitude and a longitude enable the location to be displayed on a map and analyzed spatially.

Layer Layers in a GIS system can be thought of as transparent overlays of the map, each containing a different type of geography. For example, typical layers in a map could include highways, census tracts, patient locations, and county boundaries. By keeping them in separate layers, the lines and symbols used to depict the geographical features can be applied by layer to differentiate by color or line style; for example, city boundaries can be distinguished from zip code boundaries by using a different dotted line versus solid lines.

Spatial Query Since a GIS can be thought of as essentially being a large relational database, it is possible to relate or integrate different tables based on spatial characteristics and use the spatial statistics together with a database query to identify records meeting a criterion. For example, assume you would like to identify which male patients who visited a county clinic in the past 90 days reside within two miles of a county clinic. This can be accomplished in two steps: The first step would be to identify the records that met the database query criteria (males who visited a clinic in the past 90 days). The second step would involve selecting a subset of the first query by determining which of those patients live within a two-mile radius of a clinic. This would typically be accomplished by creating a ring with a two-mile radius around each clinic and then determining which of the previously selected male patient cases are located within any of the rings.

Thematic Map A thematic (or theme) map is designed as data visualization tool. In essence, the geographic features of the map are designed to describe one or more attributes of the features. An example is a map of the U.S., with each state assigned a different color, based upon the population.

Features — Geographic features are specific places on a map. Features can be roads, regions, cities, zip codes, etc.

Projection — Since the earth is round and not flat, simple XY coordinates become inaccurate over longer distances due to the earth's curvature. Projections are mathematical algorithms to adjust coordinates such as latitude and longitude for the earth's curvature. Typical projections include NAD27 (North American Datum of 1927), which was developed using the Clarke 1866 spheroid, referring to the geometric definition of the earth's shape. NAD83 (North American Datum of 1983) is a replacement for the long-established NAD27 and is based on the GRS80 spheroid, derived from satellite imagery. A point assigned a latitude and longitude in NAD27 could be a block or more away from another point assigned the same latitude and longitude using NAD83. The significance of projection methods is that GIS users must be aware of the projections that were assigned to geocoded datasets and geography files so that layers using different projections are not mixed on the same map.

Most GIS software will automatically distinguish between layers using different methods and warn the user that the methods are inconsistent. Geocoded datasets, however, can be more problematic since they may not indicate the projection method used to assign the coordinates, leaving the user to keep track of the method and ensure that it matches the projections of other datasets and geographic layers.

TYPES OF GEOGRAPHIC FEATURES

Anything that can be depicted on a map is described as being a geographic feature. Geographic features generally fall into one of three categories:

Points are essentially locations that can be identified with just a single combination of a latitude and longitude. Points are typically used to depict locations of events, buildings, and other features that occupy a relatively small space.

Lines are features consisting of straight, curved, or jagged lines that can be used to depict features such as roads, highways, and waterways.

Polygons, sometimes called *regions*, are geographic features that have closed boundaries that contain geographic areas, such as cities, counties, and states.

In order to provide users with a way to independently manage all of the various types of geographic features in a GIS database, different types of features are normally stored in different layers. For example, the map in Figure 10.5 contains a variety of geographic features, including streets, highways, zip code boundaries, and locations of public health facilities. In database terms, each one

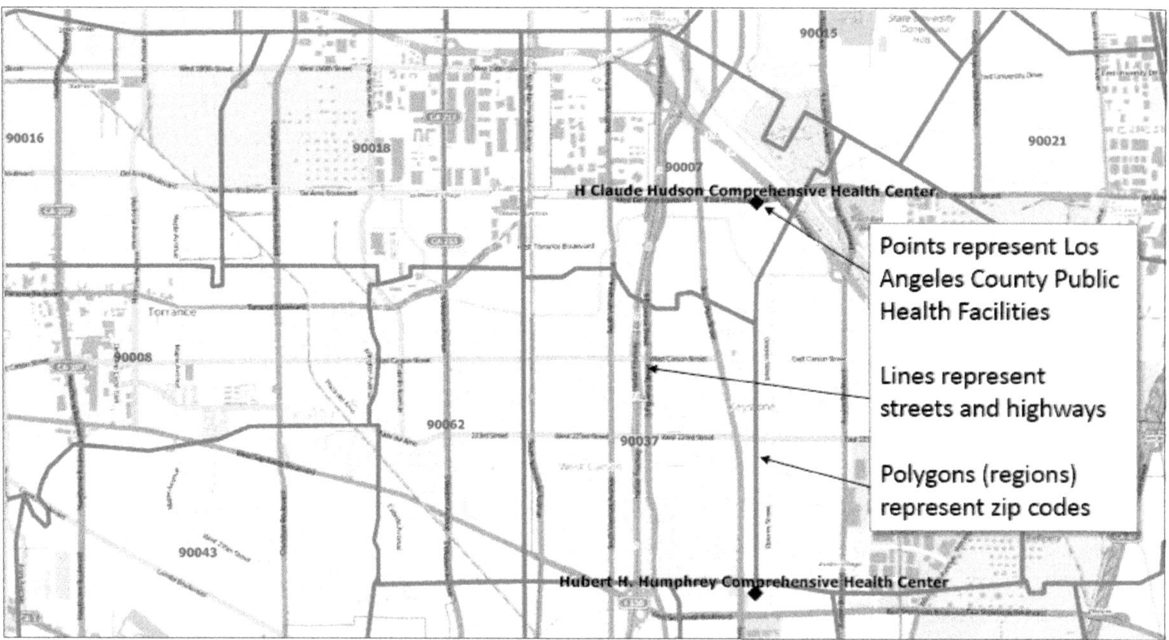

FIGURE 10.5 Example of Points, Lines, and Polygons on a Map: Los Angeles, CA.

of these types of features can be thought of as being an individual table, with the records in that table containing the attributes of the geographic features within it. For example, the zip codes are stored in a table in which each record contains attributes about a specific zip code.

CENSUS GEOGRAPHY

In order to effectively apply a geographic information system as a decision-support tool, it is first helpful to understand the dynamics of the underlying data used in GIS systems. GIS databases contain two types of data:

1. Geographic files provide locations of feature boundaries and locations such as roads, cities, states, and zip codes.
2. Attribute tables, which contain data about populations, social, commercial, environmental, economic and other characteristics of those features.

As an example, a geographic file would contain the physical boundaries of cities, formatted in such a way that those boundaries could be digitally shown as a map in GIS software. The attributes might contain fields such as the total population, employment, and median home value for each city.

In the U.S. much of the data used in GIS software can be found freely available from the *United States Census Bureau*. The U.S. Census Bureau is the agency responsible for producing and tracking much of the data relating to geographical features throughout the country. The method that is used to identify and track those features relies upon a numeric coding system, with the identifiers referred to as FIPS (Federal Information Processing System) codes. FIPS codes are based on a hierarchy of geographic features going from largest to smallest. The largest level of geographic features in the U.S. is that of the state. Each state in the U.S. is identified using a two-digit numeric code. The process for assigning the codes is actually very simple. The states are all sorted in alphabetical order and then assigned a sequential number starting with "01" for Alabama to "56" for Wyoming (several of the numbers are skipped, resulting in the last state being "56" rather than "50").

Within states there are counties, which are assigned a similar code. This is done by sorting all of the counties alphabetically within each state and then numbering them from "001" to whatever the last number turns out to be. One thing to remember are that only odd numbers are used and the only way to uniquely identify a county number is by knowing what state it is in. So, for example in California, Los Angeles County is numbered 037, but since other states are also likely to have a county numbered 037, the county code must be combined with the state code in order for it to be unique. Hence, the full code for Los Angeles County, CA, is 06037, which consists of the state code followed by the county code.

Counties are further broken down into census tracts, which are somewhat arbitrary boundaries designed to hold approximately 4,000 households. On average, California census tracts are roughly half the size of zip codes. The codes used to define census tracts consist of six digits—a four-digit code with a two-digit suffix. For example, a census tract FIPS code might be 201100. The confusing thing about census tracts is that they do not have "friendly" names as do states and counties; therefore, they can be identified only by their FIPS codes. The reason census tracts are important is that much of the detailed data the census bureau (and other government agencies) make available can be found at the census tract level, but you need to know what to ask for. The complete FIPS code for any given census tract consists of the state, county, and census tract, all concatenated together. For example, 06037201100 is the FIPS code for census tract 201100, located in Los Angeles County, CA.

The final level of geography we will discuss is the block group level. Census block groups represent fairly small neighborhoods of about 400 households, and they are the smallest geographic regions

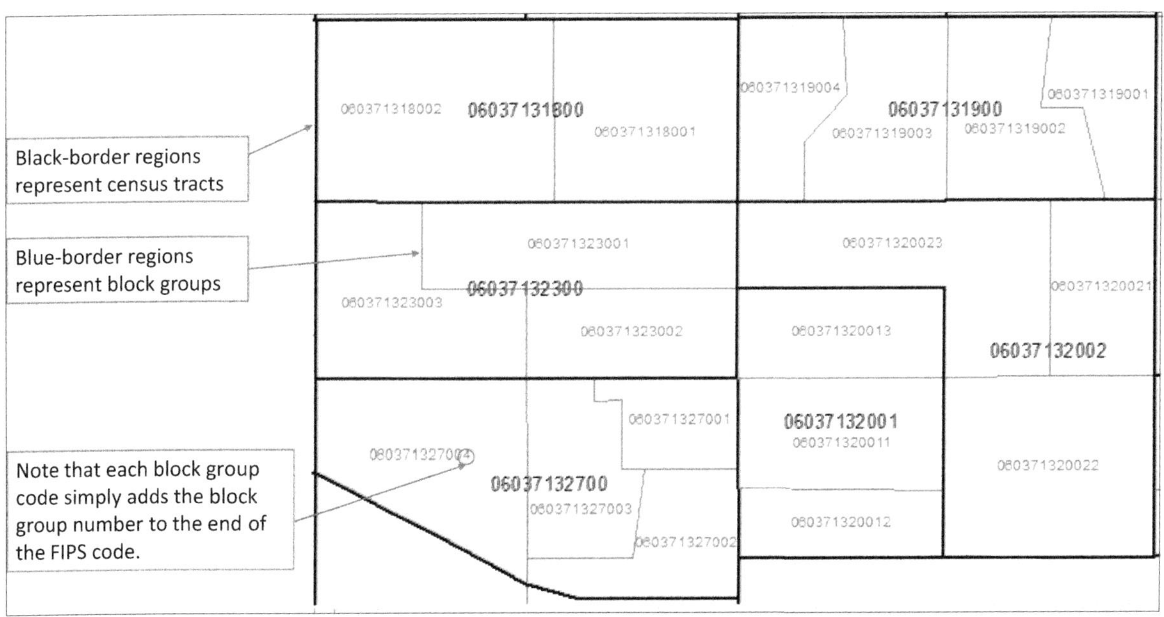

FIGURE 10.6 Example of Census Tracts (Black Borders) and Block Groups (Blue Borders).

for which the census bureau will release data. There can be up to ten block groups in any given census tract, and they are identified by a single digit at the end of the FIPS code.

The primary reason for knowing about census geography and FIPS codes is that FIPS codes allow you to access a wealth of demographic, economic, and business data about very small geographic regions. For example, if you need to conduct a health needs assessment of a smaller neighborhood, knowing which block group or block groups comprise that neighborhood allows you to request the data from the census bureau (and/or other agencies), which can then be mapped in a GIS program or analyzed in a spreadsheet or other software.

Much of the data from the census bureau can be downloaded for free directly from its website at www.census.gov. The census bureau also provides access to its own online interactive mapping capabilities and to the American Factfinder, which provides summary level reports of demography for geographic regions that you specify. Data can also be downloaded for use in a GIS system or spreadsheet.

DATA VISUALIZATION

An important feature of GIS technology is the ability to apply data visualization techniques, which are often useful for identifying patterns and relationships of data displayed from a geographic perspective. For example, a tabular report showing mortality rates of census block groups can be useful in identifying which specific block groups have relatively high or low rates. When the block groups are depicted in a thematic map, however, sets of contiguous block groups with unusually high rates can be readily identified as being within close proximity to each other. For example, a tabular report might show that five block groups have significantly above-average mortality rates, while a data visualization technique can show whether those five block groups are all clustered in the same area or if they are dispersed around the city.

In another example, clusters of points can be readily identified by viewing them on a map, whereas a simple report listing would not reveal their proximity to one another. As a risk communication tool, GIS programs provide a method to take complex information and communicate it in an easy-to-understand format to the general public. For example, environmental maps can be used to show which areas in and around a city are at an elevated historical risk for brush fire or flooding.

The following are some examples of typical GIS applications:

- **Fire risk:** GIS software is often used to identify areas that are in close proximity or inside of areas at a high risk of brush fires. GIS programs are used to assign vegetation attributes and historical burn attributes to regions in order to arrive at a probability of future fire risk.
- **Crime risk:** GIS software is used to create maps of historical crime reports by region. Areas with a high number of crime reports for violent crimes can be readily identified and analyzed to better identify crime victimization risk factors. Maps are used to communicate crime risk so that adequate precautions can be taken in high-risk areas. In many cases, additional variable such as time of day, days of the week, or types of locations (bars, convenience stores, etc.) where certain types of crimes are most likely to occur can also be graphically displayed or annotated to provide additional detail.

- **Travel:** Maps are often used to communicate diseases that are endemic to certain areas. These can be useful to determine what types of preventative precautions should be taken and what vaccinations may be required when visiting those areas.
- **Epidemiology:** GIS programs are used to better understand the geographic trends and patterns related to infectious disease transmission, vulnerability of populations, and environmental risks.
- **Health provider network planning:** GIS programs are used to analyze the relationship between healthcare provider networks and the consumers who utilize those networks. By understanding the locations of the consumers and their socioeconomic and demographic characteristics, healthcare organizations can better plan for the types of healthcare providers and their geographic locations needed to best serve consumers, while reducing wait times.

DATA SOURCES

With the increased use of GIS software as a decision-support tool, public-use GIS datasets have become freely available from a variety of sources. For example, GIS datasets are often available containing a variety of health-related data, such as:

- Locations of under-served health districts
- Mortality by cause of death
- Locations of public health facilities, hospitals, skilled nursing facilities, and other healthcare providers
- Locations of potential environmental risk sites
- Women, infant, child (WIC) clinics
- Emergency medical facilities

GIS data is often provided in one of two formats:

Point location files containing lists of locations together with latitudes and longitudes needed to display the locations in a GIS map. These types of files are often made available in a variety of commonly used formats such as text, Excel XLSX or XLS, dBase DBF, or Microsoft Access ACCDB. When mapped, these files are sometime referred to as *event layers*.

Shapefiles are a specific type of GIS file format made popular by ESRI (Environmental Systems Research Institute). The shapefile format really consists of a family of three to six different files all having the same file name but with different extensions. For example, a shapefile called *hospitals* would likely be made up of *hospitals.shp*, *hospitals.shx*, *hospitals.dbf*, and possible several other similarly named files. Shapefiles are rather ubiquitous in the GIS world and can be imported by almost all GIS programs. Many federal, state, and local agencies make public-use data available for download from their websites in shapefile format, as well as other formats.

Geodatabases are a file format utilized by Esri GIS software, as well as other programs that have the ability to import and export to the geodatabase format, such as the open-source program, QGIS.

Geodatabases have the capacity to contain multiple layers of various types of features and are optimized to work with large, complex GIS datasets.

In addition to GIS software that resides on a desktop or laptop computer, web-based GIS software has also become much more widely used in recent years. Web-based mapping programs allow users to purchase subscriptions for use of the software, and then allow the program to be accessed through a web browser. Web-based mapping environments, such as ESRI's *ArcGIS Online*, also provide collaborative environments where users can contribute maps and geographic datasets, making them available to other select users for their use, or they can be made public so that any user can access the dataset and use it as the basis for a new map or analysis.

THEMATIC MAPPING

Thematic mapping is a data visualization technique that allows spatial relationships in geographic data to be easily viewed and communicated. One of the important things to know about thematic mapping visualizations is that they can often allow the reader to observe relationships and patterns

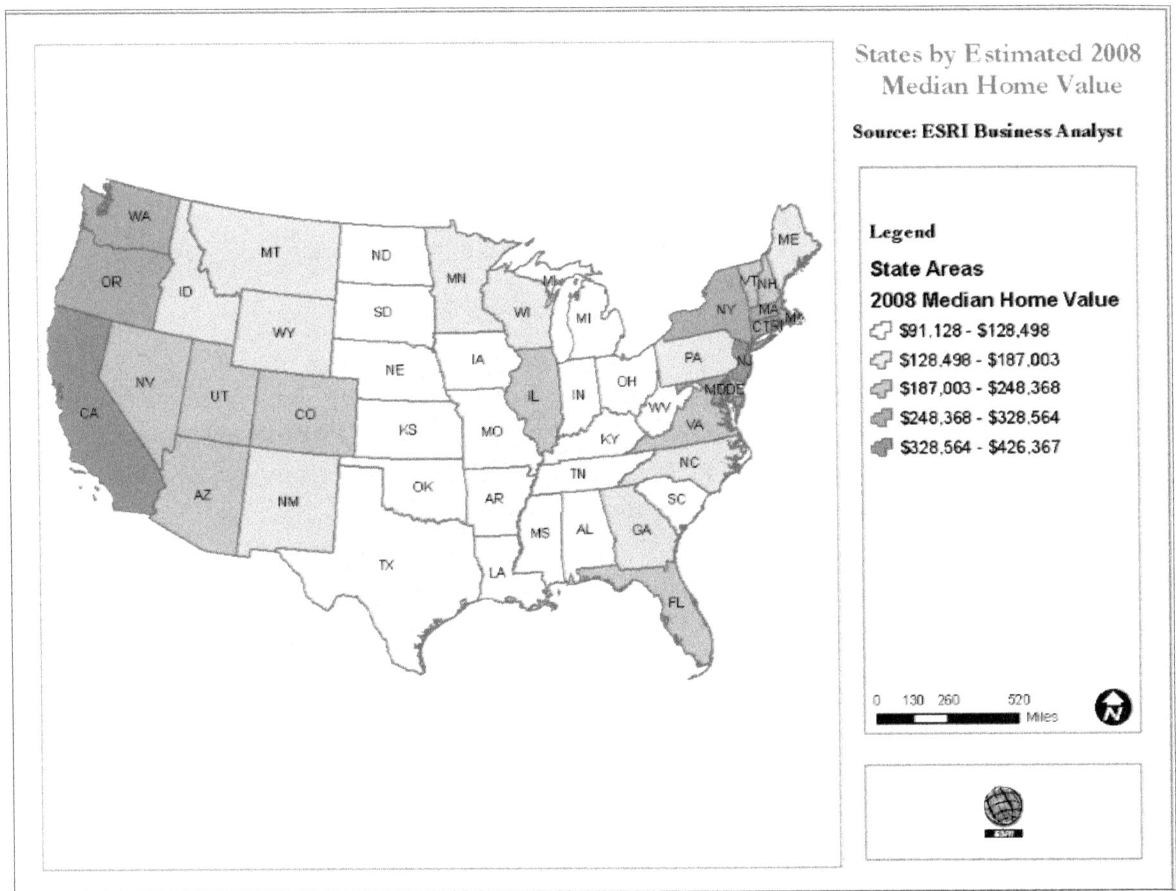

FIGURE 10.7 States by Estimated 2016 Median Home Value.

in data that would otherwise be impossible to identify. For example, the map below displays the U.S., with each state color-coded based upon its median home value. Although a tabular list of states and their corresponding home values would essentially provide the same information (and more precise information, because the exact values would be shown rather than ranges), the map below provides another interesting piece of information in that it allows you to observe the spatial relationship between home values and where the states are located.

Reviewing the map below, it should be apparent that there is a definite spatial (geographic) pattern to home values in the U.S. The highest home values are typically located along the east and west coasts, with the lowest home values in the center of the country. This pattern would be virtually impossible to identify without the use of a thematic map.

MAPPING TRAFFIC INJURIES

In another example of thematic mapping, the map below, created by the San Francisco Department of Public Health, was designed to help identify traffic corridors with the highest risk of pedestrian injuries within the city.[29,41] Layers in this map consist of pedestrian accidents resulting in severe injury or death, high-injury corridors, and a *Pedestrian Injury Counts* layer that uses a thematic approach to display circles of various sizes to visualize how many pedestrian injury accidents have occurred at each intersection. One of the powerful features of a GIS program is the ability to click on map features in order to display the attributes attached to that feature's database record. In the example below, the attributes for a pedestrian fatality accident is displayed. The interactivity of a GIS map is one of the characteristics that make it an effective analytical tool.

Through the use of different symbol types and sizes, this map provides an excellent example of how thematic mapping can help the reader identify geospatial patterns. In this case, the patterns that can be seen are the locations where severe injury and fatality accidents tend to occur most often. With that information, policy changes can be made to address the problem, such as adding traffic lights, changing speed limits, or adding/moving crosswalks.

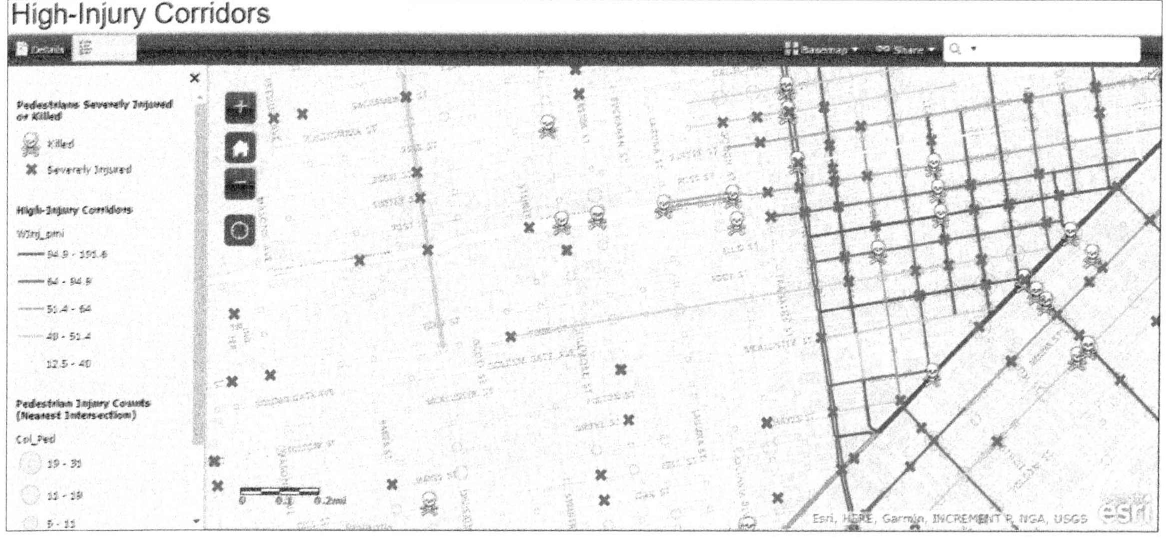

FIGURE 10.8 Screenshot from: ArcGIS Website.

The thematic map below was created as part of a study investigating areas within the country of Mozambique likely to have the highest prevalence of a tropical parasitic disease called onchocerciasis. Also known as river blindness, onchocerciasis is caused by a microscopic worm carried by the African blackfly, and is one of the leading causes of blindness on the African continent.

The study used GIS technology to predict the locations where the fly population and disease prevalence would likely be highest by predicting locations which included both ideal fly habitats and human population density. Fly habitats were determined by locating areas containing water sources, combined with elevation changes likely to produce movement and oxygenation of the water, as well as proximity to food sources. Locating populated villages in proximity to the habitats then provided a means to identify populations most likely to be at risk of contact with the flies and ultimately becoming infected with onchocerciasis.

After calculating a risk index for each region in the country, the risk index was then visualized in this thematic map, and used to prioritize areas to be surveyed in an epidemiological study for purposes of planning medical relief efforts.[30,42]

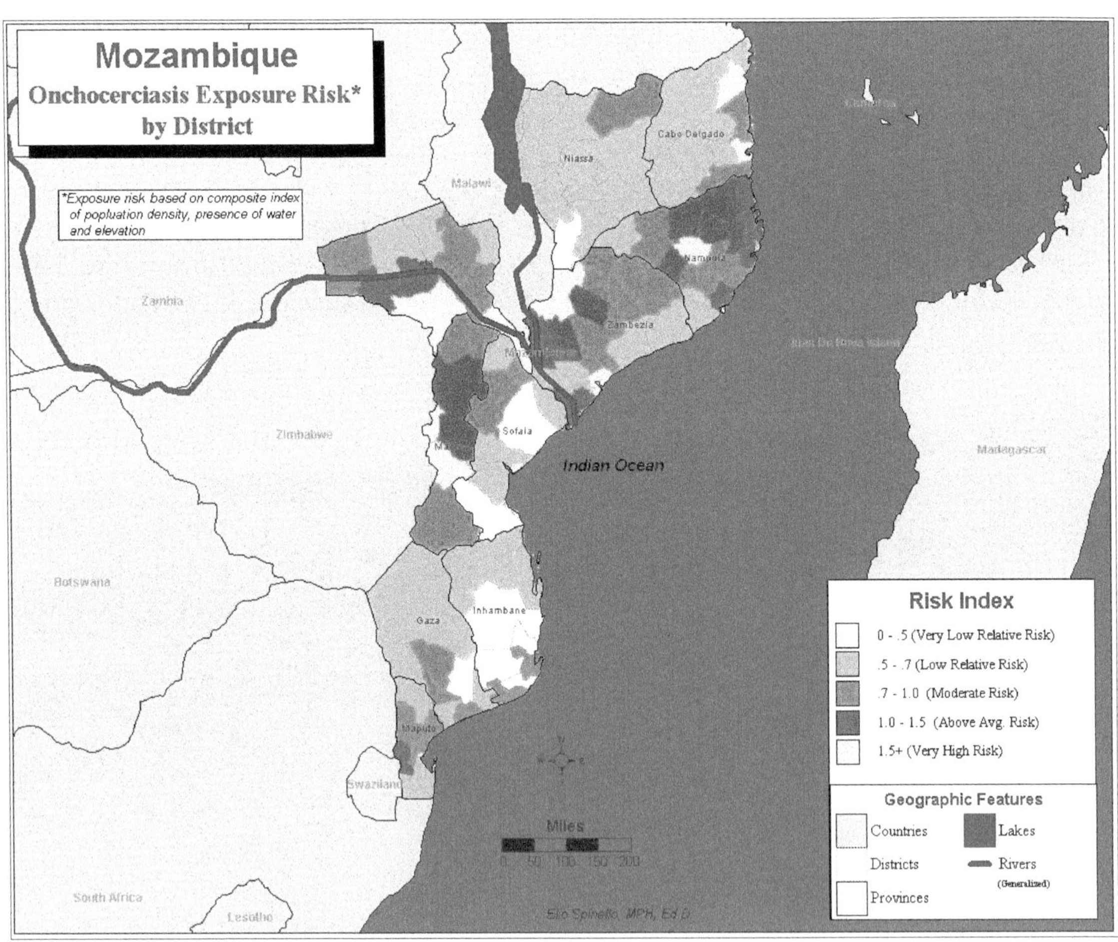

FIGURE 10.9 Onchocerciasis Risk Map for Mozambique.

SUMMARY

Spatial analysis refers to the analysis of data relative to place or location. Used by Dr. John Snow to help solve the spread of cholera, the analytical approach has become one of the key tools in epidemiology, resulting the development of Geographic Information Systems (GIS) software to facilitate the spatial analysis of data in public health, healthcare and many other industries.

GIS technology provides the healthcare and public health decision maker with a unique tool that provides the ability to view data from a geospatial perspective. GIS programs can essentially be described as relational database programs that have the capability of maintaining database records' locational information together with other more traditional database fields. With the locational attributes, GIS datasets can be analyzed from both a database perspective and a spatial perspective through techniques such as thematic mapping.

Geographic features refer to items appearing on a map. Features fall into one of three possible types: points, lines, and polygons. Geographic features are represented as records in a database table, with each table appearing as a layer in a GIS map. Thematic mapping allows maps to be produced that allow database attributes to be visualized so that geospatial patterns can be more readily identified.

RESOURCES

The following are resources that may be useful as sources of data and/or mapping software:

1. Web-based GIS software: http://www.arcgis.com
2. QGIS, A free and open source desktop GIS program: http://www.qgis.com
3. Public health GIS data available from the United States Centers for Disease Control and Prevention: http://www.cdc.gov/gis/
4. California Office of Statewide Health Planning and Development data with locations of medical provider facilities and hospitals: http://www.oshpd.ca.gov/general_info/healthcare_atlas.html
5. United States Census Bureau: http://www.census.gov/geo/maps-data/

APPLY YOUR KNOWLEDGE

1. Using a web search engine such as Google, Bing, or Yahoo, locate three analytical maps using GIS technology. For each of the three maps you find, describe at least one key observation that can be made from the map. Examples of search terms that are likely to return appropriate results may include "GIS healthcare mapping" or "GIS health (or public health) mapping."
2. Using a web search engine such as Google, Bing, or Yahoo, identify one source of downloadable geographic data in a shapefile format that can be used in a GIS program. Describe what is contained in the shapefile and how it might be used.
3. Complete the GIS exercise, Creating an Analytical Thematic Map. The objective of the exercise is to provide an opportunity to apply some of the concepts discussed in this chapter by creating a thematic map using actual public health data.

APPLY YOUR KNOWLEDGE

CREATING AN ANALYTICAL THEMATIC MAP

Please refer to Active Learning Platform for exercise.

IMAGE CREDITS

Fig. 10.1: "Dr. John Snow," https://commons.wikimedia.org/wiki/File:John_Snow.jpg. Copyright in the Public Domain.
Fig. 10.2: "Cholera Map," https://commons.wikimedia.org/wiki/File:Snow-cholera-map.jpg. Copyright in the Public Domain.
Fig. 10.3: Copyright © Wellcome Images (CC by 4.0) at "https://commons.wikimedia.org/wiki/File:Broad_Street_(latterly_Broadwick_Street),_Soho,_with_a_white_Wellcome_L0028567.jpg.
Fig. 10.4: Copyright in the Public Domain.
Fig. 10.7: Copyright © by Esri.
Fig. 10.8: Copyright © by Esri.
Fig. 10.9: Copyright in the Public Domain.
"HIPAA Security Standards: Guidance on Risk Analysis," http://www.hhs.gov/ocr/privacy/hipaa/administrative/securityrule/radraftguidance.pdf. Copyright in the Public Domain.

A

APPENDIX

Source: U.S. Department of Health & Human Services,
Office for Civil Rights

GUIDANCE ON RISK ANALYSIS REQUIREMENTS UNDER THE HIPAA SECURITY RULE[1]

INTRODUCTION

The Office for Civil Rights (OCR) is responsible for issuing annual guidance on the provisions in the HIPAA Security Rule.[2] (45 C.F.R. §§ 164.302–318.) This series of guidances will assist organizations[3] in identifying and implementing the most effective and appropriate administrative, physical, and technical safeguards to secure electronic protected health information (e-PHI). The guidance materials will be developed with input from stakeholders and the public, and will be updated as appropriate.

We begin the series with the risk analysis requirement in § 164.308(a)(1)(ii)(A). Conducting a risk analysis is the first step in identifying and implementing safeguards that comply with and carry out the standards and implementation specifications in the Security Rule. Therefore, a risk analysis is foundational, and must be understood in detail before OCR can issue meaningful guidance that specifically addresses safeguards and technologies that will best protect electronic health information.

The guidance is not intended to provide a one-size-fits-all blueprint for compliance with the risk analysis requirement. Rather, it clarifies the expectations of the Department for organizations working to meet these requirements.[4] An organization should determine the most appropriate way to achieve compliance, taking into account the characteristics of the organization and its environment.

We note that some of the content contained in this guidance is based on recommendations of the National Institute of Standards and Technology (NIST). NIST, a federal agency,

---

[1] HHS / Copyright in the Public Domain.

[2] Section 13401(c) of the Health Information Technology for Economic and Clinical (HITECH) Act.

[3] As used in this guidance the term "organizations" refers to covered entities and business associates. The guidance will be updated following implementation of the final HITECH regulations.

[4] The HIPAA Security Rule: Health Insurance Reform: Security Standards, February 20, 2003, 68 FR 8334.

publishes freely available material in the public domain, including guidelines.[5] Although only federal agencies are required to follow guidelines set by NIST, the guidelines represent the industry standard for good business practices with respect to standards for securing e-PHI.

Therefore, non-federal organizations may find their content valuable when developing and performing compliance activities.

All e-PHI created, received, maintained or transmitted by an organization is subject to the Security Rule. The Security Rule requires entities to evaluate risks and vulnerabilities in their environments and to implement reasonable and appropriate security measures to protect against reasonably anticipated threats or hazards to the security or integrity of e-PHI. Risk analysis is the first step in that process.

We understand that the Security Rule does not prescribe a specific risk analysis methodology, recognizing that methods will vary dependent on the size, complexity, and capabilities of the organization. Instead, the Rule identifies risk analysis as the foundational element in the process of achieving compliance, and it establishes several objectives that any methodology adopted must achieve.

RISK ANALYSIS REQUIREMENTS UNDER THE SECURITY RULE

The Security Management Process standard in the Security Rule requires organizations to *"[i]mplement policies and procedures to prevent, detect, contain, and correct security violations."* (45 C.F.R. § 164.308(a)(1).) Risk analysis is one of four required implementation specifications that provide instructions to implement the Security Management Process standard. Section 164.308(a)(1)(ii)(A) states:

> RISK ANALYSIS (Required).
> Conduct an accurate and thorough assessment of the potential risks and vulnerabilities to the confidentiality, integrity, and availability of electronic protected health information held by the [organization].

The following questions adapted from NIST Special Publication (SP) 800–66[6] are examples organizations could consider as part of a risk analysis. These sample questions are not prescriptive and merely identify issues an organization may wish to consider in implementing the Security Rule:

- Have you identified the e-PHI within your organization? This includes e-PHI that you create, receive, maintain or transmit.
- What are the external sources of e-PHI? For example, do vendors or consultants create, receive, maintain or transmit e-PHI?
- What are the human, natural, and environmental threats to information systems that contain e-PHI?

---

[5] The 800 Series of Special Publications (SP) are available on the Office for Civil Rights' website—specifically, *SP 800–30 - Risk Management Guide for Information Technology Systems.* (http://www.hhs.gov/ocr/privacy/hipaa/administrative/securityrule/securityruleguidance.html.)

[6] See NIST SP 800–66, Section #4 Considerations When Applying the HIPAA Security Rule. Available at http://www.hhs.gov/ocr/privacy/hipaa/administrative/securityrule/nist80066.pdf.

In addition to an express requirement to conduct a risk analysis, the Rule indicates that risk analysis is a necessary tool in reaching substantial compliance with many other standards and implementation specifications. For example, the Rule contains several implementation specifications that are labeled "addressable" rather than "required." (68 FR 8334, 8336 (Feb. 20, 2003).) An addressable implementation specification is not optional; rather, if an organization determines that the implementation specification is not reasonable and appropriate, the organization must document why it is not reasonable and appropriate and adopt an equivalent measure if it is reasonable and appropriate to do so. (See 68 FR 8334, 8336 (Feb. 20, 2003); 45 C.F.R. § 164.306(d)(3).)

The outcome of the risk analysis process is a critical factor in assessing whether an implementation specification or an equivalent measure is reasonable and appropriate. Organizations should use the information gleaned from their risk analysis as they, for example:

- Design appropriate personnel screening processes. (45 C.F.R. § 164.308(a)(3)(ii)(B).)
- Identify what data to backup and how. (45 C.F.R. § 164.308(a)(7)(ii)(A).)
- Decide whether and how to use encryption. (45 C.F.R. §§ 164.312(a)(2)(iv) and (e)(2)(ii).)
- Address what data must be authenticated in particular situations to protect data integrity. (45 C.F.R. § 164.312(c)(2).)
- Determine the appropriate manner of protecting health information transmissions. (45 C.F.R. § 164.312(e)(1).)

IMPORTANT DEFINITIONS

Unlike "availability," "confidentiality" and "integrity," the following terms are not expressly defined in the Security Rule. The definitions provided in this guidance, which are consistent with common industry definitions, are provided to put the risk analysis discussion in context. These terms do not modify or update the Security Rule and should not be interpreted inconsistently with the terms used in the Security Rule.

VULNERABILITY

Vulnerability is defined in NIST Special Publication (SP) 800–30 as *"[a] flaw or weakness in system security procedures, design, implementation, or internal controls that could be exercised (accidentally triggered or intentionally exploited) and result in a security breach or a violation of the system's security policy."*

Vulnerabilities, whether accidentally triggered or intentionally exploited, could potentially result in a security incident, such as inappropriate access to or disclosure of e-PHI. Vulnerabilities may be grouped into two general categories, technical and non-technical. Non-technical vulnerabilities may include ineffective or non-existent policies, procedures, standards or guidelines. Technical vulnerabilities may include: holes, flaws or weaknesses in the development of information systems; or incorrectly implemented and/or configured information systems.

THREAT

An adapted definition of threat, from NIST SP 800–30, is *"[t]he potential for a person or thing to exercise (accidentally trigger or intentionally exploit) a specific vulnerability."*

There are several types of threats that may occur within an information system or operating environment. Threats may be grouped into general categories such as natural, human, and environmental. Examples of common threats in each of these general categories include:

- Natural threats such as floods, earthquakes, tornadoes, and landslides.
- Human threats are enabled or caused by humans and may include intentional (e.g., network and computer based attacks, malicious software upload, and unauthorized access to e-PHI) or unintentional (e.g., inadvertent data entry or deletion and inaccurate data entry) actions.
- Environmental threats such as power failures, pollution, chemicals, and liquid leakage.

RISK

An adapted definition of risk, from NIST SP 800–30, is:

"The net mission impact considering (1) the probability that a particular [threat] will exercise (accidentally trigger or intentionally exploit) a particular [vulnerability] and (2) the resulting impact if this should occur . . . [R]isks arise from legal liability or mission loss due to—

1. *Unauthorized (malicious or accidental) disclosure, modification, or destruction of information*
2. *Unintentional errors and omissions*
3. *IT disruptions due to natural or man-made disasters*
4. *Failure to exercise due care and diligence in the implementation and operation of the IT system."*

Risk can be understood as a function of 1) the likelihood of a given threat triggering or exploiting a particular vulnerability, and 2) the resulting impact on the organization. This means that risk is not a single factor or event, but rather it is a combination of factors or events (threats and vulnerabilities) that, if they occur, may have an adverse impact on the organization.

ELEMENTS OF A RISK ANALYSIS

There are numerous methods of performing risk analysis and there is no single method or "best practice" that guarantees compliance with the Security Rule. Some examples of steps that might be applied in a risk analysis process are outlined in NIST SP 800–30.[7]

The remainder of this guidance document explains several elements a risk analysis must incorporate, regardless of the method employed.

[7] Available at http://www.hhs.gov/ocr/privacy/hipaa/administrative/securityrule/nist800-30.pdf.

SCOPE OF THE ANALYSIS

The scope of risk analysis that the Security Rule encompasses includes the potential risks and vulnerabilities to the confidentiality, availability and integrity of all e-PHI that an organization creates, receives, maintains, or transmits. (45 C.F.R. § 164.306(a).) This includes e-PHI in all forms of electronic media, such as hard drives, floppy disks, CDs, DVDs, smart cards or other storage devices, personal digital assistants, transmission media, or portable electronic media. Electronic media includes a single workstation as well as complex networks connected between multiple locations. Thus, an organization's risk analysis should take into account all of its e-PHI, regardless of the particular electronic medium in which it is created, received, maintained or transmitted or the source or location of its e-PHI.

DATA COLLECTION

An organization must identify where the e-PHI is stored, received, maintained or transmitted. An organization could gather relevant data by: reviewing past and/or existing projects; performing interviews; reviewing documentation; or using other data gathering techniques. The data on e-PHI gathered using these methods must be documented. (See 45 C.F.R. §§ 164.308(a)(1)(ii)(A) and 164.316(b)(1).)

Identify and Document Potential Threats and Vulnerabilities

Organizations must identify and document reasonably anticipated threats to e-PHI. (See 45 C.F.R. §§ 164.306(a)(2) and 164.316(b)(1)(ii).) Organizations may identify different threats that are unique to the circumstances of their environment. Organizations must also identify and document vulnerabilities which, if triggered or exploited by a threat, would create a risk of inappropriate access to or disclosure of e-PHI. (See 45 C.F.R. §§ 164.308(a)(1)(ii)(A) and 164.316(b)(1)(ii).)

Assess Current Security Measures

Organizations should assess and document the security measures an entity uses to safeguard e-PHI, whether security measures required by the Security Rule are already in place, and if current security measures are configured and used properly. (See 45 C.F.R. §§ 164.306(b)(1), 164.308(a)(1)(ii)(A), and 164.316(b)(1).)

The security measures implemented to reduce risk will vary among organizations. For example, small organizations tend to have more control within their environment. Small organizations tend to have fewer variables (i.e. fewer workforce members and information systems) to consider when making decisions regarding how to safeguard e-PHI. As a result, the appropriate security measures that reduce the likelihood of risk to the confidentiality, availability and integrity of e-PHI in a small organization may differ from those that are appropriate in large organizations.[8]

---

[8] For more information on methods smaller entities might employ to achieve compliance with the Security Rule, see #7 in the Center for Medicare and Medicaid Services' (CMS) Security Series papers, titled "Implementation for the Small Provider." Available at http://www.hhs.gov/ocr/privacy/hipaa/administrative/securityrule/smallprovider.pdf.

Determine the Likelihood of Threat Occurrence

The Security Rule requires organizations to take into account the probability of potential risks to e-PHI. (See 45 C.F.R. § 164.306(b)(2)(iv).) The results of this assessment, combined with the initial list of threats, will influence the determination of which threats the Rule requires protection against because they are "reasonably anticipated."

The output of this part should be documentation of all threat and vulnerability combinations with associated likelihood estimates that may impact the confidentiality, availability and integrity of e-PHI of an organization. (See 45 C.F.R. §§ 164.306(b)(2)(iv), 164.308(a)(1)(ii)(A), and 164.316(b)(1)(ii).)

Determine the Potential Impact of Threat Occurrence

The Rule also requires consideration of the "criticality," or impact, of potential risks to confidentiality, integrity, and availability of e-PHI. (See 45 C.F.R. § 164.306(b)(2)(iv).) An organization must assess the magnitude of the potential impact resulting from a threat triggering or exploiting a specific vulnerability. An entity may use either a qualitative or quantitative method or a combination of the two methods to measure the impact on the organization.

The output of this process should be documentation of all potential impacts associated with the occurrence of threats triggering or exploiting vulnerabilities that affect the confidentiality, availability and integrity of e-PHI within an organization. (See 45 C.F.R. §§ 164.306(a)(2), 164.308(a)(1)(ii)(A), and 164.316(b)(1)(ii).)

Determine the Level of Risk

Organizations should assign risk levels for all threat and vulnerability combinations identified during the risk analysis. The level of risk could be determined, for example, by analyzing the values assigned to the likelihood of threat occurrence and resulting impact of threat occurrence. The risk level determination might be performed by assigning a risk level based on the average of the assigned likelihood and impact levels.

The output should be documentation of the assigned risk levels and a list of corrective actions to be performed to mitigate each risk level. (See 45 C.F.R. §§ 164.306(a)(2), 164.308(a)(1)(ii)(A), and 164.316(b)(1).)

Finalize Documentation

The Security Rule requires the risk analysis to be documented but does not require a specific format. (See 45 C.F.R. § 164.316(b)(1).) The risk analysis documentation is a direct input to the risk management process.

Periodic Review and Updates to the Risk Assessment

The risk analysis process should be ongoing. In order for an entity to update and document its security measures "as needed," which the Rule requires, it should conduct continuous risk analysis to identify when updates are needed. (45 C.F.R. §§ 164.306(e) and 164.316(b)(2)(iii).) The Security Rule does not specify how frequently to perform risk analysis as part of a comprehensive risk management process. The frequency of performance will vary among covered entities. Some covered entities may perform these processes annually or as needed (e.g., bi-annual or every 3 years) depending on circumstances of their environment.

A truly integrated risk analysis and management process is performed as new technologies and business operations are planned, thus reducing the effort required to address risks identified after implementation. For example, if the covered entity has experienced a security incident, has had change in ownership, turnover in key staff or management, is planning to incorporate new technology to make operations more efficient, the potential risk should be analyzed to ensure the e-PHI is reasonably and appropriately protected. If it is determined that existing security measures are not sufficient to protect against the risks associated with the evolving threats or vulnerabilities, a changing business environment, or the introduction of new technology, then the entity must determine if additional security measures are needed. Performing the risk analysis and adjusting risk management processes to address risks in a timely manner will allow the covered entity to reduce the associated risks to reasonable and appropriate levels.[9]

IN SUMMARY

Risk analysis is the first step in an organization's Security Rule compliance efforts. Risk analysis is an ongoing process that should provide the organization with a detailed understanding of the risks to the confidentiality, integrity, and availability of e-PHI.

RESOURCES

The Security Series papers available on the Office for Civil Rights (OCR) website, http://www.hhs.gov/ocr/hipaa, contain a more detailed discussion of tools and methods available for risk analysis and risk management, as well as other Security Rule compliance requirements. Visit http://www.hhs.gov/ocr/hipaa for the latest guidance, FAQs and other information on the Security Rule.

Several other federal and non-federal organizations have developed materials that might be helpful to covered entities seeking to develop and implement risk analysis and risk management strategies. The Department of Health and Human Services does not endorse or recommend any particular risk analysis or risk management model. The documents referenced below do not constitute legally binding guidance for covered entities, nor does adherence to any or all of the standards contained in these materials prove substantial compliance with the risk analysis requirements of the Security Rule. Rather, the materials are presented as examples of frameworks and methodologies that some organizations use to guide their risk analysis efforts.

The National Institute of Standards and Technology (NIST), an agency of the United States Department of Commerce, is responsible for developing information security standards for federal agencies. NIST has produced a series of Special Publications, available at http://csrc.nist.gov/publications/PubsSPs.html, which provide information that is relevant to information technology security. These papers include:

- Guide to Technical Aspects of Performing Information Security Assessments (SP800–115)
- Information Security Handbook: A Guide for Managers (SP800–100; Chapter 10 provides a Risk Management Framework and details steps in the risk management process)

[9] For more information on methods smaller entities might employ to achieve compliance with the Security Rule, see #6 in the Center for Medicare and Medicaid Services' (CMS) Security Series papers, titled "Basics of Risk Analysis and Risk Management." Available at http://www.hhs.gov/ocr/privacy/hipaa/administrative/securityrule/riskassessment.pdf.

- An Introductory Resource Guide for Implementing the Health Insurance Portability and Accountability Act (HIPAA) Security Rule (SP800–66; Part 3 links the NIST Risk Management Framework to components of the Security Rule)
- A draft publication, Managing Risk from Information Systems (SP800–39)

The Office of the National Coordinator for Health Information Technology (ONC) has produced a risk assessment guide for small health care practices, called Reassessing Your Security Practices in a Health IT Environment, which is available at http://healthit.hhs.gov/portal/server.pt/gateway/PTARGS_0_10741_848086_0_0_18/SmallPracticeSecurityGuide-1.pdf.

The Healthcare Information and Management Systems Society (HIMSS), a private consortium of health care information technology stakeholders, created an information technology security practices questionnaire, available at http://www.himss.org/content/files/ApplicationSecurityv2.3.pdf. The questionnaire was developed to collect information about the state of IT security in the health care sector, but could also be a helpful self-assessment tool during the risk analysis process.

The Health Information Trust Alliance (HITRUST) worked with industry to create the Common Security Framework (CSF), a proprietary resource available at http://hitrustcentral.net/files. The risk management section of the document, Control Name: 03.0, explains the role of risk assessment and management in overall security program development and implementation. The paper describes methods for implementing a risk analysis program, including knowledge and process requirements, and it links various existing frameworks and standards to applicable points in an information security life cycle.

INDEX

S

T

U

V

W

Y

REFERENCES

1. Owen G, Savage N. Empirical analysis of Tor Hidden Services. *IET Information Security.* 2016;10(3):113–118.
2. DHHS U.S. Summary of HIPAA Privacy Rule. [PDF]. 2003.
3. DHHS U.S. Dermatology practice settles potential HIPAA violations. 2013;2014.
4. Medlin BD, Cazier JA. A Study of Hard Drive Forensics on Consumers' PCs: Data Recovery and Exploitation. *Journal of Management Policy and Practice.* 2011;12(1):27–35.
5. United States Department of Health and Human Services. 575-What does HIPAA require of covered entities when they dispose of PHI | HHS.gov. [Webpage]. 2015; http://www.hhs.gov/hipaa/for-professionals/faq/575/what-does-hipaa-require-of-covered-entities-when-they-dispose-information/index.html. Accessed 10/12/2016, 2016.
6. United States Health Resources and Services Administration. Destruction of Medical/Dental records Protocol. 2016; Protocol for Destruction of Medical/Dental Records. Available at: http://bphc.hrsa.gov/archive/technicalassistance/resourcecenter/services/destructionofnedicalrecordprotcol.pdf. Accessed October 13, 2016, 2016.
7. Benlian A, Hess T. Opportunities and risks of software-as-a-service: Findings from a survey of IT executives. 2011;52(1):232–246.
8. The Open Source Definition. 2013; http://opensource.org/osd. Accessed 3/20/2013, 2013.
9. Awad NF, Fitzgerald K. The deceptive behaviors that offend us most about spyware. *Communications of the ACM.* 2005;48(8):55.
10. Chang J, Venkatasubramanian KK, West AG, Lee I. Analyzing and defending against web-based malware. *ACM Computing Surveys.* 2013;45(4):1–35.
11. Davis J. Cybercriminals to launch more ransomware attacks as black market price of health data drops. *Healthcare IT News.* 2016. http://www.healthcareitnews.com/news/cybercriminals-poised-launch-more-ransomware-attacks-black-market-price-health-data-drops. Accessed 2016-10-12.
12. Symantec. Ransomware and Businesses 2016. *ISTR Special Report.* 2016:30. http://www.symantec.com/content/en/us/enterprise/media/security_response/whitepapers/ISTR2016_Ransomware_and_Businesses.pdf. Accessed October 13, 2016.

13. George T. Minimizing Exposure to Ransomware Attacks | SecurityWeek.Com. *Security Week* 2016; http://www.securityweek.com/minimizing-exposure-ransomware-attacks. Accessed 9/21/2016, 2016.
14. Belliveau J. MedStar Ransomware Attack Caused by Known Security Flaw. *HealthITSecurity* 2016; http://healthitsecurity.com/news/medstar-ransomware-attack-caused-by-known-security-flaw. Accessed 9/21/2016, 2016.
15. Cox JW. MedStar Health turns away patients after likely ransomware cyberattack. *The Washington Post.* March 29, 2016, 2016.
16. Fierce Healthcare. Lessons from the MedStar Health ransomware attack | FierceHealthcare. 2016; http://www.fiercehealthcare.com/privacy-security/lessons-from-medstar-ransomware-attack. Accessed 9/20/2016, 2016.
17. Worstall T. Yes, Apple Really Does Have A Serious Problem With Computer Viruses And Malware. *Forbes*: Forbes; 2014.
18. The Office of the National Coordinator for Health Information Technology. CyberSecurity. *Security Risk Assessment* 2014; http://www.healthit.gov/providers-professionals/cybersecurity, 2014.
19. Vijayan J. Infected USB drive blamed for '08 military cyber breach. *Computer World*: @Computerworld; 2010.
20. Info Security. HHS fines Blue Cross of Tennessee for theft of 57 hard drives. *Info Security*2012.
21. Blue Cross of Tennessee. Eastgate Hard Drive Theft. [Website]. 2010. Accessed 9/30/2016, 2016.
22. Sackett DL, Rosenberg WMC. Evidence based medicine: What it is and what it isn't. *BMJ: British Medical Journal (International Edition).* 1996;312(7023):71–72.
23. Sproule JA, Tansey C, Burns B, Fenelon G. The Web: friend or foe of the hand surgeon? *Hand Surg.* 2003;8(2):181–185.
24. Fallis D, Fricke M. Indicators of accuracy of consumer health information on the Internet: a study of indicators relating to information for managing fever in children in the home. *J Am Med Inform Assoc.* 2002;9(1):73–79.
25. Muthukumarasamy S, Osmani Z, Sharpe A, England RJ. Quality of information available on the World Wide Web for patients undergoing thyroidectomy: review. *The Journal of laryngology and otology.* 2011:1–4.
26. Thakor V, Leach MJ, Gillham D, Esterman A. The quality of information on websites selling St. John's wort. *Complementary therapies in medicine.* 2011;19(3):155–160.
27. Science Daily. Watermelon May Have Viagra-effect. 2008; http://www.sciencedaily.com/releases/2008/06/080630165707.htm. Accessed September 10, 2014, 2014.
28. Science Watch. Risks and Benefits: Harvard's Walter C. Willett on Epidemiology. *Essential Science Indicators* [Website]. 2008. Accessed June 15, 2012, 2012.
29. Health on the Net Foundation. HONcode: Principles - Quality and trustworthy health information. 2014; http://www.hon.ch/HONcode/Pro/Conduct.html, 2014.
30. HON. Health on the Net Foundation Website. 2011; H. Available at. Accessed February 15, 2011, 2011.
31. Koo M. Complementary and alternative medicine on wikipedia: opportunities for improvement. *Evidence-based complementary and alternative medicine : eCAM.* 2014;2014:105186.

32. Hasty RT, Garbalosa RC, Barbato VA, et al. Wikipedia vs peer-reviewed medical literature for information about the 10 most costly medical conditions. *The Journal of the American Osteopathic Association.* 2014;114(5):368–373.
33. Phillips J, Lam C, Palmisano L. Analysis of the accuracy and readability of herbal supplement information on Wikipedia. *Journal of the American Pharmacists Association : JAPhA.* 2014;54(4):406–414.
34. McGlinchey D. Nuclear agency managers among diploma mill users. 2004; http://www.govexec.com/management/2004/05/nuclear-agency-managers-among-diploma-mill-users/16667/.
35. Leung R. Diplomas For Sale. *60 Minutes* 2014; http://www.cbsnews.com/news/diplomas-for-sale-08-11-2004/. Accessed September 21, 2014, 2014.
36. Brandt KA, Lehmann HP. Teaching literature searching in the context of the World Wide Web. *Proc Annu Symp Comput Appl Med Care.* 1995:888–892.
37. SSRB. Best Practice Spreadsheet Modeling Standards. *Best Practice Spreadsheet Modeling Standards* 2014; http://www.bestpracticemodelling.com/resources?page=/resources/standards. Accessed 7/5/2014, 2014.
38. SSRB. Best Practice Modeling Resource. 2014;2014:Standards for spreadsheet modeling.
39. California Department of Public Health. *California Cancer Registry.* 2011.
40. A. D. A. M. Editorial Board. Color blindness. 2013.
41. Cowles S. San Francisco Pedestrian Injuries - High Injury Corridors. 2012; http://www.arcgis.com/home/item.html?id=7cb523571fb14e8b9d54b9435d10ba3b. Accessed 8/28/2014, 2014.
42. Centers for Disease Control and Prevention. CDC Map Gallery. 2006; http://www.cdc.gov/gis/mg_mozambique_risk.htm. Accessed 10/10/2014, 2014.

ABOUT THE AUTHOR

Dr. Elio Spinello has been a faculty member in the California State University, Northridge, Department of Health Sciences since 1992. In addition to teaching at CSUN, he serves as the Technology Coordinator for the CSUN College of Health and Human Development. He is also an adjunct professor at the Pepperdine University Graduate School of Education and Psychology, and an adjunct professor for the University of Redlands School of Business MBA program.

When he is not teaching, Dr. Spinello is a partner in RPM Consulting, LLC, a management consulting firm that provides research, training, system development, and decision support services to a variety of large and small organizations in the fields of healthcare, financial services, and public safety. He has been a consultant to the State of California Employment Development Department, and the Los Angeles County Sheriff's Department, as well as a number of universities through the U.S. Dr. Spinello holds an MPH, as well as an EdD in Educational Technology from Pepperdine University, where his dissertation and subsequent research focused on the use of computer simulations of infectious disease outbreaks in the training of public health professionals.

Elio resides in Southern California with his family and a very noisy cocker spaniel named Maggie. He can be reached at elio@drspinello.com.

CPSIA information can be obtained
at www.ICGtesting.com
Printed in the USA
FSOW03n0415310817
38206FS